NEW
CONCISE

PROJECT
MATHS 3A

FOR LEAVING CERT ORDINARY LEVEL

GEORGE HUMPHREY, BRENDAN GUILDEA, GEOFFREY REEVES
LOUISE BOYLAN

g **GILL** EDUCATION

Gill Education
Hume Avenue
Park West
Dublin 12
www.gilleducation.ie

Gill Education is an imprint of M.H. Gill & Co.

© George Humphrey, Brendan Guildea, Geoffrey Reeves and
Louise Boylan 2012

978 07171 5358 9

Print origination by MPS Limited

Any links to external websites should not be construed as an endorsement
by Gill Education of the content or views of the linked materials.

For permission to reproduce photographs, the authors and publisher gratefully
acknowledge the following:

© Alamy: 265; © Getty Images: 242T, 242B, 271C, 271B, 291.

The authors and publisher have made every effort to trace all copyright
holders, but if any has been inadvertently overlooked we would be pleased to
make the necessary arrangement at the first opportunity.

Contents

Acknowledgments

The authors would like to thank Sorcha Forde, David Grimes, Elaine Guildea, Jessica Hayden, Colman Humphrey, Allison Lynch and Gráinne McKnight who helped with the proofreading, checked the answers and made many valuable suggestions that are included in the final text.

The authors also wish to express their thanks to the staff of Gill & Macmillan, and special thanks to Kristin Jensen, for her advice, guidance and untiring assistance in the preparation and presentation of the book.

Preface

New Concise Project Maths 3A is one of two books covering the new Leaving Certificate Ordinary Level course for students taking the 2014 exam and onwards. The second book is *New Concise Project Maths 3B*.

New Concise Project Maths 3A incorporates the approach to the teaching of mathematics envisaged in **Project Maths**. It reflects the greater emphasis on the understanding of mathematical concepts, developing problem-solving skills and relating mathematics to everyday events.

The authors strongly empathise with the main aims and objectives of the new Project Maths syllabus and examination. In the worked examples, a numbered, step-by-step approach is used throughout the book to help with problem solving. The constructions are demonstrated with excellent diagrams. There is a comprehensive range of carefully graded exercises to reflect the new exam. Exam-style in-context questions are included to enhance students' understanding of everyday practical applications of mathematics. The emphasis is on a clear and practical presentation of the material. Simple and concise language is used throughout, instead of technical language, which is not required in the exam.

Additional teachers' resources, including a **Digital Flipbook**, are provided online at www.gillmacmillan.ie.

An excellent resource for teachers and students is the dynamic software package **GeoGebra**. This package is of particular use for coordinate geometry, geometry and graphing functions. It can be accessed at www.geogebra.org.

George Humphrey
Brendan Guildea
Geoffrey Reeves
Louise Boylan
April 2012

CHAPTER 1

ALGEBRA

Evaluating expressions (substitution)

A **substitute** is used to replace something. In football, a substitute replaces another player. In algebra, when we replace letters with numbers when evaluating expressions, we call it **substitution**. When you are substituting numbers in an expression, it is good practice to put a bracket around the number that replaces the letter. (Remember: **BEMDAS** the order of operations.)

EXAMPLE

Find the value of the following.

(i) $4(a - b)^a$ when $a = 2$ and $b = -1$

(ii) $\dfrac{5(x - y)}{3(x^2 + y^2)}$ when $x = 2$ and $y = -1$

Solution:

(i) $\quad 4(a - b)^a$

$\quad = 4[(2) - (-1)]^2$

$\quad = 4[2 + 1]^2$

$\quad = 4(3)^2$

$\quad = 4(9)$

$\quad = 36$

(ii) $\dfrac{5(x - y)}{3(x^2 + y^2)}$

$\quad = \dfrac{5[(2) - (-1)]}{3[(2)^2 + (-1)^2]}$

$\quad = \dfrac{5(2 + 1)}{3(4 + 1)}$

$\quad = \dfrac{5(3)}{3(5)} = \dfrac{15}{15} = 1$

Exercise 1.1

Evaluate each of the following in questions 1–22.

1. $3 + 4 \times 5$
2. $-3 + 7$
3. $-5 + 2$
4. $-1 - 5$
5. $8 - 10$
6. $5(-2)$
7. $-3(4)$
8. $-2(-4)$
9. $2(3)^2$
10. $(-4)^2$
11. $5(-2)^2$
12. $-4(-5)^2$
13. $-20 \div 5$
14. $12 \div -6$
15. $-18 \div -3$
16. $-8 \div 8$
17. $(5)^2 - 2(5)$
18. $(4)^2 - 2(4) - 8$
19. $(-3)^2 - 4(-3) - 21$
20. $\dfrac{6 + 2}{6 - 2}$
21. $\dfrac{18 + 2 \times 3}{2(5 - 1)}$
22. $\dfrac{5^2 - 7}{3^2 - 7}$

Evaluate each of the expressions in questions 23–32 for the given values of the variables.

23. $x^2 + 2x + 3$ when $x = 1$

24. $x^2 - 3x + 2$ when $x = -2$

25. $a^2 + 2\sqrt{a} - 20$ when $a = 4$

26. $x^2 - 5xy$ when $x = 3$ and $y = -2$

27. $3(2p - q)$ when $p = -4$ and $q = 5$

28. $(a - b)^a$ when $a = 2$ and $b = -1$

29. $\dfrac{3x - 2y - 1}{5}$ when $x = 13$ and $y = 14$

30. $\dfrac{p^2 + 4q}{2(q + 1)}$ when $p = -2$ and $q = 3$

31. $\sqrt{3a - 2b}$ when $a = 4$ and $b = -2$

32. $(3x^2 - 11)^{\frac{1}{2}}$ when $x = 5$

33. Find the value of $5x - 3y$ when $x = \dfrac{5}{2}$ and $y = \dfrac{2}{3}$.

34. Find the value of $\dfrac{ab - c}{2}$ when $a = 3$, $b = \dfrac{2}{3}$ and $c = 1$.

35. Find the value of $\dfrac{a + b - 1}{a - b + 1}$ when $a = \dfrac{1}{2}$ and $b = \dfrac{2}{3}$.

36. A car increases its speed from u km/h to v km/h in a time, t hrs.

    The distance, d km, that it has travelled is given by the formula $d = \dfrac{t}{4}(u + v)$.

    Calculate d when $t = 12$, $u = 3$ and $v = 7$.

37. x people share the cost of travelling y km in z cars.

    The amount, €A, each has to pay is given by the formula $A = \dfrac{z\left(8 + \dfrac{y}{5}\right)}{x}$.

    Find the value of A when $x = 17$, $y = 300$ and $z = 18$.

38. x and y are positive or negative whole numbers such that $2x + y = 8$. Find four pairs of values for x and y that make this equation balance. For example, $x = 5$ and $y = -2$ make the equation balance.

39. $A = 3p + 2q$ where p and q are different positive whole numbers. Choose values for p and q such that A is:

    (i) Even   (ii) Odd   (iii) Divisible by 5   (iv) A perfect square   (v) A prime number

40. x and y are positive whole numbers. Explain why $(6x + 4y)$ is always even.

41. Patrick knows that a, b and c have the values 5, 6 and 10 but he does not know which variable has which value.

    (i) What is the maximum value that the expression $3a + 2b - 5c$ could have?

    (ii) What is the minimum value that the expression $5a - b + 2c$ could have?

42. The number x is a positive whole number. Write, in terms of x, the next two positive whole numbers greater than x. Show that the sum of these three numbers is always a multiple of 3.

Simplifying algebraic expressions

> Only terms that are the same can be added.

EXAMPLE

Simplify: **(i)** $2(a^2 + 3a) - a(2a + 5) + a$ **(ii)** $(2x + 3)(x^2 - 5x - 4)$

Solution:

(i)
$$2(a^2 + 3a) - a(2a + 5) + a$$
$$= 2a^2 + 6a - 2a^2 - 5a + a$$
$$= 2a^2 - 2a^2 + 6a + a - 5a$$
$$= 2a$$

(ii)
$$(2x + 3)(x^2 - 5x - 4)$$
$$= 2x(x^2 - 5x - 4) + 3(x^2 - 5x - 4)$$
$$= 2x^3 - 10x^2 - 8x + 3x^2 - 15x - 12$$
$$= 2x^3 - 10x^2 + 3x^2 - 8x - 15x - 12$$
$$= 2x^3 - 7x^2 - 23x - 12$$

Exercise 1.2

Simplify each of the following in questions 1–11.

1. $4x + 3x$
2. $8x - 6x$
3. $5x - 8x$
4. $-2x - 4x$
5. $-x + 5x$
6. $2a - 9a$
7. $-8y - 6y$
8. $-4b + 7b$
9. $2x^2 + 3x^2 + 4x^2$
10. $-2a^2 + 5a^2 - a^2$
11. $-x^2 + 3x^2 + 5x^2 - 4x^2$

Multiply the terms in questions 12–19.

12. $(2x)(3x)$
13. $(-2x)(5x)$
14. $(3x^2)(-4x)$
15. $(-2x^2)(-5x)$
16. $(-x)(-x)$
17. $(-3a)(-4a)$
18. $(3y^2)(-5y)$
19. $(-2p)(-4p^2)$

Expand (remove the brackets) for each of the following in questions 20–26 and simplify.

20. $(x + 2)(x + 3)$
21. $(2x + 5)(x - 4)$
22. $(3x - 2)(2x - 5)$
23. $a(a - b) + b(a - b) + b^2$
24. $2(x^2 + 3x) - x(2x + 5) + x$
25. $a(a + 1) + 2a(a - 3) + 3(2a - a^2)$
26. $a(b + c) - b(c - a) - c(a - b)$

27. Match up the following Algebra Snap cards into groups. Which card is the odd one out?

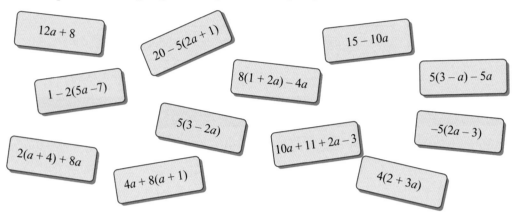

$12a + 8$

$20 - 5(2a + 1)$

$15 - 10a$

$1 - 2(5a - 7)$

$8(1 + 2a) - 4a$

$5(3 - a) - 5a$

$5(3 - 2a)$

$-5(2a - 3)$

$2(a + 4) + 8a$

$10a + 11 + 2a - 3$

$4a + 8(a + 1)$

$4(2 + 3a)$

In questions 28–31, show that each of the following reduces to a constant (number) and find that constant.

28. $3(4x + 5) - 2(6x + 4)$

29. $3a(2a + 3) - 6a(a + 2) + 3(a + 1)$

30. $(x - 3)(x + 5) - x(x + 2) + 15$

31. $a(b + c) - b(c + a) - c(a - b)$

32. Write down the simplest possible expression for the perimeter of each shape.

(i)

a

a　　a

a

(ii)

$5x$

$2x$　　$2x$

$5x$

(iii)

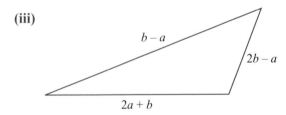

$b - a$

$2b - a$

$2a + b$

33. Write down the simplest possible expression for the area of each shape.

(i)

$2x$

$5x$

(ii)

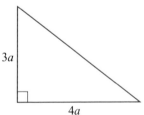

$3a$

$4a$

(iii)

5

$4x$　　3

34. The rectangle is made up of 24 squares. Its length is 16 y m. Write down its area in terms of y.

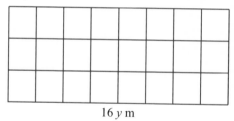

16 y m

35. In a magic square, the sum of each row, column and diagonal is the same. Which of the following squares are magic squares? In each case, justify your answer.

(i)

$p^2 - 2$	$p^2 - 1$	$p^2 + 3$
$p^2 + 5$	p^2	$p^2 - 5$
$p^2 - 3$	$p^2 + 1$	$p^2 + 2$

(ii)

$a + b$	$a - b - c$	$a + c$
$a - b + c$	a	$a + b - c$
$a - c$	$a + b + c$	$a - b$

(iii)

$y - x$	$3x + 2y$	x
$3x$	$x + y$	$2y - x$
$x + 2y$	x	$3x + y$

36. John wrote the following: $4(3x - 1) + 10(2x + 3) = 7x - 4 + 20x + 30 = 27x - 26$.
John has made two mistakes in his working. Explain the mistakes that John has made.

Single variable linear equations

A equation is solved with the following method:

> Whatever you do to one side, you must do **exactly the same** to the other side.

Note: Keep balance in mind.

The solution of an equation is the number that makes both sides balance.

EXAMPLE

Solve: (i) $4(x + 5) - 2(x + 3) = 12$

(ii) $\dfrac{x - 1}{4} - \dfrac{1}{20} = \dfrac{2x - 3}{5}$

Solution:

(i) $4(x + 5) - 2(x + 3) = 12$

$\quad\quad 4x + 20 - 2x - 6 = 12$ (remove brackets)

$\quad\quad\quad\quad\quad 2x + 14 = 12$ (simplify the left-hand side)

$\quad\quad\quad\quad\quad\quad 2x = -2$ (subtract 14 from both sides)

$\quad\quad\quad\quad\quad\quad\quad x = -1$ (divide both sides by 2)

(ii)   The LCM of 4, 5 and 20 is 20. Therefore, we multiply each part by 20.

$\dfrac{(x - 1)}{4} - \dfrac{(1)}{20} = \dfrac{(2x - 3)}{5}$ (put brackets on top)

$\dfrac{20(x - 1)}{4} - \dfrac{20(1)}{20} = \dfrac{20(2x - 3)}{5}$ (multiply each part by 20)

$5(x - 1) - 1 = 4(2x - 3)$ (divide the bottom into the top)

$5x - 5 - 1 = 8x - 12$ (remove the brackets)

$5x - 6 = 8x - 12$ (simplify the left-hand side)

$5x = 8x - 6$ (add 6 to both sides)

$-3x = -6$ (subtract $8x$ from both sides)

$3x = 6$ (multiply both sides by -1)

$x = 2$ (divide both sides by 3)

Exercise 1.3

Solve each of the following equations in questions 1–22.

1. $2x = 10$
2. $3x = -12$
3. $-4x = -8$
4. $-5x = 15$
5. $3x - 1 = 11$
6. $7x + 1 = 22$
7. $4x + 7 = -13$
8. $3x - 1 = -10$
9. $5(x + 4) - 3(x - 4) = 40$
10. $10(x + 4) = 3(2x + 5) + 1$
11. $2(7 + x) - 4(x + 3) = 15(x - 1)$
12. $2 - 6(2 - x) = 5(x + 3) - 23$
13. $5 + 2(x - 1) = x + 4(x - 3)$

14. $11 - 2(2x - 5) = 5(2x + 1) - 4(3x - 1)$

15. $\dfrac{x}{2} + \dfrac{x}{3} = \dfrac{5}{6}$

16. $\dfrac{3x}{4} = \dfrac{2x}{3} + \dfrac{5}{12}$

17. $\dfrac{x + 2}{3} + \dfrac{x + 5}{4} = \dfrac{5}{2}$

18. $\dfrac{x - 1}{5} = \dfrac{17}{5} - \dfrac{x + 3}{2}$

19. $\dfrac{x}{5} - \dfrac{11}{15} = \dfrac{x - 3}{6}$

20. $\dfrac{3x - 1}{2} = \dfrac{x}{4} + \dfrac{9}{2}$

21. $\frac{1}{3}(4x + 1) - \frac{1}{2}(2x + 1) - \frac{1}{6} = 0$

22. $\frac{5}{6}(3x - 4) - \frac{3}{2}(4x + 2) = \frac{2}{3}$

23. A and B have the same number of coins.
A has two bags of coins and 23 extra coins.

B has three bags of coins and six extra coins.

Each bag has the same number of coins in it. How many coins are in each bag?

24. Find the value of x in each balance.

(i)

(ii)

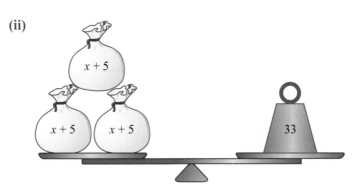

(iii)

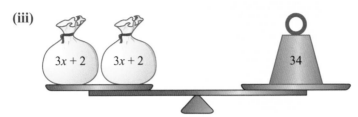

25. The perimeter of the isosceles triangle shown is 64 cm.
  (i) Using this information, write down an equation in terms of x.
  (ii) Solve the equation to find x.
  (iii) What is the length of the base, $(5x - 1)$ cm?

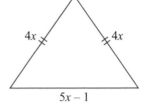

26. Two cylindrical buckets hold 18 litres and 6 litres of liquid, respectively. Another $2x$ litres of liquid are added to each bucket so that the first one now holds twice as much as the second one.
  (i) Express the volume of liquid in each bucket in terms of x.
  (ii) Form an equation in x.
  (iii) Solve the equation to find the value of x.

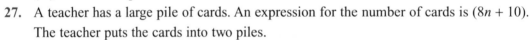

27. A teacher has a large pile of cards. An expression for the number of cards is $(8n + 10)$. The teacher puts the cards into two piles.
  (i) If one pile has $(3n + 6)$ cards, how many cards are in the other pile?
  (ii) One pile has $(5n + 1)$ cards. If there are 61 cards in this pile, how many cards are in the second pile?

28. Three consecutive numbers (e.g. 3, 4, 5) are x, $x + 1$ and $x + 2$. When the three numbers are added together the result is 33.
  (i) Use this information to form an equation.
  (ii) Solve the equation to find the value of x.
  (iii) What are the three numbers?

29. A girl bought a coat for $€\frac{x}{2}$ and a hat for $€\frac{x}{5}$. The total amount of money she spent was €70.
  (i) Use this information to form an equation.
  (ii) Solve the equation to find the value of x.
  (iii) Find the cost of her hat.

30. A rectangle has sides 8 cm and $(5x + 3)$ cm. A smaller rectangle with sides 5 cm and $(2x + 1)$ cm is cut from the larger rectangle. If the remaining area is 139 cm^2, calculate the value of x.

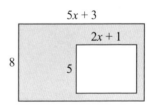

31. **(i)** What is an equilateral triangle?

   (ii) Could the triangle shown be an equilateral triangle? Justify your answer.

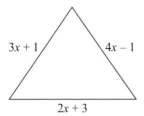

Simultaneous linear equations

Simultaneous linear equations in two variables are solved with the following steps.

1. Write both equations in the form $ax + by = k$, where a, b and k are whole numbers, and label the equations ① and ②.

2. Multiply one or both of the equations by a number in order to make the coefficients of x or y the same, but of opposite sign.

3. Add to remove the variable with equal coefficients but of opposite sign.

4. Solve the resultant equation to find the value of the remaining unknown (x or y).

5. Substitute this value in equation ① or ② to find the value of the other unknown.

EXAMPLE 1

Solve for x and y: $2x + 3y - 8 = 0$ and $\dfrac{3x}{2} + y - 1 = 0$.

Solution:

First write both equations in the form $ax + by = k$ and label the equations ① and ②.

$$2x + 3y - 8 = 0$$

$$2x + 3y = 8 \quad ① \quad \text{(in the form } ax + by = k \text{: label the equation ①)}$$

$$\frac{3x}{2} + y - 1 = 0$$

$$3x + 2y - 2 = 0 \quad \text{(multiply each part by 2)}$$

$$3x + 2y = 2 \quad ② \quad \text{(in the form } ax + by = k \text{: label the equation ②)}$$

Now solve between equations ① and ②:

$$2x + 3y = 8 \qquad ①$$
$$3x + 2y = 2 \qquad ②$$

$4x + 6y = 16$	① × 2
$-9x - 6y = -6$	② × -3
$-5x = 10$	(add)
$5x = -10$	
$x = -2$	

Put $x = -2$ into ① or ②:

$$2x + 3y = 8 \qquad ①$$

$$2(-2) + 3y = 8$$
$$-4 + 3y = 8$$
$$3y = 12$$
$$y = 4$$

∴ The solution is $x = -2$ and $y = 4$.

Solution containing fractions

If the solution contains fractions, the substitution can be difficult. In such cases, the following method is useful:

> 1. Eliminate y and find x.
> 2. Eliminate x and find y.

EXAMPLE 2

Solve the simultaneous equations $2x + 3y = -2$ and $3x + 7y = -6$.

Solution:

Both equations are in the form $ax + by = k$. Number the equations ① and ②.

1. Eliminate y and find x.

$2x + 3y = -2$	①
$3x + 7y = -6$	②
$14x + 21y = -14$	① × 7
$-9x - 21y = 18$	② × -3
$5x = 4$	(add)
$x = \frac{4}{5}$	

2. Eliminate x and find y.

$2x + 3y = -2$	①
$3x + 7y = -6$	②
$6x + 9y = -6$	① × 3
$-6x - 14y = 12$	② × -2
$-5y = 6$	(add)
$5y = -6$	
$y = -\frac{6}{5}$	

∴ The solution is $x = \frac{4}{5}$ and $y = -\frac{6}{5}$.

Note: This method can also be used if the solution does not contain fractions.

Exercise 1.4

Solve for x and y in questions 1–27.

1. $3x + 2y = 8$
   $2x - y = 3$

2. $5x - 3y = 14$
   $2x + y = 10$

3. $2x + y = 13$
   $x + 2y = 11$

4. $x + y = 7$
   $2x + y = 12$

5. $2x - 3y = 5$
   $x + y = -5$

6. $2x + y = 7$
   $3x - 2y = 0$

7. $x + y = 10$
   $x - y = 4$

8. $2x - 5y = 11$
   $3x + 2y = 7$

9. $2x + 3y = 12$
   $x + y = 5$

10. $2x - y = -3$
    $x - 2y = -3$

11. $2x - 3y - 14 = 0$
    $3x + 4y + 13 = 0$

12. $x - 4y - 3 = 0$
    $3x - y + 2 = 0$

13. $x - 2y = 0$
    $2(x + 3) = 3y + 5$

14. $5x + y = 19$
    $2x - y = 2(y - x)$

15. $3(x + y) + 2(y - x) = 4$
    $2(x - 2) = 3(y - 3)$

16. $3x + y = 9$
    $\dfrac{x}{2} - y = -2$

17. $2x - 5y = 19$
    $\dfrac{3x}{2} + \dfrac{4y}{3} = -1$

18. $3x - 4y = -3$
    $\dfrac{x}{2} + \dfrac{y}{3} = \dfrac{5}{2}$

19. $2x + 7y = 3$
    $x + y = \dfrac{x - 2y + 1}{2}$

20. $2(x - 5) = 3y$
    $\dfrac{2x + 1}{5} + \dfrac{x + y}{2} = 1$

21. $3x - 2y = y - 6x$
    $\dfrac{5x - 3y + 2}{2} = \dfrac{x - 2y + 4}{3}$

In questions 22–27, the solutions contain fractions.

22. $7x - 3y = 6$
    $3x - 6y = 1$

23. $5x + y = 10$
    $3x - y = 2$

24. $4x - 3y = 6$
    $2x + 6y = 13$

25. $2x + y = 2$
    $5x + 10y = 11$

26. $2x + 3y = 8$
    $2x - 3y = 2$

27. $x - y = 1$
    $3x + 5y = 7$

28. Seven books and three magazines cost €82. Two books and one magazine cost €24. Let €x be the price of a book and €y be the price of a magazine.

    (i) Write down an equation in x and y to show the price of
       (a) seven books and three magazines (b) two books and one magazine.

    (ii) Solve your two equations simultaneously.

    (iii) What is the price of (a) a book (b) a magazine?

    (iv) Calculate the price of 10 books and six magazines.

29. Here are four equations:
    A: $2x - y = 8$ B: $3x + y = 20$ C: $4x + 3y = 26$ D: $3x + 2y = 11$
    Here are four sets of (x, y) values: $(1, 4)$, $(5, 2)$, $(3, -2)$, $(-1, 23)$.
    Match each pair of (x, y) values to one of the equations, A, B, C or D.

30. The opposite sides in a parallelogram are equal in length. Use this information to calculate the values of x and y for the following parallelograms (all dimensions are in cm).

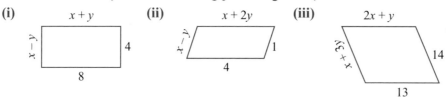

(i) $x + y$ **(ii)** $x + 2y$ **(iii)** $2x + y$

31. Solve for x and y.

(i)   **(ii)**

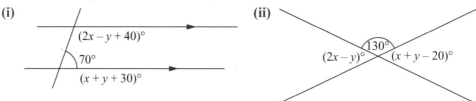

32. Andrew played a computer game. He scored 49 points by destroying five satellites and three planets and he scored 31 points by destroying three satellites and two planets. By letting $x =$ the number of points for destroying a satellite and $y =$ the number of points for destroying a planet, form two equations in x and y. By solving these equations, calculate the number of points Andrew scored for destroying a satellite and for destroying a planet.

33. Angela used her mobile phone to send eight text messages and four picture messages and was charged €1·44. When she sent three text messages and two picture messages she was charged €0·62. By letting $x =$ the cost of sending a text message and $y =$ the cost of sending a picture message, form two equations in x and y. By solving these equations, find the cost of each type of message.

34. The number in each square is the sum of the numbers in the two circles on either side of the square.

(i) P, Q, R and S are positive whole numbers. Calculate the value of P, Q, R and S.

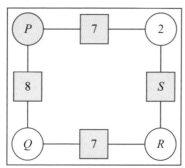

(ii) A, B, C, D and E are positive whole numbers. If $A = 3$, calculate the value of B, C, D and E.

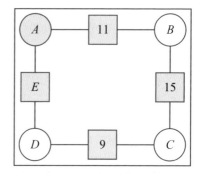

35. Each fruit symbol stands for a missing number. Calculate the value of each fruit.

(i)  = 30

(ii)  = 22

(iii) + + = 40

(iv) − − = 2

(v) + + + = 50

(vi) + + + + = 54

Factors required to solve quadratic equations

There are three types of quadratic expression we have to factorise to solve quadratic equations.

	Type	Example	Factors
1.	Quadratic trinomials	$2x^2 - 7x + 3$	$(2x - 1)(x - 3)$
2.	Taking out the HCF	$x^2 - x$	$x(x - 1)$
3.	Difference of two squares	$x^2 - 25$	$(x - 5)(x + 5)$

1. Quadratic trinomials
Factorising quadratic trinomials
Quadratic trinomials can be broken up into **two** types.

1. **Final term positive**

    When the final term is positive, the signs inside the middle of the brackets will be the **same,** either two pluses or two minuses. Keep the sign of the middle term given in the question.

    > Middle term plus: (number x + number)(number x + number)   (two pluses)
    > Middle term minus: (number x − number)(number x − number)   (two minuses)

2. **Final term negative**

    When the final term is negative, the signs inside the middle of the brackets will be **different**.

    > (number x + number)(number x − number)   (different signs)
    >
    > or
    >
    > (number x − number)(number x + number)   (different signs)

In both cases the factors can be found by trial and improvement. The test is to multiply the inside terms, multiply the outside terms and add the results to see if you get the middle term of the original quadratic trinomial.

EXAMPLE

Factorise each of the following.

(i) $x^2 + x - 20$ (ii) $2x^2 - 11x + 5$ (iii) $5x^2 - x - 6$

Solution:

(i) $x^2 + x - 20$

Final term $-$,

$\therefore$ the factors are $(x + \text{number})\,(x - \text{number})$

or

$(x - \text{number})\,(x + \text{number})$.

Factors of 20
1×20
2×10
4×5

Note: It is good practice to begin the trial and improvement with $(x + \text{number})(x - \text{number})$.

$(x + 2)(x - 10)$ $2x - 10x = -8x$ (no)

$(x + 4)(x - 5)$ $4x - 5x = -x$ (no, wrong sign)

On our second trial we have the correct number in front of x but of the wrong sign. So we just swap the signs:

$(x - 4)(x + 5)$ $-4x + 5x = x$ (yes, this is the middle term)

$\therefore x^2 + x - 20 = (x - 4)(x + 5)$

(ii) $2x^2 - 11x + 5$

The factors of $2x^2$ are $2x$ and x.

Final term $+$ and middle term $-$,

$\therefore$ the factors are $(2x - \text{number})(x - \text{number})$.

Factors of 5
1×5

1. $(2x - 5)(x - 1)$ middle term $= -5x - 2x = -7x$ (no)

2. $(2x - 1)(x - 5)$ middle term $= -x - 10x = -11x$ (yes)

$\therefore 2x^2 - 11x + 5 = (2x - 1)(x - 5)$

(iii) $5x^2 - x - 6$

The factors of $5x^2$ are $5x$ and x.

Final term $-$,

$\therefore$ the factors are $(5x + \text{number})(x - \text{number})$.

Factors of 6
1×6
2×3

Note: The signs inside these brackets could be swapped.

1. $(5x + 1)(x - 6)$ middle term $= x - 30x = -29x$ (no)

2. $(5x + 6)(x - 1)$ middle term $= 6x - 5x = x$ (no, wrong sign)

The second attempt has the wrong sign of the coefficient of the middle term. Therefore, all that is needed is to swap the signs in the middle of the brackets.

3. $(5x - 6)(x + 1)$ middle term $= -6x + 5x = -x$ (yes)

$$\therefore 5x^2 - x - 6 = (5x - 6)(x + 1)$$

2. Taking out the highest common factor (HCF)

EXAMPLE

Factorise: **(i)** $x^2 - 3x$ **(ii)** $2x^2 + x$

Solution:

(i) $x^2 - 3x$
    $= x(x - 3)$ (take out the highest common factor x)

(ii) $2x^2 + x$
    $= x(2x + 1)$ (take out the highest common factor x)

3. Difference of two squares

We factorise the difference of two squares with the following steps.

1. Write each term as a perfect square with brackets.
2. Use the rule $a^2 - b^2 = (a - b)(a + b)$.

In words: $(\text{first})^2 - (\text{second})^2 = (\text{first} - \text{second})(\text{first} + \text{second})$.

EXAMPLE

Factorise: **(i)** $x^2 - 16$ **(ii)** $x^2 - 1$

Solution:

(i) $x^2 - 16$
    $= (x)^2 - (4)^2$ (write each term as a perfect square in brackets)
    $= (x - 4)(x + 4)$ (apply the rule, $(\text{first} - \text{second})(\text{first} + \text{second})$)

(ii) $x^2 - 1$

   $= (x)^2 - (1)^2$ (write each term as a perfect square in brackets)

   $= (x - 1)(x + 1)$ (apply the rule, (first $-$ second)(first $+$ second))

Exercise 1.5

Factorise each of the following quadratic trinomials in questions 1–24.

1. $x^2 + 4x + 3$
2. $x^2 - 6x + 5$
3. $x^2 + 2x - 8$
4. $x^2 - 3x - 10$
5. $x^2 - 5x + 4$
6. $x^2 + 9x + 20$
7. $x^2 + x - 12$
8. $x^2 - 2x - 15$
9. $x^2 + 13x + 30$
10. $x^2 - 3x - 28$
11. $2x^2 + 5x + 3$
12. $2x^2 - 7x + 6$
13. $2x^2 + 9x - 5$
14. $2x^2 - x - 6$
15. $3x^2 + 16x + 5$
16. $3x^2 - 22x + 7$
17. $3x^2 + 10x - 8$
18. $3x^2 - x - 2$
19. $5x^2 + 8x + 3$
20. $5x^2 - 17x + 6$
21. $5x^2 + 9x - 2$
22. $5x^2 - 19x - 4$
23. $7x^2 - 36x + 5$
24. $11x^2 + 31x - 6$

Factorise each of the following by taking out the highest common factor in questions 25–33.

25. $x^2 + 2x$
26. $x^2 - 3x$
27. $x^2 + 4x$
28. $x^2 - 5x$
29. $x^2 + 6x$
30. $x^2 - x$
31. $x^2 + x$
32. $2x^2 + 3x$
33. $2x^2 - 5x$

Factorise each of the following using the difference of two squares in questions 34–39.

34. $x^2 - 4$
35. $x^2 - 16$
36. $x^2 - 25$
37. $x^2 - 64$
38. $x^2 - 100$
39. $x^2 - 49$

40. Expand (remove the brackets) each of the following and factorise your answer.

   (i) $x^2 - 2 + 2(3x + 5)$ (ii) $3(x^2 + 4x) - 2(x^2 + 3x) - x$ (iii) $5(x^2 - 1) - 4(x^2 + 1)$

41. Write down an expression for the missing lengths, l, of each of the following rectangles.

(i)

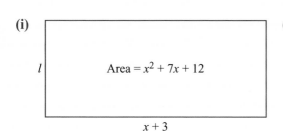

(ii)

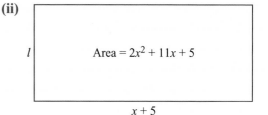

(iii)

$$l \begin{array}{|c|} \hline \\ \text{Area} = 3x^2 + 17x + 10 \\ \\ \hline \end{array}$$

$$3x + 2$$

EXAMPLE

Factorise $8x^2 + 2x - 15$.

Solution:

$8x^2 + 2x - 15$

The factors of $8x^2$ are $8x$ and x or $4x$ and $2x$.

Factors of 15
11×5
3×5

∴ The factors are:

$(8x + \text{number})(x - \text{number})$ or $(4x + \text{number})(2x - \text{number})$

Note: The signs inside these brackets could be swapped.

1. $(8x + 3)(x - 5)$ middle term $= 3x - 40x = -37x$ (no)

2. $(8x + 5)(x - 3)$ middle term $= 5x - 24x = -19x$ (no)

3. $(4x + 3)(2x - 5)$ middle term $= 6x - 20x = -14x$ (no)

4. $(4x + 5)(2x - 3)$ middle term $= 10x - 12x = -2x$ (no, wrong sign)

The fourth attempt has the wrong sign of the coefficient of the middle term. Therefore, all that is needed is to swap the signs in the middle of the brackets.

5. $(4x - 5)(2x + 3)$ middle term $= -10x + 12x = 2x$ (yes)

$$\boxed{\therefore 8x^2 + 2x - 15 = (4x - 5)(2x + 3)}$$

Exercise 1.6

Factorise each of the following.

1. $4x^2 + 8x + 3$
2. $4x^2 - 21x + 5$
3. $6x^2 + 11x + 3$
4. $6x^2 - 13x + 2$
5. $6x^2 - x - 2$
6. $8x^2 - 25x + 3$
7. $8x^2 + 6x - 5$
8. $9x^2 - 18x + 5$
9. $10x^2 - x - 3$

Quadratic equations

A quadratic equation is an equation in the form
$$ax^2 + bx + c = 0$$
where a, b and c are constants and $a \neq 0$.

Solving a quadratic equation means finding the two values of the variable which satisfy the equation. These values are called the **roots** of the equation. Sometimes the two roots are the same.

There are three types of quadratic equation we will meet on our course:

1. $x^2 - 2x - 3 = 0$ (three terms)
2. $x^2 - 5x = 0$ (no constant term)
3. $x^2 - 16 = 0$ (no x term)

Quadratic equations are solved with the following steps.

Method 1

1. Write the equation in the form $ax^2 + bx + c = 0$, where a, b and c are whole numbers.

    (If necessary, multiply both sides by -1 to make the coefficient of x^2 positive.)
2. Factorise the left-hand side.
3. Let each factor $= 0$.
4. Solve each simple equation.

Method 2

The roots of the quadratic equation $ax^2 + bx + c = 0$ are given by the formula:
$$x = \frac{-b \pm \sqrt{b^2 - 4ac}}{2a}$$

Notes:
1. The whole of the top of the right-hand side, including $-b$, is divided by $2a$.
2. It is often called the $-b$ or quadratic formula.
3. Before using the formula, make sure every term is on the left-hand side, i.e. write the equation in the form $ax^2 + bx + c = 0$.

Note: If $\sqrt{b^2 - 4ac}$ is a whole number, then $ax^2 + bx + c$ can be factorised.
The formula can still be used even if $ax^2 + bx + c$ can be factorised.

Quadratic equation type 1

EXAMPLE

Solve for x: $3x^2 - 5x - 12 = 0$.

Solution:

Method 1: Using factors

$$3x^2 - 5x - 12 = 0$$

$$(3x + 4)(x - 3) = 0 \qquad \text{(factorise the left-hand side)}$$

$$3x + 4 = 0 \qquad \text{or} \qquad x - 3 = 0 \qquad \text{(let each factor = 0)}$$

$$3x = -4 \qquad \text{or} \qquad x = 3$$

$$x = -\tfrac{4}{3} \qquad \text{or} \qquad x = 3 \qquad \text{(solve each simple equation)}$$

Method 2: Using the formula $x = \dfrac{-b \pm \sqrt{b^2 - 4ac}}{2a}$

$$3x^2 - 5x - 12 = 0$$

$$x = \frac{-b \pm \sqrt{b^2 - 4ac}}{2a}$$

$$x = \frac{5 \pm \sqrt{(-5)^2 - 4(3)(-12)}}{2(3)} \qquad (a = 3,\ b = -5,\ c = -12)$$

$$x = \frac{5 \pm \sqrt{25 + 144}}{6}$$

$$x = \frac{5 \pm \sqrt{169}}{6}$$

$$x = \frac{5 \pm 13}{6}$$

$$x = \frac{5 + 13}{6} \qquad \text{or} \qquad x = \frac{5 - 13}{6}$$

$$x = \frac{18}{6} \qquad \text{or} \qquad x = -\frac{8}{6}$$

$$x = 3 \qquad \text{or} \qquad x = -\frac{4}{3}$$

Quadratic equation type 2

 EXAMPLE

Solve for x: $x^2 + 5x = 0$.

Solution:

$$x^2 + 5x = 0 \qquad \text{(every term is on the left-hand side)}$$
$$x(x + 5) = 0 \qquad \text{(factorise the left-hand side)}$$
$$x = 0 \quad \text{or} \quad x + 5 = 0 \qquad \text{(let each factor = 0)}$$
$$x = 0 \quad \text{or} \quad x = -5 \qquad \text{(solve each simple equation)}$$

Note: It is important **not** to divide both sides by x, otherwise the root $x = 0$ is lost.

Quadratic equation type 3

 EXAMPLE

Solve for x: $x^2 - 4 = 0$.

Solution:

We will use two methods to solve this quadratic equation.

Method 1

$$x^2 - 4 = 0 \qquad \text{(every term is on the left-hand side)}$$
$$(x)^2 - (2)^2 = 0 \qquad \text{(difference of two squares)}$$
$$(x - 2)(x + 2) = 0 \qquad \text{(factorise the left-hand side)}$$
$$x - 2 = 0 \quad \text{or} \quad x + 2 = 0 \qquad \text{(let each factor = 0)}$$
$$x = 2 \quad \text{or} \quad x = -2 \qquad \text{(solve each simple equation)}$$

Method 2

$$x^2 - 4 = 0$$
$$x^2 = 4 \qquad \text{(add 4 to both sides)}$$
$$x = \pm\sqrt{4} \qquad \text{(take the square root of both sides)}$$
$$x = \pm 2$$
$$x = 2 \quad \text{or} \quad x = -2$$

Note: The examples in type 2 and type 3 could have been solved using the formula.

Exercise 1.7

Solve for x in each of the following quadratic equations in questions 1–33.

1. $(x - 2)(x - 3) = 0$ **2.** $(x + 5)(x - 4) = 0$ **3.** $(x - 3)(x + 7) = 0$

4. $x(x + 3) = 0$ **5.** $x(x - 5) = 0$ **6.** $x(x - 8) = 0$

7. $(x - 6)(x + 6) = 0$ **8.** $(x - 4)(x + 4) = 0$ **9.** $(x - 10)(x + 10) = 0$

In questions 10, 17, 21 and 23, verify your answers.

10. $x^2 - 7x + 12 = 0$ **11.** $x^2 + 6x + 8 = 0$ **12.** $x^2 - 2x - 15 = 0$

13. $x^2 - 6x + 5 = 0$ **14.** $x^2 + 3x - 10 = 0$ **15.** $x^2 + x - 20 = 0$

16. $x^2 - 6x - 7 = 0$ **17.** $x^2 - 9x + 14 = 0$ **18.** $x^2 - 5x - 24 = 0$

19. $x^2 - 4x = 0$ **20.** $x^2 + 6x = 0$ **21.** $x^2 - 2x = 0$

22. $x^2 - 9 = 0$ **23.** $x^2 - 25 = 0$ **24.** $x^2 - 1 = 0$

25. $2x^2 + 5x + 3 = 0$ **26.** $2x^2 - 7x + 6 = 0$ **27.** $2x^2 + 7x - 4 = 0$

28. $3x^2 + 10x - 8 = 0$ **29.** $3x^2 + 2x - 5 = 0$ **30.** $3x^2 - 7x + 2 = 0$

31. $5x^2 + 9x - 2 = 0$ **32.** $7x^2 + 5x - 2 = 0$ **33.** $2x^2 + 7x - 15 = 0$

In questions 34–39, first express each equation in the form $ax^2 + bx + c = 0$, where a, b and c are positive or negative whole numbers.

34. $\frac{1}{3}x^2 - x - 6 = 0$ **35.** $\frac{x^2}{4} - \frac{x}{2} - 2 = 0$ **36.** $\frac{x^2}{10} + \frac{x}{5} = \frac{3}{2}$

37. $\frac{1}{2}x^2 + x = 0$ **38.** $\frac{1}{4}x^2 - x = 0$ **39.** $\frac{1}{3}x^2 - 12 = 0$

40. Simplify $(2x - 1)(x + 1) - 2(x + 7)$ and factorise the simplified expression. Hence, solve $(2x - 1)(x + 1) - 2(x + 7) = 0$. Verify your answers.

Solve each of the following equations in questions 41–43.

41. $x(2x + 7) + 6 = 0$ **42.** $(x + 3)(x + 5) = 3 + x$ **43.** $(x - 1)^2 - 4 = 0$

44. Two whole numbers, x and $(x + 8)$, are multiplied together. The result is 84.

    (i) Write down an equation in x.

    (ii) Show that this equation can be expressed as $x^2 + 8x - 84 = 0$.

    (iii) Solve the equation to find the values of the two whole numbers.

45. A rectangular flowerbed measures $(2x + 5)$ m by $(x + 3)$ m. It has an area of 45 m². Find the value of x. Verify your answer.

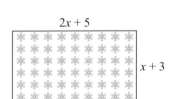

46. The triangle and the rectangle have equal areas, where $x > 0$.

   (i) Find the value of x and verify your answer.

   (ii) Find the perimeter of the triangle.

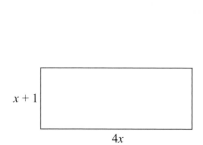
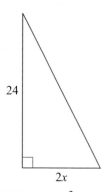

47. This rectangle is made up of four parts with areas of x^2, $5x$, $4x$ and 20 square units. If the area of the rectangle is 56 cm^2, calculate the value of x and verify your answer.

x^2	$5x$
$4x$	20

48. A square has length x cm. An open box is to be made by cutting 2 cm squares from each corner and folding up the sides. The volume of the box is 72 cm^3. Find the dimensions of the box.

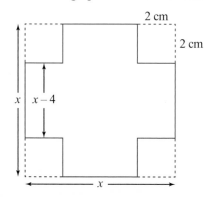
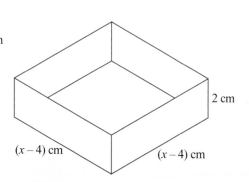

49. A closed rectangular box has a square base of side x cm. The height of the box is 2 cm. The total surface area of the box is 90 cm^2. Write down an equation in x to represent this information and use it to calculate x. Verify your answer.

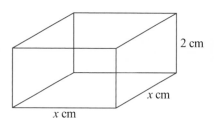

50. *AT* is a tangent to a circle of centre *O*, where *T* is a point on the circle.
$|OT| = x$ cm, $|AT| = (x + 2)$ cm and
$|OA| = (x + 4)$ cm.

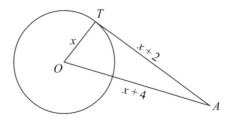

(i) Write down $|\angle OTA|$, giving a reason for your answer.

(ii) If the area of $\triangle OTA = 24$ cm^2, calculate the value of x and verify your answer.

(iii) Use another method to calculate the value of x.

Simplifying surds

Numbers such as $\sqrt{2}$, $\sqrt{3}$, $\sqrt{5}$ and $\sqrt{7}$ are called **surds**. They cannot be written as fractions. They are also called **irrational numbers**. Below is a property of surds that we use when solving quadratic equations with the quadratic formula.

Property	Example
1. $\sqrt{ab} = \sqrt{a}\sqrt{b}$	$\sqrt{20} = \sqrt{4 \times 5} = \sqrt{4}\sqrt{5} = 2\sqrt{5}$

When simplifying surds, the key idea is to find the largest possible square number bigger than 1 that will divide evenly into the number under the square root symbol.

The square numbers greater than 1 are 4, 9, 16, 25, 36, 49, 64, 81, 100, 121, 144, etc.

You can use your calculator to help you find the largest possible square number that will divide exactly into the number under the square root symbol. Try 4, then try 9, then try 16 and so on until you find the largest possible square number that will divide exactly.

EXAMPLE

Express (i) $\sqrt{18}$ (ii) $\sqrt{75}$ (iii) $\sqrt{80}$ in the form $a\sqrt{b}$, where $a \neq 1$.

Solution:
(i) $\sqrt{18} = \sqrt{9 \times 2} = \sqrt{9}\sqrt{2} = 3\sqrt{2}$
(ii) $\sqrt{75} = \sqrt{25 \times 3} = \sqrt{25}\sqrt{3} = 5\sqrt{3}$
(iii) $\sqrt{80} = \sqrt{16 \times 5} = \sqrt{16}\sqrt{5} = 4\sqrt{5}$

Quadratic formula

In many quadratic equations, $ax^2 + bx + c$ cannot be resolved into factors. When this happens the formula **must** be used. To save time trying to look for factors, a clue that you must use the formula is often given in the question. When the question requires an approximate answer, e.g. 'correct to two decimal places', 'correct to three significant figures', 'correct to the nearest integer' or 'express your answer in surd form', then the formula must be used.

The roots of the quadratic equation $ax^2 + bx + c = 0$ are given by the formula

$$x = \frac{-b \pm \sqrt{b^2 - 4ac}}{2a}.$$

Notes: 1. The whole of the top of the right-hand side, including $-b$, is divided by $2a$.

2. It is often called the $-b$ or quadratic formula.

3. Before using the formula, make sure every term is on the left-hand side, i.e. write the equation in the form $ax^2 + bx + c = 0$.

EXAMPLE

Solve the equation $x^2 - 4x + 1 = 0$.

Write your answers:
  (i) In the form $a \pm \sqrt{b}$, where $a, b \in \mathbb{N}$
 (ii) Correct to one decimal place

Solution:
The clues, write your answers **(i)** in the form $a \pm \sqrt{b}$ and   **(ii)** correct to one decimal place, mean we have to use the formula.
  (i) Answers in the form $a \pm \sqrt{b}$

$$x^2 - 4x + 1 = 0$$

$$x = \frac{-b \pm \sqrt{b^2 - 4a}}{2a}$$

$$x = \frac{4 \pm \sqrt{(-4)^2 - 4(1)(1)}}{2(1)} \qquad (a = 1, b = -4, c = 1)$$

$$x = \frac{4 \pm \sqrt{16 - 4}}{2}$$

$$x = \frac{4 \pm \sqrt{12}}{2}$$

$$x = \frac{4 \pm 2\sqrt{3}}{2}$$

$$(\sqrt{12} = \sqrt{4 \times 3} = \sqrt{4}\sqrt{3} = 2\sqrt{3})$$

$$x = \frac{4}{2} \pm \frac{2\sqrt{3}}{2}$$

$$x = 2 \pm \sqrt{3}$$

(ii) Correct to one decimal place

$x = 2 \pm \sqrt{3}$

$x = 2 + \sqrt{3}$ or $x = 2 - \sqrt{3}$

$x = 2 + 1{\cdot}732050808$ or $x = 2 - 1{\cdot}732050808$

$x = 3{\cdot}732050808$ or $x = 0{\cdot}2679491924$

$x = 3{\cdot}7$ or $x = 0{\cdot}3$, correct to one decimal place

Exercise 1.8

Write questions 1–10 in the form $a\sqrt{b}$, where $a \neq 1$.

1. $\sqrt{8}$ 2. $\sqrt{24}$ 3. $\sqrt{45}$ 4. $\sqrt{32}$ 5. $\sqrt{27}$

6. $\sqrt{48}$ 7. $\sqrt{54}$ 8. $\sqrt{125}$ 9. $\sqrt{90}$ 10. $\sqrt{50}$

Solve each of the following equations in questions 11–19, writing your answers (i) in the form $a \pm \sqrt{b}$ (ii) correct to two decimal places.

11. $x^2 - 2x - 4 = 0$ 12. $x^2 + 2x - 2 = 0$ 13. $x^2 - 4x - 1 = 0$

14. $x^2 + 6x + 7 = 0$ 15. $x^2 - 6x + 4 = 0$ 16. $x^2 + 8x + 13 = 0$

17. $x^2 + 10x + 23 = 0$ 18. $x^2 - 10x + 18 = 0$ 19. $x^2 + 12x + 33 = 0$

In questions 20–22, write your answer in the form $\dfrac{a \pm \sqrt{b}}{c}$.

20. $2x^2 - 2x - 1 = 0$ 21. $4x^2 + 2x - 1 = 0$ 22. $9x^2 + 6x - 1 = 0$

Solve each of the following equations in questions 23–25, giving your answers correct to two decimal places.

23. $x^2 - 4x - 14 = 0$ 24. $2x^2 - x - 2 = 0$ 25. $5x^2 + 7x - 4 = 0$

26. (i) A rectangle has dimensions $(x + 3)$ m by $(x + 1)$ m. If the area of the rectangle is 10 m^2, find the value of x correct to two decimal places.

(ii) Calculate the error by using your value of x.

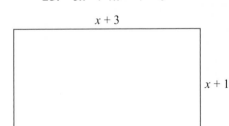

27. **(i)** Solve for x, $x(x - 2) = 3 + 2x$ and give your solution in the from $a \pm \sqrt{b}$, where $a, b \in \mathbb{N}$.
    (ii) Write one of your solutions correct to two decimal places.
    (iii) Using this value, show that the difference between the values of the left-hand side and the right-hand side of the given equation is less than 0.1.

28. The diagram shows a trapezium. The measurements on the diagram are in cm.

    The lengths of the parallel sides are x cm and 14 cm.

    The height of the trapezium is $2x$ cm.

    The area of the trapezium is 100 cm².

    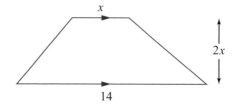

    (i) Show that $x^2 + 14x - 100 = 0$.
    (ii) Find the value of x. Give your answer correct to one decimal place.
    (iii) Calculate the error by using this value of x.

Quadratic equations in fractional form

Quadratic equations in fractional form are solved with the following steps.

1. Multiply each part of the equation by the LCM of the expressions on the bottom.
2. Simplify both sides (no fractions left).
3. Proceed as in the previous section on solving quadratic equations.

EXAMPLE 1

Solve for x: $x - 2 - \dfrac{8}{x} = 0$.

Solution:

$$x - 2 - \frac{8}{x} = 0$$

$$x^2 - 2x - 8 = 0 \qquad \text{(multiply each term by } x\text{)}$$

$$(x + 2)(x - 4) = 0 \qquad \text{(factorise the left-hand side)}$$

$$x + 2 = 0 \quad \text{or} \quad x - 4 = 0 \qquad \text{(let each factor} = 0)$$

$$x = -2 \quad \text{or} \quad x = 4 \qquad \text{(solve each simple equation)}$$

EXAMPLE 2

Solve the equation: $\dfrac{3}{2} - \dfrac{1}{x} = \dfrac{1}{x-1}$.

Solution:

$$\dfrac{3}{2} - \dfrac{1}{x} = \dfrac{1}{(x-1)}$$
(put brackets on $(x-1)$)

$$2x(x-1)\left(\dfrac{3}{2}\right) - 2x(x-1)\left(\dfrac{1}{x}\right) = 2x(x-1)\dfrac{1}{(x-1)}$$
(the LCM is $2x(x-1)$)
(multiply each part by $2x(x-1)$)

$$3x(x-1) - 2(x-1) = 2x$$
(simplify both sides)

$$3x^2 - 3x - 2x + 2 = 2x$$
(remove the brackets)

$$3x^2 - 3x - 2x + 2 - 2x = 0$$
(every term on the left-hand side)

$$3x^2 - 7x + 2 = 0$$
(simplify the left-hand side)

$$(3x - 1)(x - 2) = 0$$
(factorise the left-hand side)

$$3x - 1 = 0 \quad \text{or} \quad x - 2 = 0$$
(let each factor $= 0$)

$$3x = 1 \quad \text{or} \quad x = 2$$

$$x = \tfrac{1}{3} \quad \text{or} \quad x = 2$$
(solve each simple equation)

Exercise 1.9

Solve for x in questions 1–27.

1. $x - 3 + \dfrac{2}{x} = 0$

2. $x - 7 + \dfrac{12}{x} = 0$

3. $x + 2 - \dfrac{15}{x} = 0$

4. $x - \dfrac{2}{x} = 1$

5. $2x = 5 - \dfrac{3}{x}$

6. $3x = \dfrac{3}{x} - 8$

7. $x - \dfrac{4}{x} = 0$

8. $x = \dfrac{25}{x}$

9. $x = \dfrac{1}{x}$

10. $1 = \dfrac{3}{x} - \dfrac{4}{x+1}$

11. $6 = \dfrac{1}{x} - \dfrac{1}{x+3}$

12. $1 = \dfrac{9}{x+8} + \dfrac{1}{x}$

13. $4 = \dfrac{1}{x} - \dfrac{3}{x-2}$

14. $\dfrac{1}{20} = \dfrac{1}{x} - \dfrac{1}{x+1}$

15. $3 = \dfrac{1}{x} - \dfrac{2}{x-2}$

16. $\dfrac{3}{x-1} - \dfrac{2}{x+1} = 1$

17. $\dfrac{5}{2x-1} + 1 = \dfrac{6}{x}$

18. $\dfrac{1}{x} - \dfrac{1}{x+2} = \dfrac{1}{4}$

19. $\dfrac{2}{x} - \dfrac{3}{x+1} = \dfrac{1}{2}$

20. $\dfrac{2}{x-1} - \dfrac{1}{x+2} = \dfrac{1}{2}$

21. $\dfrac{3}{x-2} - \dfrac{1}{x} = \dfrac{5}{4}$

In questions 22 to 24, write your answers correct to two decimal places:

22. $x + \dfrac{1}{x} = 3$

23. $4 = \dfrac{1}{x+1} + \dfrac{2}{x}$

24. $\dfrac{1}{x+2} - \dfrac{1}{x} = 3$

In questions 25 to 27, write your answers in the form $a + \sqrt{b}, \quad a, b \in \mathbb{N}$:

25. $x - \dfrac{1}{x} = 2$

26. $\dfrac{3}{x+1} + \dfrac{1}{x-1} = 1$

27. $\dfrac{1}{3} = \dfrac{2}{x} - \dfrac{1}{x+1}$

28. **(i)** Write $\dfrac{1}{x+1} + \dfrac{2}{x-3}$ as a single fraction.

(ii) Hence or otherwise, find, correct to one decimal place, the two solutions of:

$$\frac{1}{x+1} + \frac{2}{x-3} = 1$$

29. **(i)** Write $\dfrac{1}{x+1} + \dfrac{1}{x-1}$ as a single fraction.

(ii) Hence or otherwise, solve the equation $\dfrac{1}{2} = \dfrac{1}{x+1} + \dfrac{1}{x-1}$,

giving your solutions in the form $a \pm \sqrt{b}, a, b \in \mathbb{N}$.

Constructing a quadratic equation when given its roots

This is the reverse process to solving a quadratic equation by using factors.

EXAMPLE

Find a quadratic equation with roots **(i)** -2 and 3 **(ii)** $\frac{2}{3}$ and $-\frac{1}{5}$.

Write your answers in the form $ax^2 + bx + c = 0, \quad a, b, c \in \mathbb{Z}$.

Solution:

(i) Roots -2 and 3

Let $x = -2$ and $x = 3$

$x + 2 = 0$ and $x - 3 = 0$

$(x + 2)(x - 3) = 0$

$x^2 - 3x + 2x - 6 = 0$

$x^2 - x - 6 = 0$

(ii) Roots $\frac{2}{3}$ and $-\frac{1}{5}$

Let $x = \frac{2}{3}$ and $x = -\frac{1}{5}$

$3x = 2$ and $5x = -1$

$3x - 2 = 0$ and $5x + 1 = 0$

$(3x - 2)(5x + 1) = 0$

$15x^2 + 3x - 10x - 2 = 0$

$15x^2 - 7x - 2 = 0$

Note: $0 \times 0 = 0$

Exercise 1.10

In questions 1–20, construct a quadratic equation with roots.

(In each case, write your answer in the form $ax^2 + bx + c = 0$, $a, b, c \in \mathbb{Z}$.)

1. 2, 3
2. −1, 2
3. −2, 5
4. −1, 4
5. −3, −2
6. 4, 5
7. −3, 4
8. −8, 3
9. −3, 3
10. 2, 2
11. −2, 0
12. 0, 5
13. −1, 1
14. $\frac{1}{2}$, 3
15. $-\frac{1}{3}$, 2
16. $-3, \frac{1}{2}$
17. $-1, \frac{5}{2}$
18. $\frac{1}{3}, \frac{1}{2}$
19. $\frac{1}{3}, -\frac{2}{3}$
20. $\frac{1}{2}, \frac{3}{4}$

21. The equation $x^2 + mx + n = 0$ has roots −3 and 5. Find the values of m and n.

22. The equation $ax^2 + bx + c = 0$ has roots $-\frac{1}{2}$ and $\frac{2}{5}$. Find one set of values of a, b and c, where $a, b, c \in \mathbb{Z}$.

Simultaneous equations, one linear and one quadratic

The solution of a pair of simultaneous equations where one is linear (line) and one is quadratic (curve) represents the points of intersection of a line and a curve. Graphing a line and a curve will lead to three possibilities.

1.	2.	3.
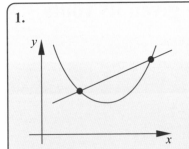	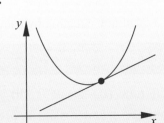	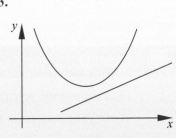
Two points of intersection Line meets the curve in two different points	**One point of intersection** Line is a tangent to the curve	**No point of intersection** Line misses the curve

The **method of substitution** is used to solve between a linear equation and a quadratic equation. The method involves three steps.

1. From the linear equation, express one variable in terms of the other.
2. Substitute this into the quadratic equation and solve.
3. Substitute **separately** the value(s) obtained in step 2 into the linear equation in step 1 to find the corresponding value(s) of the other variable.

EXAMPLE 1

Solve for x and y: $x + 3 = 2y$ and $xy - 7y + 8 = 0$.

Solution:

$x + 3 = 2y$ and $xy - 7y + 8 = 0$

1. $x + 3 = 2y$ (get x on its own from the linear equation)

       $x = 2y - 3$ (x on its own)

2. $xy - 7y + 8 = 0$

    $(2y - 3)y - 7y + 8 = 0$ (put in $(2y - 3)$ for x)

    $2y^2 - 3y - 7y + 8 = 0$ (remove the brackets)

      $2y^2 - 10y + 8 = 0$ (simplify the left-hand side)

       $y^2 - 5y + 4 = 0$ (divide both sides by 2)

    $(y - 1)(y - 4) = 0$ (factorise the left-hand side)

     $y - 1 = 0$ or $y - 4 = 0$ (let each factor $= 0$)

       $y = 1$ or $y = 4$ (solve each simple equation)

3.   Substitute $y = 1$ and $y = 4$ separately into the linear equation.

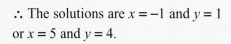

$y = 1$	$y = 4$
$x = 2y - 3$	$x = 2y - 3$
$x = 2(1) - 3$	$x = 2(4) - 3$
$x = 2 - 3$	$x = 8 - 3$
$x = -1$	$x = 5$
$x = -1, y = 1$	$x = 5, y = 4$

$\therefore$ The solutions are $x = -1$ and $y = 1$
or $x = 5$ and $y = 4$.

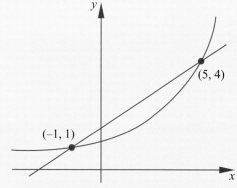

The line and the curve meet at the points $(-1, 1)$ and $(5, 4)$.

EXAMPLE 2

Solve for x and y: $x + y = 7$ and $x^2 + y^2 = 29$.

Solution:

$x + y = 7$ and $x^2 + y^2 = 29$

1. $x + y = 7$ (get x or y on its own from the linear equation)

       $y = 7 - x$ (y on its own)

2.
$$x^2 + y^2 = 29$$
$$x^2 + (7 - x)^2 = 29 \qquad \text{(put in } (7-x) \text{ for } y)$$
$$x^2 + 49 - 14x + x^2 = 29 \qquad ((7-x)^2 = 49 - 14x + x^2)$$
$$2x^2 - 14x + 49 = 29 \qquad \text{(simplify the left-hand side)}$$
$$2x^2 - 14x + 20 = 0 \qquad \text{(subtract 29 from both sides)}$$
$$x^2 - 7x + 10 = 0 \qquad \text{(divide both sides by 2)}$$
$$(x - 2)(x - 5) = 0 \qquad \text{(factorise the left-hand side)}$$
$$x - 2 = 0 \quad \text{or} \quad x - 5 = 0 \quad \text{(let each factor} = 0)$$
$$x = 2 \quad \text{or} \quad x = 5 \quad \text{(solve each simple equation)}$$

3. Substitute $x = 2$ and $x = 5$ separately into the linear equation.

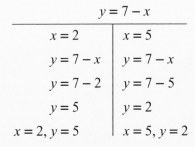

$y = 7 - x$	
$x = 2$	$x = 5$
$y = 7 - x$	$y = 7 - x$
$y = 7 - 2$	$y = 7 - 5$
$y = 5$	$y = 2$
$x = 2, y = 5$	$x = 5, y = 2$

$\therefore$ The solutions are

$x = 2$ and $y = 5$ or $x = 5$ and $y = 2$.

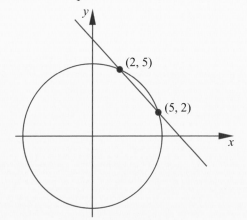

The line and curve meet at the points (2, 5) and (5, 2).

Exercise 1.11

1. Solve each of the following pairs of simultaneous equations.

    (i) $y = x - 5$ and $y = x^2 - 5x + 3$ **(ii)** $y = 3x + 2$ and $y = x^2 + x - 1$

2. In the following, $f(x)$ represents the line and $g(x)$ represents the curve. In each case, find the coordinates of the points of intersection.

(i) $f(x) = x + 3$ $g(x) = x^2 - 2x - 7$ (ii) $f(x) = 2x - 3$ $g(x) = 9 + x - x^2$

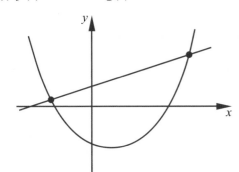

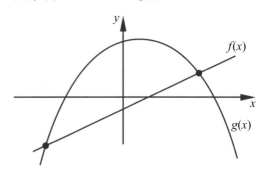

3. Verify that the line $4x - y - 7 = 0$ is a tangent to the curve $y = x^2 - 2x + 2$ and find the coordinates of the point of contact.

Solve each of the following pairs of simultaneous equations in questions 4–6.

4. $x + y = 5$
   $xy = 6$

5. $x - y = 1$
   $xy = 2$

6. $2x + y - 6 = 0$
   $xy = 4$

Write down the expansion of each of the following in questions 7–14.

7. $(x + 3)^2$

8. $(x - 2)^2$

9. $(y - 1)^2$

10. $(y + 3)^2$

11. $(2 + x)^2$

12. $(1 - 2x)^2$

13. $(3 - 2x)^2$

14. $(3 - 5y)^2$

Solve each of the following for x and y in questions 15–23.

15. $x + y = 3$
    $x^2 + y^2 = 17$

16. $x - y = 1$
    $x^2 + y^2 = 25$

17. $y = x + 1$
    $x^2 + y^2 = 1$

18. $x - 2y = 0$
    $x^2 + y^2 = 20$

19. $x = 2y + 5$
    $x^2 + y^2 = 25$

20. $x + y = 5$
    $x^2 + y^2 = 13$

21. $x - y - 4 = 0$
    $y^2 + 3x = 16$

22. $x = 3 - y$
    $x^2 - y^2 + 3 = 0$

23. $2x + y = 1$
    $x^2 + xy + y^2 = 7$

24. (i) Solve for x and y: $y = 10 - 2x$ and $x^2 + y^2 = 25$.

    (ii) Hence, find the two possible values of $x^3 + y^3$.

25. A rectangle has dimensions as shown. Its perimeter is 14 cm and its area is 12 cm².

    (i) Derive the equations $x + y = 7$ and $xy = 12$.

    (ii) Solve the equations and deduce the dimensions of the rectangle.

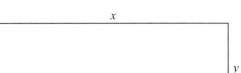

26. A right-angled triangle has dimensions as shown.
Its perimeter is 24 cm and its area is 24 cm^2.

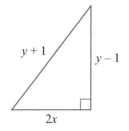

   (i) Derive the equations $x + y = 12$ and $xy - x = 24$,
   where $x < y$.

   (ii) Solve the equations and deduce the dimensions
   of the triangle.

27. The graph below shows a line $f(x) =$
$x + 1$ and a curve $g(x) = -x^2 + 10x - 7$.
The line represents the top flat
surface of a hill and the curve
represents the flight path of a
projectile.

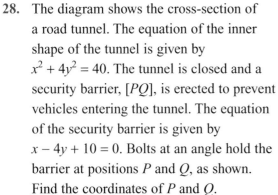

   The projectile is fired from point A
   and it lands at point B.

   (i) Find the coordinates of points A
   and B.

   (ii) Calculate $|AB|$.

28. The diagram shows the cross-section of
a road tunnel. The equation of the inner
shape of the tunnel is given by
$x^2 + 4y^2 = 40$. The tunnel is closed and a
security barrier, $[PQ]$, is erected to prevent
vehicles entering the tunnel. The equation
of the security barrier is given by
$x - 4y + 10 = 0$. Bolts at an angle hold the
barrier at positions P and Q, as shown.
Find the coordinates of P and Q.

29. A model railway bridge is supported
by straight bars connected to an arch,
as shown. The arch is resting on the
ground. The ground is represented by
the x-axis and the arch is symmetrical
about the y-axis.

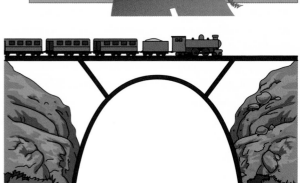

   The equations of the straight bars
   are given by $2x - y + 6 = 0$ and
   $2x + y - 6 = 0$.

The equation of the arched frame is given by $20x^2 + y^2 = 180$.

The equation of the railway track is given by $y = 16$.

Find the coordinates of the points where:

(i) The straight bars meet the arched frame

(ii) The straight bars meet the railway line

Inequalities

The four inequality symbols are:

1.	$>$ means greater than	**2.**	$\geq$ means greater than or equal to
3.	$<$ means less than	**4.**	$\leq$ means less than or equal to

Algebraic expressions that are linked by one of the four inequality symbols are called **inequalities**. For example, $3x - 1 \leq 11$ and $-3 < 2x - 1 \leq 7$ are inequalities.

Solving inequalities is exactly the same as solving equations, with the following exception:

Multiplying or dividing both sides of an inequality by a **negative** number
reverses the direction of the inequality symbol.

That is:

$>$ changes to $<$ $\geq$ changes to $\leq$

$<$ changes to $>$ $\leq$ changes to $\geq$

For example, $5 > -3$ is true. If we multiply both sides by -1, it gives $-5 < 3$, which is also true.

Solving an inequality means finding the values of x that make the inequality true.

The following rules apply to graphing inequalities on a number line:

Number line for $x \in \mathbb{N}$ or $x \in \mathbb{Z}$, use **dots**.

Number line for $x \in \mathbb{R}$, use a **full** heavy line.

Note: Inequalities can be turned around. For example:

$5 \leq x$ means the same as $x \geq 5$

$8 \geq x \geq 3$ means the same as $3 \leq x \leq 8$

Single variable linear inequalities

EXAMPLE 1

Find the solution set of $14 - 3x \geq 2$, $x \in \mathbb{N}$ and graph your solution on the number line.

Solution:

$$14 - 3x \geq 2$$

$$-3x \geq -12 \qquad \text{(subtract 14 from both sides)}$$

$$3x \leq 12 \qquad \text{(multiply both sides by } -1 \text{ and reverse the inequality symbol)}$$

$$x \leq 4 \qquad \text{(divide both sides by 3)}$$

As $x \in \mathbb{N}$, this is the set of natural numbers less than or equal to 4.
Thus, the values of x are 1, 2, 3 and 4.

Number line:

Note: As $x \in \mathbb{N}$, dots are used on the number line.

EXAMPLE 2

Solve the inequality $3x - 2 < 7x + 6$, $x \in \mathbb{R}$ and illustrate the solution on the number line.

Solution:

$$3x - 2 < 7x + 6$$

$$3x < 7x + 8 \qquad \text{(add 2 to both sides)}$$

$$-4x < 8 \qquad \text{(subtract } 7x \text{ from both sides)}$$

$$4x > -8 \qquad \text{(multiply both sides by } -1 \text{ and reverse the inequality)}$$

$$x > -2 \qquad \text{(divide both sides by 4)}$$

This is the set of real numbers greater than -2 (-2 is **not** included).

Number line:

A circle is put around -2 to indicate that it is **not** part of the solution.

Note: As $x \in \mathbb{R}$, we use full heavy shading on the number line.

EXAMPLE 3

(i) Find A, the solution set of $7x - 1 \leq 27$, $x \in \mathbb{Z}$.

(ii) Find B, the solution set of $\dfrac{5 - 3x}{2} \leq 4$, $x \in \mathbb{Z}$.

(iii) Find $A \cap B$ and graph your solution on the number line.

Solution:

(i) A: $7x - 1 \leq 27$

$\qquad 7x \leq 28$

$\qquad\quad x \leq 4$

(ii) B: $\dfrac{5 - 3x}{2} \leq 4$

$\qquad 5 - 3x \leq 8$

$\qquad$ (multiply both sides by 2)

$\qquad\quad -3x \leq 3$

$\qquad\quad\ \ 3x \geq -3$

$\qquad\qquad x \geq -1$

(iii) $A \cap B$: combining the two inequalities:

$$-1 \leq x \leq 4$$

This is the set of positive and negative whole numbers between -1 and 4, including -1 and 4.

Number line:

Note: As $x \in \mathbb{Z}$, dots are used on the number line.

Double inequalities

A double inequality is one like $-3 \leq 2x + 1 \leq 7$.

There are two methods for solving double inequalities.

Method 1

> Whatever we do to one part, we do the same to all three parts.

Method 2

> 1. Write the double inequality as two separate simple inequalities.
> 2. Solve each simple inequality and combine their solutions.

EXAMPLE

Solve the inequality $-6 \le 5x - 1 < 9, \quad x \in \mathbb{R}$.
Graph your solution on a number line.

Solution:

Method 1:   Do the same to all three parts.

$$-6 \le 5x - 1 < 9$$
$$-5 \le 5x < 10 \qquad \text{(add 1 to each part)}$$
$$-1 \le x < 2 \qquad \text{(divide each part by 5)}$$

Method 2:   Write the double inequality as two separate inequalities.

$$-6 \le 5x - 1 \qquad\qquad \text{and} \qquad\qquad 5x - 1 < 9$$
$$-6 \le 5x - 1 \qquad\qquad\qquad\qquad\qquad 5x - 1 < 9$$
$$-5 \le 5x \qquad\qquad\qquad\qquad\qquad\qquad 5x < 10$$
$$-1 \le x \qquad\qquad\qquad\qquad\qquad\qquad x < 2$$

$$-1 \le x < 2 \qquad\qquad \text{(combining solutions)}$$

Number line:

A circle is put around 2 to indicate that 2 is **not** included in the solution.

Note: As $x \in \mathbb{R}$, we use full heavy shading on the number line.

Exercise 1.12

Solve each of the following inequalities in questions 1–18. In each case, graph your solution on the number line.

1. $2x + 1 \ge 7, \quad x \in \mathbb{R}$
2. $3x + 1 \le 13, \quad x \in \mathbb{R}$
3. $5x - 3 > 3x + 1, \quad x \in \mathbb{N}$
4. $8x - 1 < 3x + 9, \quad x \in \mathbb{R}$
5. $2x - 1 \ge 4x - 7, \quad x \in \mathbb{R}$
6. $6x - 10 \le 9x + 5, \quad x \in \mathbb{Z}$
7. $2(x + 4) < 2 - x, \quad x \in \mathbb{R}$
8. $4(x - 2) \ge 5(2x - 1) - 9, \quad x \in \mathbb{R}$
9. $\dfrac{x}{2} + \dfrac{x}{3} \ge \dfrac{5}{6}, \quad x \in \mathbb{R}$
10. $\dfrac{3x}{5} - \dfrac{x}{2} \le \dfrac{3}{10}, \quad x \in \mathbb{R}$

11. $2x + 1 \leq 5, \quad x \in \mathbb{N}$

12. $4x - 15 \leq 1, \quad x \in \mathbb{N}$

13. $13 - 2x < 3, \quad x \in \mathbb{N}$

14. $12 - 5x > 2, \quad x \in \mathbb{N}$

15. $4 \leq 2x \leq 10, \quad x \in \mathbb{N}$

16. $-4 \leq 3x - 1 < 11, \quad x \in \mathbb{Z}$

17. $-7 \leq 5x + 3 < 18, \quad x \in \mathbb{R}$

18. $-5 < 4x + 7 \leq 35, \quad x \in \mathbb{R}$

19. (i) Find the solution set of (a) $A: x - 1 \geq 2, \quad x \in \mathbb{R}$ (b) $B: x + 4 \leq 9, \quad x \in \mathbb{R}$.

    (ii) Find $A \cap B$ and graph your solution on the number line.

20. (i) Find the solution set of (a) $H: 2x - 3 \leq 5, \quad x \in \mathbb{R}$ (b) $K: 3x + 2 \geq -4, \quad x \in \mathbb{R}$.

    (ii) Find $H \cap K$ and graph your solution on the number line.

21. (i) Find the solution set E of $2x + 7 \leq 19, \quad x \in \mathbb{R}$.

    (ii) Find the solution set H of $3 - 2x \leq 11, \quad x \in \mathbb{R}$.

    (iii) Find $E \cap H$.

22. (i) Find the solution set H of $2x + 5 \geq -1, \quad x \in \mathbb{R}$.

    (ii) Find the solution set K of $7 - 3x \geq 4, \quad x \in \mathbb{R}$.

    (iii) Find $H \cap K$ and graph your solution on a number line.

23. (i) Find A, the solution set of $3x - 2 \leq 4, \quad x \in \mathbb{Z}$.

    (ii) Find B, the solution set of $\dfrac{1 - 3x}{2} < 5, \quad x \in \mathbb{Z}$.

    (iii) List the elements of $A \cap B$.

24. (i) Find the solution set E of $9 - 2x \geq 7, \quad x \in \mathbb{N}$.

    (ii) Find the solution set H of $\frac{1}{4}x - \frac{1}{3} \leq \frac{5}{12}, \quad x \in \mathbb{N}$.

    (iii) Write down the elements of the set $H \setminus E$.

25. Find the smallest natural number k such that $2x + 4(x + 3) + 7(2x + 4) < 20(x + k)$.

26. Show that there are no real numbers which simultaneously satisfy the two inequalities $2x - 1 \geq 9$ and $3x + 2 \leq 14$. Explain your answer.

27. Write down the values of x that satisfy each of the following.

    (i) $x - 1 \leq 4$, where x is a positive, even number.

    (ii) $x + 4 < 6$, where x is a positive, odd number.

    (iii) $2x - 13 < 37$, where x is a square number.

    (iv) $2x + 5 < 27$, where x is a prime number.

28. Aishling said, 'I thought of a whole number, multiplied it by 5 then subtracted 3. The answer was between 11 and 23.' List the whole numbers that Aishling could have used.

29. The lengths of the sides of a triangle are $(2x + 3)$ cm, $(2x + 2)$ cm and x cm. Find the range of values of x for which this triangle exists.

30. Match the words with the correct inequality shown on the right.

    (i) x is less than 6   **(ii)** x is greater than or equal to 6

  (iii) x is greater than 6   **(iv)** x is less than or equal to 6

   (v) x is at least 6   **(vi)** x has a maximum value of 6

 (vii) x is at most 6   **(viii)** x has a minimum value of 6

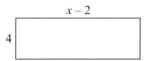

A: $x \geq 6$
B: $x > 6$
C: $x \leq 6$
D: $x < 6$

31.   **(i)** A rectangle has dimensions as shown. Explain why $x > 2$.

     (ii) The number of centimetres in its perimeter is greater than the number of square centimetres in its area. Write an equality to represent this information and solve it to find the range of values of x.

$x - 2$

4

32. A family has four children. The table shows some information about their ages in years.

Name	Andrew	Bernadette	Catherine	Dermot
Age in years	n	$2n + 6$	14	22

    (i) Bernadette is older than Catherine but younger than Dermot. Calculate Andrew's possible ages.

   (ii) Could any of these children be twins? Justify your answer.

33. The diagram shows a map of an island. A gold coin is buried at a place where the x and y coordinates are positive whole numbers. Use the clues to work out the coordinates where the gold coin is buried.

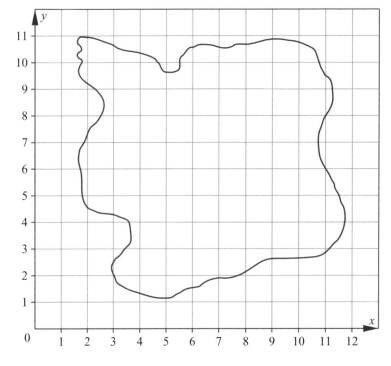

Clues:

   (i) $x > 7$

  (ii) $y > 6$

 (iii) $x + y = 17$

 (iv) One of x and y is prime and the other is not

Changing the subject of a formula

When we rearrange a formula so that one of the variables is given in terms of the others, we are **changing the subject of the formula**.

Changing the subject of a formula is solved with the following method:

> Whatever you do to one side, you must do **exactly the same** to the other side.

Note: Keep balance in mind. Whatever letter comes after the word 'express' is to be on its own.

EXAMPLE

(i)   Given that $px - q = r$, express x in terms of p, q and r, where $p \neq 0$.

(ii)   Given that $u^2 + 2as = v^2$, express s in terms of v, u and a.

(iii)   Express x in terms of r and s when $r - \dfrac{x}{s} = 1$, $\quad s \neq 0$.

(iv)   Express t in terms of p and q when $p = \dfrac{q - t}{3t}$, $\quad t \neq 0$.

Solution:

(i) $px - q = r$

$$px = r + q \qquad \text{(add } q \text{ to both sides)}$$

$$\frac{px}{p} = \frac{r + q}{p} \qquad \text{(divide both sides by } p\text{)}$$

$$x = \frac{r + q}{p} \qquad \text{(simplify the left-hand side)}$$

(ii) $u^2 + 2as = v^2$

$$2as = v^2 - u^2 \qquad \text{(subtract } u^2 \text{ from both sides)}$$

$$\frac{2as}{2a} = \frac{v^2 - u^2}{2a} \qquad \text{(divide both sides by } 2a\text{)}$$

$$s = \frac{v^2 - u^2}{2a} \qquad \text{(simplify the left-hand side)}$$

(iii) $r - \dfrac{x}{s} = 1$

$$sr - \frac{sx}{s} = s(1) \qquad \text{(multiply each part by } s\text{)}$$

$$sr - x = s \qquad \left(\frac{sx}{s} = x \text{ and } s(1) = s\right)$$

$$-x = s - sr \qquad \text{(subtract } sr \text{ from both sides)}$$

$$x = -s + sr \qquad \text{(multiply both sides by } -1\text{)}$$

(iv) $p = \dfrac{q-t}{3t}$

$3tp = \dfrac{3t(q-t)}{3t}$ (multiply both sides by $3t$)

$3tp = q - t$ (simplify the right-hand side)

$3tp + t = q$ (add t to both sides)

$t(3p + 1) = q$ (take out the common factor t on the left-hand side)

$\dfrac{t(3p+1)}{3p+1} = \dfrac{q}{3p+1}$ (divide both sides by $(3p+1)$)

$t = \dfrac{q}{3p+1}$ (simplify the left-hand side)

Exercise 1.13

Change each of the formulae in questions 1–30 to express the letter in square brackets in terms of the others.

1. $2a - b = c$ [a]
2. $3p + q = r$ [p]
3. $ab - c = d$ [a]
4. $u + at = v$ [t]
5. $3a + 2b = 5c$ [b]
6. $3q - 4p = 2r$ [q]
7. $2(a - b) = c$ [a]
8. $a(b - c) = d$ [b]
9. $x(y + z) = w$ [y]
10. $\frac{1}{2}a = b$ [a]
11. $\frac{b}{2} + c = a$ [b]
12. $s + \frac{t}{3} = r$ [t]
13. $\frac{a}{2} + \frac{b}{3} = c$ [a]
14. $\frac{p+q}{2} = r$ [q]
15. $r = \frac{1}{3}(p - q)$ [p]
16. $a = \frac{b - 2c}{3}$ [c]
17. $x + \frac{w}{y} = z$ [w]
18. $2p + \frac{3q}{r} = s$ [q]
19. $\frac{p - 3r}{q} = 5$ [p]
20. $s = \frac{p}{q} + \frac{r}{q}$ [q]
21. $\frac{2a}{b} - \frac{3c}{b} = d$ [b]
22. $\frac{1}{2}(3a + b) = \frac{1}{3}c$ [a]
23. $u^2 + 2as = v^2$ [a]
24. $a = \frac{b}{4} - 2c$ [c]
25. $\frac{1}{2}at^2 = s$ [a]
26. $v = \frac{1}{3}\pi r^2 h$ [h]
27. $s = ut + \frac{1}{2}at^2$ [a]
28. $r = \frac{1}{s} + t$ [s]
29. $p + \frac{t}{q} = r$ [q]
30. $x - \frac{y}{z} = w$ [z]

31. The formula for finding the speed, v, of a body after accelerating for t seconds is given by $v = u + at$. **(i)** Express t in terms of u, v and a. **(ii)** Find t when $v = 650$, $u = 50$ and $a = 15$.

32. **(i)** The area of a trapezium is given by
$A = \left(\dfrac{a + b}{2} \right) h$. Express h in terms of A, a and b.

   (ii) Find the value of h when $A = 150$, $a = 10$ and $b = 15$.

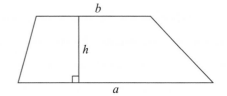

33. The diagram shows a rectangle of length l and width w. Its perimeter is P and its area is A. Express:

   (i) P in terms of l and w **(ii)** w in terms of P and l

   (iii) A in terms of l and w **(iv)** w in terms of A and l

   (v) Hence, express A in terms of P and l.

34. A farmer wants to fence off part of his garden. He buys 18 m of fencing and uses it to make three sides of a rectangle, using a fence as the fourth side, as shown. The length of one side of the rectangle is x m and the length of the other side is y m.

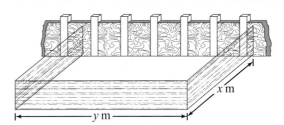

   (i) Write down an equation in x and y to represent this information.

   (ii) Express y in terms of x.

   (iii) If the area of the rectangle is 40 m², explain why $xy = 40$.

   (iv) Using your answer from part **(ii)**, write down an equation in x only to represent the area of the rectangle and solve this equation to find the values of x and y.

35. Temperatures can be measured in degrees Celsius (°C), degrees Fahrenheit (°F) or degrees Kelvin (°K). The relationships between the scales of temperature are given by

$$C = \frac{5(F - 32)}{9} \quad \text{and} \quad K = C + 273.$$

   (i) Express F in terms of **(a)** C **(b)** K.

   (ii) Hence or otherwise, calculate F when **(a)** $C = 10$ and **(b)** $K = 123$.

Notation for indices

We use a shorthand called **index notation** to indicate repeated multiplication.

For example, we write $2 \times 2 \times 2 \times 2 \times 2$ as 2^5.

This is read as '2 to the power of 5'.

The power or index simply tells you how many times a number is multiplied by itself.

> 2 is the **base**.
>
> 5 is the **index** or **power**.

Rules of indices

1. $a^m \times a^n = a^{m+n}$ Example: $2^4 \times 2^3 = 2^{4+3} = 2^7$

    Multiplying powers of the same number: **add** the indices.

2. $\dfrac{a^m}{a^n} = a^{m-n}$ Example: $\dfrac{3^9}{3^5} = 3^{9-5} = 3^4$

    Dividing powers of the same number: **subtract** the index on the bottom from the index on top.

3. $(a^m)^n = a^{mn}$ Example: $(4^5)^3 = 4^{5 \times 3} = 4^{15}$

    Raising the power of a number to a power, multiply the indices.

4. $(ab)^m = a^m b^m$ Example: $(2 \times 3)^5 = 2^5 \times 3^5$

    Raising a product to a power, every factor is raised to the power.

5. $\left(\dfrac{a}{b}\right)^m = \dfrac{a^m}{b^m}$ Example: $\left(\dfrac{2}{5}\right)^3 = \dfrac{2^3}{5^3}$

    Raising a fraction to a power, **both** top and bottom are raised to the power.

6. $a^0 = 1$ Example: $4^0 = 1$

    Any number to the power of zero is 1.

7. $a^{-m} = \dfrac{1}{a^m}$ Example: $5^{-2} = \dfrac{1}{5^2}$

    A number with a negative index is equal to its reciprocal with a positive index.

    Note: If a term is brought from the top to the bottom of a fraction (or vice versa), the sign of its index is changed.

8. $a^{m/n} = (a^{1/n})^m$ Example: $32^{3/5} = (32^{1/5})^3$

    Take the root first and then raise to the power (or vice versa).

$8^{\frac{1}{3}}$ means the number that multiplied by itself three times will equal 8.

Thus, $8^{\frac{1}{3}} = 2$, as $2 \times 2 \times 2 = 8$.

Similarly, $25^{\frac{1}{2}} = 5$, as $5 \times 5 = 25$, and $81^{\frac{1}{4}} = 3$, as $3 \times 3 \times 3 \times 3 = 81$.

Note: $\sqrt{a} = a^{\frac{1}{2}}$, for example $\sqrt{16} = 16^{\frac{1}{2}} = 4$.

Also, $\sqrt{a}\sqrt{a} = a^{\frac{1}{2}} \cdot a^{\frac{1}{2}} = a^{\frac{1}{2}+\frac{1}{2}} = a^1 = a$.

Alternative notation: $a^{\frac{1}{n}} = {}^n\sqrt{a}$ Example: $8^{\frac{1}{3}} = {}^3\sqrt{8}$

$a^{\frac{m}{n}} = {}^n\sqrt{a^m}$ Example: $32^{\frac{2}{5}} = {}^5\sqrt{32^2}$

When dealing with fractional indices, the calculations are simpler if the root is taken first and the result is raised to the power.

For example, $16^{\frac{3}{4}} = (16^{\frac{1}{4}})^3 = (2)^3 = 8$

(root first)   (power next)

Using a calculator

A calculator can be used to evaluate an expression such as $32^{\frac{3}{5}}$.

$$\left(\boxed{\blacksquare}\ \ 32\ \ \boxed{y^x}\ \ (3 \div 5)\ \ \boxed{=} \right)$$

The calculator will give an answer of 8.

However, there are problems when dealing with negative indices or raising a fraction to a power, as the calculator can give the answer as a decimal.

For example, $8^{-\frac{2}{3}} = \dfrac{1}{8^{\frac{2}{3}}} = \dfrac{1}{(8^{\frac{1}{3}})^2} = \dfrac{1}{(2)^2} = \dfrac{1}{4}$

Using a calculator,

$$\left(\boxed{\blacksquare}\ \ 8\ \ \boxed{y^x}\ \boxed{+/-}\ \ (2 \div 3)\ \ \boxed{=} \right)$$ gives an answer of 0·25.

Note: $\frac{1}{4} = 0.25$

Also, $\left(\dfrac{8}{27}\right)^{\frac{2}{3}} = \dfrac{8^{\frac{2}{3}}}{27^{\frac{2}{3}}} = \dfrac{(8^{\frac{1}{3}})^2}{(27^{\frac{1}{3}})^2} = \dfrac{(2)^2}{(3)^2} = \dfrac{4}{9}$

Using a calculator,

$$\left(\boxed{\blacksquare}\ \ \boxed{(}\ 8 \div 27\ \boxed{)}\ \boxed{y^x}\ (2 \div 3)\ \boxed{=} \right)$$ gives an answer of 0·444444444 . . .

Note: $\frac{4}{9} = 0.444444444 \ldots$

Avoid using a calculator with negative indices or when raising a fraction to a power.

EXAMPLE 1

Write the following without indices. **(i)** 6^{-2} **(ii)** $81^{\frac{1}{2}}$ **(iii)** $27^{\frac{4}{3}}$ **(iv)** $32^{\frac{3}{5}}$

Solution:

(i) $6^{-2} = \dfrac{1}{6^2} = \dfrac{1}{36}$

(ii) $81^{\frac{1}{2}} = 9$

(iii) $27^{\frac{4}{3}} = (27^{\frac{1}{3}})^4\ (27^{\frac{1}{3}})^4 = (3)^4 = 81$

(iv) $32^{\frac{3}{5}} = (32^{\frac{1}{5}})^3 = (2)^3 = 8$

EXAMPLE 2

Write the following as a power of 2.   (i) 8   (ii) $8^{\frac{4}{3}}$ (iii) $\sqrt{8}$ (iv) 4^{-3}

Solution:

(i) $8 = 2^3$

(ii) **Method 1**
$$8^{\frac{4}{3}} = (2^3)^{\frac{4}{3}} = 2^{3 \times \frac{4}{3}} = 2^4$$

(ii) **Method 2**
$$8^{\frac{4}{3}} = (8^{\frac{1}{3}})^4 = (2)^4 = 16 = 2^4$$

(iii) $\sqrt{8} = (8)^{\frac{1}{2}} = (2^3)^{\frac{1}{2}} = 2^{3 \times \frac{1}{2}} = 2^{\frac{3}{2}}$

(iv) $4^{-3} = (4)^{-3} = (2^2)^{-3} = 2^{2 \times -3} = 2^{-6}$

Exercise 1.14

Express questions 1–20 with a single index.

1. $2^3 \times 2^4$
2. $5^2 \times 5^7$
3. $7^3 \times 7$
4. $3 \times 3^4 \times 3^2$
5. $\dfrac{3^7}{3^5}$
6. $\dfrac{2^8}{2^5}$
7. $\dfrac{3^4}{3^6}$
8. $\dfrac{5}{5^4}$
9. $(3^2)^4$
10. $(5^3)^2$
11. $(\sqrt{5})^4$
12. $(\sqrt{3})^3$
13. $\dfrac{2^2}{\sqrt{2}}$
14. $\dfrac{3^4}{\sqrt{3}}$
15. $\dfrac{\sqrt{2}}{2^3}$
16. $\dfrac{\sqrt{5}}{5^2}$
17. $a^{\frac{2}{3}} \times a^{\frac{4}{3}}$
18. $a^{\frac{1}{2}} \times a^{\frac{1}{2}} \times a^2$
19. $\dfrac{a^{\frac{7}{2}}}{a^{\frac{3}{2}}}$
20. $\dfrac{a^2 \times a^{\frac{5}{2}}}{a^{\frac{1}{2}}}$

Express questions 21–32 in the form a^p, where $a \in N$ and $p \neq 1$.

21. 4
22. 25
23. 36
24. 27
25. 16
26. 49
27. 32
28. 81
29. 125
30. 128
31. 243
32. 216

Write questions 33–62 without indices.

33. 2^3
34. 3^2
35. 4^3
36. 5^2
37. 6^2
38. 5^3
39. 3^4
40. 5^3
41. 7^2
42. 2^4
43. 6^3
44. 8^0
45. 3^{-1}
46. 4^{-2}
47. 5^{-3}
48. 2^{-5}
49. 3^{-2}
50. 10^{-3}
51. $9^{\frac{1}{2}}$
52. $25^{\frac{1}{2}}$
53. $8^{\frac{1}{3}}$
54. $64^{\frac{1}{3}}$
55. $32^{\frac{1}{5}}$
56. $216^{\frac{1}{3}}$
57. $4^{\frac{3}{2}}$
58. $4^{-\frac{3}{2}}$
59. $8^{\frac{4}{3}}$
60. $8^{-\frac{4}{3}}$
61. $27^{\frac{2}{3}}$
62. $27^{-\frac{2}{3}}$

63. Express 64 in the form a^b in three different ways, where $a \in \mathbb{N}$ and $b \neq 1$.

64. Express 81 in the form a^b in two different ways, where $a \in \mathbb{N}$ and $b \neq 1$.

Express questions 65–88 in the form 2^n or 3^n or 5^n or 7^n.

65. 8	**66.** 9	**67.** 25	**68.** 49
69. 16	**70.** 125	**71.** $\sqrt{2}$	**72.** $\sqrt{3}$
73. $\sqrt{5}$	**74.** $\sqrt{7}$	**75.** $2\sqrt{2}$	**76.** $(2\sqrt{2})^2$
77. $\dfrac{4}{\sqrt{2}}$	**78.** $\dfrac{9}{\sqrt{3}}$	**79.** $\dfrac{25}{\sqrt{5}}$	**80.** $\sqrt{125}$
81. $\dfrac{1}{\sqrt{7}}$	**82.** $\dfrac{125}{\sqrt{5}}$	**83.** $\left(\dfrac{4}{\sqrt{2}}\right)^2$	**84.** $\left(\dfrac{1}{\sqrt{3}}\right)^2$
85. $\left(\dfrac{\sqrt{5}}{25}\right)^2$	**86.** $\left(\dfrac{\sqrt{8}}{2}\right)^2$	**87.** $\left(\dfrac{25}{\sqrt{5}}\right)^2$	**88.** $\left(\dfrac{\sqrt{3}}{9}\right)^2$

89. Show that: **(i)** $\left(\dfrac{\sqrt{a}}{a^2}\right)^2 = a^{-3}$ **(ii)** $\dfrac{(a\sqrt{a})^3}{a^4} = \sqrt{a}$

90. Two of the numbers $9^{\frac{1}{2}}$, 9^{-1}, 27^0, $(-3)^2$ and 3^{-2} are equal. Write down these two values. Justify your answer.

91. The foundation for a building is in the shape of the letter L, as shown. The shape is formed from two squares of dimensions x m and $\sqrt{x}$ m.

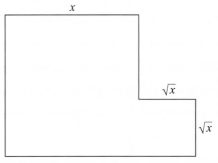

(i) Write down an expression in terms of x of the area of the foundation.

(ii) If the area of the foundation is 42 m², write a quadratic equation in terms of x and calculate the value of x.

92. (i) Simplify $(x + \sqrt{x})(x - \sqrt{x})$ when $x > 0$.

(ii) Hence or otherwise, find the value of x for which $(x + \sqrt{x})(x - \sqrt{x}) = 6$.

93. (i) Simplify: **(a)** $\sqrt{a^2}$ **(b)** $\sqrt{b^2}$ **(c)** $\sqrt{x^2}$ **(d)** $\sqrt{(x+3)^2}$

(ii) Factorise: **(a)** $x^2 + 2x + 1$ **(b)** $x^2 + 4x + 4$

(iii) Simplify $\sqrt{x^2 + 4x + 4} + \sqrt{x^2 + 2x + 1}$, given that $x \geq 0$.

(iv) Given that $x \geq 0$, solve for x: $\sqrt{x^2 + 4x + 4} + \sqrt{x^2 + 2x + 1} = x^2$.

94. Express the following in the form $x^{\frac{a}{b}}$.

   (i) $\sqrt{x}$ **(ii)** $\sqrt[3]{x}$ **(iii)** $\sqrt[3]{x^2}$ **(iv)** $\sqrt[4]{x^3}$

Exponential equations

Exponent is another name for power or index.

An equation involving the variable in the power is called an **exponential equation**.

For example, $3^{2x+3} = 9$ is an exponential equation.

Exponential equations are solved with the following steps.

1. Write all the numbers as powers of the same number (usually a prime number).

2. Write both sides as one power of the same number using the laws of indices.

3. Equate these powers and solve the equation.

EXAMPLE

Find the value of x if: (i) $4^{x+1} = 128$ (ii) $5^{3x+1} = \dfrac{125}{\sqrt{5}}$

Solution:

(i) 1. $\qquad 4^{x+1} = 128$ (both 4 and 128 can be written as powers of 2)

$\qquad\qquad (2^2)^{x+1} = 2^7$ ($4 = 2^2$ and $128 = 2^7$)

2. $\qquad 2^{2(x+1)} = 2^7$ (multiply the indices on the left-hand side)

$\qquad\qquad 2^{2x+2} = 2^7$ ($2(x+1) = 2x + 2$)

3. $\qquad 2x + 2 = 7$ (equate the powers)

$\qquad\qquad 2x = 5$

$\qquad\qquad x = \frac{5}{2}$

(ii) 1. $\qquad 5^{3x+1} = \dfrac{125}{\sqrt{5}}$ (both 125 and $\sqrt{5}$ can be written as powers of 5)

$\qquad\qquad 5^{3x+1} = \dfrac{5^3}{5^{1/2}}$ ($125 = 5^3$ and $\sqrt{5} = 5^{1/2}$)

2. $\qquad 5^{3x+1} = 5^{3 - \frac{1}{2}}$ (subtract index on the bottom from the index on top)

$\qquad\qquad 5^{3x+1} = 5^{2\frac{1}{2}}$ ($3 - \frac{1}{2} = 2\frac{1}{2}$)

3. $\qquad 3x + 1 = 2\frac{1}{2}$ (equate the powers)

$\qquad\qquad 6x + 2 = 5$ (multiply both sides by 2)

$\qquad\qquad 6x = 3$

$\qquad\qquad x = \frac{1}{2}$

Exercise 1.15

Solve questions 1–24 for x.

1. $5^{2x} = 5^8$
2. $3^{2x+1} = 3^7$
3. $2^{3x-1} = 2^5$
4. $7^{5x-1} = 7^4$

5. $2^x = 4$
6. $3^{x+1} = 9$
7. $2^{x-2} = 16$
8. $3^{2x-1} = 27$

9. $9^{x+1} = 81$
10. $4^{2x-5} = 64$
11. $5^{x+1} = 125$
12. $7^{3x-1} = 49$

13. $4^x = 8$
14. $9^{2x} = 27$
15. $16^{x+1} = 32$
16. $49^x = 7^{2+x}$

17. $3^x = \dfrac{1}{9}$
18. $2^x = \dfrac{1}{8}$
19. $7^x = \dfrac{1}{49}$
20. $5^{2x-1} = \dfrac{1}{125}$

21. $9^{x+1} = \dfrac{1}{27}$
22. $4^{x-3} = \dfrac{1}{32}$
23. $25^{x-2} = \dfrac{1}{125}$
24. $8 \times 2^x = \dfrac{1}{128}$

25. Express $32^{\frac{4}{5}}$ in the form 4^n. Hence or otherwise, solve $4^{2x-1} = 32^{\frac{4}{5}}$.

26. Express $2^5 - 2^4$ in the form 2^n. Hence, solve $2^{3x-5} = 2^5 - 2^4$.

27. Find the two values of x for which $\dfrac{2^{x^2}}{2^x} = 4$.

28. Express $\dfrac{4}{\sqrt{2}}$ in the form $2^{\frac{a}{b}}$. Hence, solve for x: $2^{2x+1} = \dfrac{4}{\sqrt{2}}$.

29. (i) Write each of the following as a power of 2.

   (a) $\sqrt{2}$
   (b) 8
   (c) $8^{4/3}$
   (d) $8\sqrt{2}$

   (ii) Hence, solve for x.

   (a) $2^{5x-1} = 8^{4/3}$
   (b) $2^{5x-4} = 8\sqrt{2}$
   (c) $2^{3x+1} = (8\sqrt{2})^2$

30. (i) Write each of the following as a power of 3.

   (a) $\sqrt{3}$
   (b) $\dfrac{1}{\sqrt{3}}$
   (c) 81
   (d) $\dfrac{81}{\sqrt{3}}$

   (ii) Hence, solve for x.

   (a) $3^{2x} = \sqrt{3}$
   (b) $3^{2x-1} = \dfrac{1}{\sqrt{3}}$
   (c) $3^{x-2} = \dfrac{81}{\sqrt{3}}$

31. (i) Write each of the following as a power of 5.

   (a) 125
   (b) $\sqrt{5}$
   (c) $\dfrac{125}{\sqrt{5}}$
   (d) $\left(\dfrac{125}{\sqrt{5}}\right)^2$

   (ii) Hence, solve for x.

   (a) $5^{3x+1} = \sqrt{5}$
   (b) $5^{2x+3} = \dfrac{125}{\sqrt{5}}$
   (c) $5^{2x-1} = \left(\dfrac{125}{\sqrt{5}}\right)^2$

32. (i) Simplify $\sqrt{x}\left(\sqrt{x} + \dfrac{1}{\sqrt{x}}\right)$, where $x > 0$.

   (ii) Hence or otherwise, solve for x and verify your answer: $\sqrt{x}\left(\sqrt{x} + \dfrac{1}{\sqrt{x}}\right) = 5$.

33. **(i)** Write down the formula for the area of a triangle.

   (ii) The triangle shown has a base length of $2x\sqrt{x}$ cm and perpendicular height of $\sqrt{x}$ cm.

   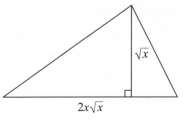

   (a) Express its area, A, in terms of x.

   (b) If $A = 81$ cm^2, calculate the value of x and verify your answer.

34. The rectangle shown has a length of 4 m and a width of 2^k m.

   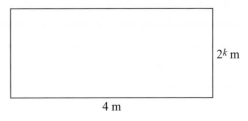

   (i) Express its area, A, in the form 2^{k+p} m^2.

   (ii) Calculate k if:

   (a) $A = 32$ m^2

   (b) $A = 4\sqrt{2}\,$m^2

35. In each case, verify your answer.

   (i) Express b in terms of a and c where $\dfrac{8a - 5b}{b} = c$.

   (ii) Hence or otherwise, evaluate b when $a = 2^{\frac{5}{2}}$ and $c = 3^3$.

Midpoint of a line segment

If (x_1, y_1) and (x_2, y_2) are two points, their midpoint is given by the formula:

$$\text{Midpoint} = \left(\frac{x_1 + x_2}{2}, \frac{y_1 + y_2}{2} \right)$$

In words:

$$\left(\frac{\text{add the } x \text{ coordinates}}{2}, \frac{\text{add the } y \text{ coordinates}}{2} \right)$$

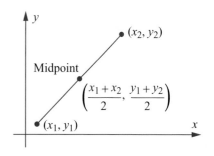

EXAMPLE 1

$P(5, 6)$ and $Q(7, -4)$ are two points. Find the coordinates of R, the midpoint of $[PQ]$.

Solution:

$P(5, 6)$ $Q(7, -4)$
(x_1, y_1) (x_2, y_2)
$x_1 = 5, y_1 = 6$ $x_2 = 7, y_2 = -4$

$$\text{Midpoint } R = \left(\frac{x_1 + x_2}{2}, \frac{y_1 + y_2}{2} \right)$$

$$= \left(\frac{5 + 7}{2}, \frac{-4 + 6}{2} \right)$$

$$= \left(\frac{12}{2}, \frac{2}{2} \right) = (6, 1)$$

$P(5, 6)$ $R(6, 1)$ $Q(7, -4)$

An alternative approach is to consider the midpoint of a line segment as the **average** of its end points.

EXAMPLE 2

$A(-1, 7)$ and $B(9, 3)$ are two points. Find the coordinates of C, the midpoint of $[AB]$.

Solution:

Add points		
A	$(-1,$	$7)$
B	$(9,$	$3)$
	$(-1 + 9,$	$7 + 3)$
	$(8,$	$10)$
Midpoint C	$(4,$	$5)$ Divide each coordinate by 2

Given the midpoint

In some questions we will be given the midpoint and one end point of a line segment and be asked to find the other end point.

To find the other end point, use the following method.

1. Make a rough diagram.
2. Find the translation that maps (moves) the given end point to the midpoint.
3. Apply the same translation to the midpoint to find the other end point.

EXAMPLE 3

If $M(6, 5)$ is the midpoint of $[PQ]$ and $P = (3, 7)$, find the coordinates of Q.

Solution:
Step 1: Rough diagram.

$P(3, 7)$ → $M(6, 5)$ → $Q(\,,\,)$ [missing coordinates]

Step 2: Translation from P to M. Rule: Add 3 to x, subtract 2 from y.

Step 3: Apply this translation to M.
$$M(6, 5) \rightarrow (6 + 3, 5 - 2) = (9, 3)$$
$\therefore$ The coordinates of Q are $(9, 3)$.

Exercise 2.1

In questions 1–12, find the midpoints of each of the following line segments whose end points are as follows.

1. $(3, 2)$ and $(5, 4)$
2. $(6, 8)$ and $(4, -2)$
3. $(10, 0)$ and $(8, -6)$
4. $(-3, 7)$ and $(-9, 3)$
5. $(-6, -5)$ and $(-10, -1)$
6. $(-8, 7)$ and $(4, -3)$
7. $(8, 8)$ and $(-2, -2)$
8. $(-7, 5)$ and $(9, -7)$
9. $(5, -1)$ and $(2, -3)$
10. $\left(3\frac{1}{2}, 1\frac{1}{4}\right)$ and $\left(2\frac{1}{2}, \frac{3}{4}\right)$
11. $\left(2\frac{1}{2}, -1\frac{1}{2}\right)$ and $\left(1\frac{1}{2}, \frac{1}{2}\right)$
12. $\left(5\frac{1}{2}, 7\frac{1}{4}\right)$ and $\left(-2\frac{1}{2}, -2\frac{1}{4}\right)$

13. If $M(3, 1)$ is the midpoint of $[PQ]$ and $P = (1, 0)$, find the coordinates of Q.

14. If $M(-3, -3)$ is the midpoint of $[AB]$ and $A = (-1, -5)$, find the coordinates of B.

15. The point $(4, -2)$ is the midpoint of the line segment joining $(-2, 1)$ and (p, q). Find the value of p and the value of q.

16. The point (1, 6) is the midpoint of the line segment joining (a, b) and (4, 7). Find the value of a and the value of b.

17. If the midpoint of (p, q) and (−4, 7) is the same as the midpoint of (4, −3) and (−2, 7), find the value of p and the value of q.

18. Five street lights are to be placed in a line and evenly spaced. If the first light is placed at (2, 3) and the last is at (10, 15), where should the others be placed?

Distance between two points

If (x_1, y_1) and (x_2, y_2) are two points, the distance, d, between them is given by the formula:

$$d = \sqrt{(x_2 - x_1)^2 + (y_2 - y_1)^2}$$

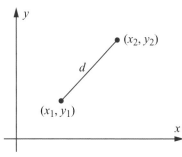

Note: Always decide which point is (x_1, y_1) and which point is (x_2, y_2) before you use the formula. The distance between the points A and B is written $|AB|$.

EXAMPLE

$A(5, 2)$, $B(8, 6)$, $C(6, −1)$ and $D(5, 7)$ are four points.

Calculate:　　(i) $|AB|$　　(ii) $|CD|$

Solution:

(i) $A(5, 2)$　　and　$B(8, 6)$
　　(x_1, y_1)　　　　(x_2, y_2)
　　$x_1 = 5, y_1 = 2$　　$x_2 = 8, y_2 = 6$

$$|AB| = \sqrt{(x_2 - x_1)^2 + (y_2 - y_1)^2}$$
$$= \sqrt{(8 - 5)^2 + (6 - 2)^2}$$
$$= \sqrt{(3)^2 + (4)^2}$$
$$= \sqrt{9 + 16}$$
$$= \sqrt{25} = 5$$

(ii) $C(6, −1)$　　and　$D(5, 7)$
　　(x_1, y_1)　　　　(x_2, y_2)
　　$x_1 = 6, y_1 = −1$　　$x_2 = 5, y_2 = 7$

$$|CD| = \sqrt{(x_2 - x_1)^2 + (y_2 - y_1)^2}$$
$$= \sqrt{(5 - 6)^2 + (7 + 1)^2}$$
$$= \sqrt{(-1)^2 + (8)^2}$$
$$= \sqrt{1 + 64}$$
$$= \sqrt{65}$$

Exercise 2.2

In questions 1–12, find the distance between each of the following pairs of points.

1. (5, 2) and (8, 6)
2. (1, 1) and (7, 9)
3. (3, 4) and (5, 5)
4. (1, −3) and (2, 5)
5. (2, 0) and (5, 0)
6. (3, −4) and (3, 2)
7. (3, −6) and (−3, −4)
8. (−2, 2) and (−7, −3)
9. (−7, −2) and (−1, −4)
10. (2, −4) and (−4, 2)
11. $\left(\frac{1}{2}, \frac{1}{2}\right)$ and $\left(2\frac{1}{2}, 1\frac{1}{2}\right)$
12. $\left(\frac{3}{2}, -\frac{1}{2}\right)$ and $\left(\frac{9}{2}, \frac{1}{2}\right)$

13. Verify that the triangle with vertices $A(3, -2)$, $B(-2, 1)$ and $C(1, 6)$ is isosceles. (An isosceles triangle has two sides of equal length.)

14. Find the radius of a circle with centre (2, 2) and containing the point (5, 6).

15. $A(3, 2)$, $B(-1, 5)$ and $C(6, 0)$ are three points.

   (i) Which point is nearest to (2, 1)?

   (ii) Which point is furthest from (2, 1)?

16. $X(2, 3)$, $Y(-1, 6)$ and $Z(1, 8)$ are three points. Show that $|XY|^2 + |YZ|^2 = |XZ|^2$.

17. Find the coordinates of M, the midpoint of the line segment joining $P(7, 4)$ and $Q(-1, -2)$. Show that $|PM| = |QM|$.

18. $A(6, 2)$, $B(-4, -4)$ and $C(4, -10)$ are the coordinates of the triangle ABC.

   (i) Find the coordinates of P, the midpoint of $[AB]$.

   (ii) Find the coordinates of Q, the midpoint of $[AC]$.

   (iii) Verify that $|PQ| = \frac{1}{2}|BC|$.

19. $A(1, 0)$, $B(6, 1)$, $C(9, 4)$ and $D(4, 3)$ form a quadrilateral $ABCD$.

   (i) Draw these points on a coordinated diagram.

   (ii) What type of quadrilateral is $ABCD$?

   (iii) Find the length of each side. Are each pair of opposite sides equal in measure?

   (iv) Find the midpoint of the diagonal $[AC]$.

   (v) How could you show that the diagonals bisect each other?

20. $A(-6, 3)$, $B(14, 18)$ and $C(50, -30)$ form a triangle. Show that the length of each side is less than the sum of the other two.

21. A map of a shopping centre is shown here.

   (i) Why is it easier to calculate $|AP|$ than $|PQ|$?

   (ii) Which is the shorter path from A to B?

   (iii) Would it be possible to reduce the distance on either path?

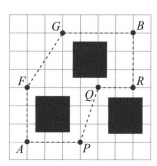

22. A group of nine houses is situated at (2, 2), (2, 6), (−1, 10), (−1, 14), (3, 18), (7, 14), (7, 10), (10, 6) and (10, 2).

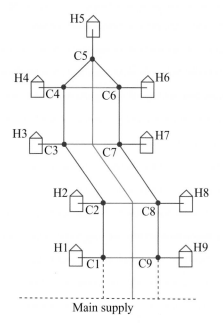

Each house is to be connected to a new fibre optic cable for TV and internet and each house is already wired to a suitable connecting point near it. Each of the connecting points is 2 units from its corresponding house.

Two options are available:

A. Create a ring from the main supply to connecting points C1 to C9. This is shown in blue on the diagram. C1 and C9 are each 3 units from the main supply.

B. Put a single cable down the centre of the road and use longer connections to each of C1 to C9. This is shown in red.

   (i) What are the coordinates of each of the connecting points?

  (ii) If option A is used, what is the total length of fibre optic cable needed?

 (iii) If option B is used, what is the total length of fibre optic cable needed?

  (iv) Why would the service supplier choose the option requiring the greater amount of cable?

Slope of a line

All mathematical graphs are read from **left to right**.

The measure of the steepness of a line is called the **slope**.

The vertical distance (up or down) is called the **rise**.

The horizontal distance (left or right) is called the **run**.

The slope of a line is defined as:

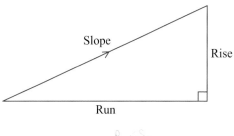

$$\text{Slope} = \frac{\text{Rise}}{\text{Run}}$$

Note: This is also equal to the tangent ratio in trigonometry.

      The rise can be negative, and in this case it is often called the **fall** or **drop**.

      If the rise is zero, then the slope is also zero.

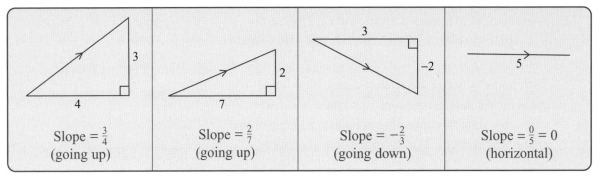

| $\text{Slope} = \frac{3}{4}$ (going up) | $\text{Slope} = \frac{2}{7}$ (going up) | $\text{Slope} = -\frac{2}{3}$ (going down) | $\text{Slope} = \frac{0}{5} = 0$ (horizontal) |

Slope of a line when given two points on the line

If a line contains two points (x_1, y_1) and (x_2, y_2), then the slope of the line is given by the formula:

$$m = \frac{y_2 - y_1}{x_2 - x_1}$$

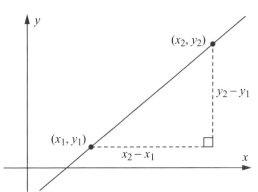

EXAMPLE

Find the slope of a line containing the points $(-2, 5)$ and $(3, 8)$.

Solution:

$(-2, 5)$ $(3, 8)$

(x_1, y_1) (x_2, y_2)

$x_1 = -2, y_1 = 5$ $x_2 = 3, y_2 = 8$

$$\text{Slope} = \frac{y_2 - y_1}{x_2 - x_1}$$
$$= \frac{8 - 5}{3 + 2}$$
$$= \frac{3}{5}$$

Parallel lines

> If two lines are **parallel**, they have equal slopes (and vice versa).

Consider the parallel lines l_1 and l_2.

In each case, the line makes the same angle with the x-axis.

Let m_1 be the slope of l_1 and let m_2 be the slope of l_2.

As $l_1 \| l_2$, then $m_1 = m_2$.

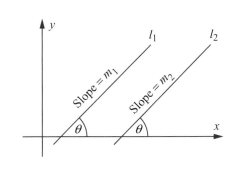

Perpendicular lines

If two lines are **perpendicular**, when we multiply their slopes we always get -1 (and vice versa).

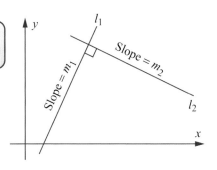

Consider the perpendicular lines l_1 and l_2.

Let m_1 be the slope of l_1 and let m_2 be the slope of l_2.

As $l_1 \perp l_2$, then $m_1 \times m_2 = -1$.

Note: If we know the slope of a line and we need to find the slope of a line perpendicular to it, simply do the following:

Turn the known slope upside down and change its sign.

For example, if a line has a slope of $-\frac{3}{4}$, then the slope of a line perpendicular to it has a slope of $\frac{4}{3}$ (turn upside down and change its sign), because $-\frac{3}{4} \times \frac{4}{3} = -1$.

EXAMPLE 1

$A(2, 4)$, $B(7, 8)$, $C(2, 0)$ and $D(7, 4)$ are four points. Show that $AB \parallel CD$.

Solution:

Let m_1 = the slope of AB and m_2 = the slope of CD.

$A(2, 4)$	$B(7, 8)$	$C(2, 0)$	$D(7, 4)$
(x_1, y_1)	(x_2, y_2)	(x_1, y_1)	(x_2, y_2)
$x_1 = 2, y_1 = 4$	$x_2 = 7, y_2 = 8$	$x_1 = 2, y_1 = 0$	$x_2 = 7, y_2 = 4$

$$m_1 = \frac{y_2 - y_1}{x_2 - x_1} \qquad\qquad m_2 = \frac{y_2 - y_1}{x_2 - x_1}$$

$$= \frac{8 - 4}{7 - 2} \qquad\qquad\qquad = \frac{4 - 0}{7 - 2}$$

$$= \frac{4}{5} \qquad\qquad\qquad\qquad = \frac{4}{5}$$

$$m_1 = m_2$$
$$\therefore AB \parallel CD$$

EXAMPLE 2

$P(2, 5)$, $Q(6, 3)$ and $R(0, 1)$ are three points. Verify that $PQ \perp PR$.

Solution:

Let m_1 = the slope of PQ and m_2 = the slope of PR.

$P(2, 5)$	$Q(6, 3)$	$P(2, 5)$	$R(0, 1)$
(x_1, y_1)	(x_2, y_2)	(x_1, y_1)	(x_2, y_2)
$x_1 = 2, y_1 = 5$	$x_2 = 6, y_2 = 3$	$x_1 = 2, y_1 = 5$	$x_2 = 0, y_2 = 1$

$$m_1 = \frac{y_2 - y_1}{x_2 - x_1} \qquad\qquad m_2 = \frac{y_2 - y_1}{x_2 - x_1}$$

$$= \frac{3 - 5}{6 - 2} \qquad\qquad\qquad = \frac{1 - 5}{0 - 2}$$

$$= \frac{-2}{4} \qquad\qquad\qquad\qquad = \frac{-4}{-2}$$

$$= -\frac{1}{2} \qquad\qquad\qquad\qquad = 2$$

$$m_1 \times m_2 = -\frac{1}{2} \times 2 = -1$$

$$\therefore PQ \perp PR$$

Exercise 2.3

1. Write down the slope of the line t in each of the following.

    (i) 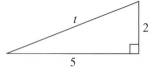   (ii) 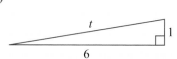   (iii)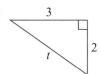

2. The diagram shows lines a, b, c, d, e and f.

    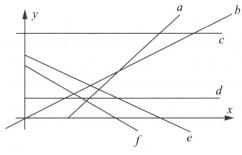

    (i)   Which lines have a negative slope?
    (ii) Which lines have a zero slope?
    (iii) Which lines have a positive slope?

In questions 3–12, find the slope of the line containing each given pair of points.

3. (1, 2) and (4, 5)

4. (2, 2) and (6, 8)

5. (2, 0) and (10, 8)

6. (0, 0) and (3, 5)

7. (5, 7) and (8, 4)

8. (−4, 6) and (7, −2)

9. (−3, −6) and (−5, −4)

10. (−2, 3) and (−3, −7)

11. $\left(\frac{3}{2}, \frac{1}{2}\right)$ and $\left(\frac{7}{2}, -\frac{3}{2}\right)$

12. $\left(-\frac{1}{4}, \frac{7}{2}\right)$ and $\left(\frac{3}{4}, \frac{3}{2}\right)$

13. $A(−4, −3)$, $B(−1, 1)$, $C(2, 2)$ and $D(5, 6)$ are four points. Verify that $AB \parallel CD$.

14. $P(4, 3)$, $Q(−2, 0)$, $R(−1, 1)$ and $S(−2, 3)$ are four points. Show that $PQ \perp RS$.

15. $X(8, −4)$, $Y(7, −1)$ and $Z(1, −3)$ are three points. Prove that $XY \perp ZY$.

16. $A(−6, 2)$, $B(−2, 1)$ and $C(0, 9)$ are the vertices of triangle ABC. Prove that $|\angle ABC| = 90°$.

17. Show that the points $A(6, −4)$, $B(5, −1)$, $C(−1, −3)$ and $D(0, −6)$ are the vertices of a rectangle.

18. The line k has a slope of $-\frac{3}{4}$. Find the slope of l if $k \perp l$.

19. The line m has a slope of $\frac{5}{3}$. Find the slope of l if $m \perp l$.

20. The line t has a slope of $-\frac{1}{3}$. Find the slope of k if $t \parallel k$.

21. The line l has a slope of $\frac{1}{4}$. Find the slope of m if $l \perp m$.

22. The line k has a slope of $−3$. Find the slope of l if $l \perp k$.

23. The height of a tree in 2007 was 6·5 m tall. By 2010, its height was 8 m.

   (i) By finding the slope, find the rate of growth of the tree per year.

   (ii) If the tree continues to grow at this rate, what should its height be in 2020?

24. A mountain has ski stations at the following points:

   (0, 0), (10, 5), (24, 7), (30, 9), (40, 12), (30, 15), (15, 17), (35, 22) and (25, 30).

   The skiing sections are graded Beginners, Experienced and Expert. Beginners sections must have a slope below $\frac{1}{3}$, while Expert sections have slopes greater than $\frac{3}{4}$.

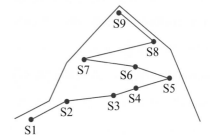

   (i) Show this on a coordinated graph.

   (ii) Calculate the slope of each section.

   (iii) Why are some of the slopes negative?

   (iv) How would each section be graded?

25. The brakes on a car are tested on a hill as shown on the diagram. It is considered unsafe to park a car on steeper hills. A road follows the following path over a mountain:

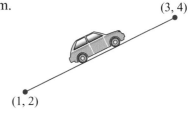

(0, 0), (2, 5), (4, 7), (6, 8), (10, 11), (13, 7), (16, 5), (20, 3) and (25, 0).

    (i) Show this on a coordinated graph.

    (ii) Calculate the slope of each section.

    (iii) Why are some of the slopes negative?

    (iv) Which sections are safe for parking?

26. Would a plane flying in a straight line from Dublin (−6, 53·5) to Luxembourg (6, 49·5) fly directly over either Birmingham (−2, 52·5) or London (0, 51·5)?

Equation of a line 1

Plot the points (−1, 8), (0, 6), (1, 4), (2, 2), (3, 0) and (4, −2).

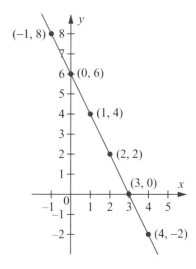

The points all lie on the same straight line. In this set of points there is the same relationship (connection, link) between the x coordinate and the y coordinate for each point.

If we double the x coordinate and add the y coordinate, the result is always 6.

That is:

$$2x + y = 6$$

This result will hold for every other point on the line. We say '$2x + y = 6$' is the equation of the line.

Note: $2x + y - 6 = 0$ is also the equation of the line.

To verify that a point belongs to a line

Once we have the equation of a line, we can determine if a point is on the line or not on the line. If a point belongs to a line, its coordinates will satisfy the equation of the line. We substitute the coordinates of the point into the equation of the line. If they satisfy the equation, then the point is **on** the line. Otherwise, the point is **not** on the line.

EXAMPLE 1

Investigate if the points $(2, -1)$ and $(5, -4)$ are on the line $5x + 3y - 7 = 0$.

Solution:

$(2, -1)$ $5x + 3y - 1 = 0$	$(5, -4)$ $5x + 3y - 1 = 0$
Substitute $x = 2$ and $y = -1$	Substitute $x = 5$ and $y = -4$
$5(2) + 3(-1) - 7$	$5(5) + 3(-4) - 7$
$= 10 - 3 - 7$	$= 25 - 12 - 7$
$= 10 - 10$	$= 25 - 19$
$= 0$	$= 6 \neq 0$

Satisfies equation.

$\therefore (2, -1)$ is on the line.

Does not satisfy equation.

$\therefore (5, -4)$ is not on the line.

 EXAMPLE 2

The equation of the line l is $5x + 4y + 3 = 0$ and the equation of the line m is $3x + ty - 8 = 0$.

The point $(-3, k)$ is on l and the point $(2, -1)$ is on the line m.

Find the value of k and the value of t.

Solution:

$5x + 4y + 3 = 0$	$3x + ty - 8 = 0$
Substitute $x = -3$ and $y = k$	Substitute $x = 2$ and $y = -1$
$(-3, k)$: $5(-3) + 4(k) + 3 = 0$	$(2, -1)$: $3(2) + t(-1) - 8 = 0$
$-15 + 4k + 3 = 0$	$6 - t - 8 = 0$
$4k - 12 = 0$	$-t - 2 = 0$
$4k = 12$	$-t = 2$
$k = 3$	$t = -2$

Exercise 2.4

In questions 1–10, find which of the given points are on the corresponding line.

1. $(4, 1)$; $x + y - 5 = 0$
2. $(3, -1)$; $2x + 3y - 3 = 0$
3. $(2, 2)$; $5x - 4y - 1 = 0$
4. $(-3, -2)$; $6x - 7y + 4 = 0$
5. $(-4, 3)$; $3x + 2y - 8 = 0$
6. $(5, 2)$; $3x - 7y - 1 = 0$

7. $(-3, -1)$; $4x + y - 15 = 0$ 8. $(2, 1)$; $x - 4y = 0$

9. $\left(\frac{5}{2}, \frac{3}{2}\right)$; $6x - 2y - 12 = 0$ 10. $\left(\frac{2}{3}, \frac{1}{3}\right)$; $3x - 6y + 3 = 0$

11. l is the line $x - 4y - 5 = 0$. Verify that the point $P(1, -1)$ is on l.

12. The point $(1, 2)$ is on the line $3x + 2y = k$. Find the value of k.

13. The point $(t, 3)$ is on the line $4x - 3y + 1 = 0$. Find the value of t.

14. The point $(-3, k)$ is on the line $5x + 4y + 3 = 0$. Find the value of k.

15. The point $(1, -2)$ is on the line $4x + ky - 14 = 0$. Find the value of k.

16. The point $(-3, -4)$ is on the line $ax - 5y - 8 = 0$. Find the value of a.

Equation of a line 2

To find the equation of a line we need:

1. The slope of the line, m.   2. A point on the line, (x_1, y_1).
   Then use the formula: $\boxed{(y - y_1) = m\,(x - x_1)}$

In short, we need the **slope** and a **point** on the line.

Note: The formula given in the mathematical tables is $y - y_1 = m(x - x_1)$.

The extra brackets will make it easier to use when the value of m is a fraction.

EXAMPLE

Find the equation of the following lines.

(i) Containing the point $(2, -3)$ with slope 3

(ii) Containing the point $(-4, 2)$ with slope $-\frac{2}{3}$

Solution:

Containing $(2, -3)$ with slope 3:

$$x_1 = 2, \quad y_1 = -3, \quad m = 3$$
$$(y - y_1) = m(x - x_1)$$
$$(y + 3) = 3(x - 2)$$
$$y + 3 = 3x - 6$$
$$-3x + y + 3 + 6 = 0$$
$$-3x + y + 9 = 0$$
$$3x - y - 9 = 0$$

Containing $(-4, 2)$ with slope $-\frac{2}{3}$:

$$x_1 = -4, \quad y_1 = 2, \quad m = -\frac{2}{3}$$
$$(y - y_1) = m(x - x_1)$$
$$(y - 2) = -\tfrac{2}{3}(x + 4)$$
$$\text{(multiply both sides by 3)}$$
$$3(y - 2) = -2(x + 4)$$
$$3y - 6 = -2x - 8$$
$$2x + 3y - 6 + 8 = 0$$
$$2x + 3y + 2 = 0$$

Exercise 2.5

In questions 1–10, find the equation of each of the following lines.

1. Containing (4, 1) with slope 2

2. Containing (−1, −1) with slope 3

3. Containing (0, −2) with slope −1

4. Containing (5, −3) with slope −5

5. Containing (0, 0) with slope 4

6. Containing (4, −7) with slope $\frac{3}{5}$

7. Containing (−3, −1) with slope $-\frac{4}{3}$

8. Containing (2, −5) with slope $\frac{5}{4}$

9. Containing (3, −3) with slope $-\frac{1}{6}$

10. Containing (−2, −1) with slope $-\frac{5}{7}$

11. Find the equation of the line k through (2, −1), the slope of k being $\frac{2}{5}$.

12. Find the equation of the line l through (3, −2), the slope of l being $-\frac{1}{2}$.

13. The time required to cook a particular food is 30 minutes plus 20 minutes per kilogram.

    (i) How long would it take to cook 2 kilograms?

    (ii) How long would it take to cook 5 kilograms?

    (iii) Find the equation of the line containing the point (0, 30) with slope 20.

    (iv) Using a suitable scale, graph this line and label the axes as *Time (mins)* and *Kilograms*, as appropriate.

    (v) Use your graph to find:

        (a) The time needed to cook 3 kilograms

        (b) The time needed to cook 4 kilograms

        (c) How much food can be safely cooked in 2 hours

Equation of a line 3

To find the equation of a line, we need the **slope** and **one point** on the line.

However, in many questions one or both of these are missing.

 EXAMPLE

Find the equation of the line that contains the points $(-4, 7)$ and $(1, 3)$.

Solution:

The slope is missing. We first find the slope and use **either one** of the two points to find the equation.

$$(-4, 7) \quad (1, 3)$$
$$(x_1, y_1) \quad (x_2, y_2)$$
$$x_1 = -4, y_1 = 7 \quad x_2 = 1, y_2 = 3$$

$$m = \frac{y_2 - y_1}{x_2 - x_1}$$

$$= \frac{3 - 7}{1 + 4}$$

$$= \frac{-4}{5}$$

$$m = -\frac{4}{5}$$

Containing $(-4, 7)$ with slope $-\frac{4}{5}$:

$$x_1 = -4, \quad y_1 = 7, \quad m = -\frac{4}{5}$$

$$(y - y_1) = m(x - x_1)$$

$$(y - 7) = -\frac{4}{5}(x + 4)$$

$$5(y - 7) = -4(x + 4)$$

(multiply both sides by 5)

$$5y - 35 = -4x - 16$$

$$4x + 5y - 35 + 16 = 0$$

$$4x + 5y - 19 = 0$$

Exercise 2.6

In questions 1–9, find the equation of the line containing the given pair of points.

1. $(2, 5)$ and $(6, 9)$
2. $(1, 8)$ and $(3, 4)$
3. $(4, -6)$ and $(5, -3)$
4. $(1, 1)$ and $(5, 3)$
5. $(8, -3)$ and $(-6, 7)$
6. $(-6, -1)$ and $(-1, 2)$
7. $(1, -5)$ and $(3, -6)$
8. $(2, -2)$ and $(4, 3)$
9. $\left(\frac{1}{2}, -\frac{5}{2}\right)$ and $\left(-\frac{3}{2}, \frac{3}{2}\right)$

10. $A(3, -2)$, $B(2, 3)$ and $C(5, 7)$ are three points. Find the equation of the line containing A if it is:

    (i) Parallel to BC
    (ii) Perpendicular to BC

11. Find the equation of the perpendicular bisectors of the line segments joining:

    (i) $(2, 3)$ and $(6, 1)$
    (ii) $(-1, 2)$ and $(-3, -2)$

12. Find the equation of the line l containing $(5, -1)$ and passing through the midpoint of $(6, 3)$ and $(-2, -1)$.

13. The line l contains the points $(2, 2)$ and $(-1, 4)$. The line k contains the point $(-4, 1)$ and $k \perp l$. Find the equation of k.

14. At age 12, a boy was 140 cm tall. When he reached 16, his height was 170 cm.

    (i) Using an appropriate scale, show these points on a coordinated graph.

    (ii) Use your graph to estimate the height of the boy when:

        (a) He was nine years old

        (b) He will be 20 years old

    (iii) Form an equation that describes the boy's growth.

    (iv) Why is this not a good method of predicting height?

    (v) If growth occurs in stages, could height be described by linking sections of different lines? Explain your answer.

    (vi) Show a possible graph on the same page, making sure it shows the correct heights at ages 12 and 16.

15. A taxi journey is charged as a fixed amount plus an amount per kilometre. A journey of 4 km cost €8 and a journey of 12 km cost €12.

    (i) Express the costs as points in the form (journey, cost).

    (ii) Find the equation of the line passing through these points.

    (iii) Plot the points and construct a line showing the cost of a taxi journey.

    (iv) From your graph, or otherwise, find the fixed charge and the charge per kilometre.

Equation of a line 4

The equation of a line is usually written in one of two ways. The first is:

$$ax + by + c = 0$$

In this format, all the terms are on the left side of the equation and it is usual to write the term involving x first, followed by the y term and then the constant. The line $3x - 6y + 11 = 0$ is in this format.

The second way is:

$$y = mx + c$$

This time, the terms are arranged so that the y is on its own on the left and the other terms are on the right (the x term followed by the constant). The line $y = -4x + 3$ is an example.

EXAMPLE

(i) Write $2x - 3y - 6 = 0$ in the form $y = mx + c$.

(ii) Write $y = \frac{3}{4}x - 3$ in the form $ax + by + c = 0$.

Solution:

(i)

$$2x - 3y - 6 = 0$$
$$-3y = -2x + 6$$
$$3y = 2x - 6$$
$$y = \frac{2}{3}x - 2$$

(ii)

$$y = \frac{3}{4}x - 3$$
$$4y = 3x - 12$$
$$-3x + 4y + 12 = 0$$
$$3x - 4y - 12 = 0$$

Exercise 2.7

In questions 1–9, write the equation of the line in the form $y = mx + c$.

1. $2x + 3y - 9 = 0$
2. $5x - 2y - 12 = 0$
3. $3x - 2y - 8 = 0$
4. $4x - 3y + 21 = 0$
5. $3x - y + 8 = 0$
6. $2x - 3y - 15 = 0$
7. $x + 2y - 16 = 0$
8. $x + 2y - 4 = 0$
9. $5x + 2y + 10 = 0$

In questions 10–18, write the equation of the line in the form $ax + by + c = 0$.

10. $y = 3x + 7$
11. $y = -2x + 11$
12. $y = -8x - 5$
13. $y = \frac{2}{3}x + 1$
14. $y = \frac{3}{5}x - 6$
15. $y = \frac{1}{3}x + 3$
16. $y = -\frac{3}{4}x - 9$
17. $y = -\frac{2}{3}x - 2$
18. $y = -\frac{5}{6}x + 4$

Slope of a line when given its equation

To find the slope of a line when given its equation, do the following.

Method 1

> Get y on its own, and the number in front of x is the slope.

Note: The number in front of x is called the **coefficient** of x.

The number on its own is called the y **intercept**.

In short, write the line in the form:

$$y = mx + c$$

$$y = (\text{slope})x + (\text{where the line cuts the } y\text{-axis})$$

Method 2

> If the line is in the form $ax + by + c = 0$, then $-\dfrac{a}{b}$ is the slope.

In words: Slope $= -\dfrac{\text{Number in front of } x}{\text{Number in front of } y}$

Note: When using this method, make sure every term is on the left-hand side in the given equation of the line.

EXAMPLE 1

Find the slope of the following lines.   (i) $3x - y - 5 = 0$ (ii) $5x + 4y - 12 = 0$

Solution:

Method 1:

(i)
$$3x - y - 5 = 0$$
$$-y = -3x + 5$$
$$y = 3x - 5$$

$\downarrow$

Compare to $y = mx + c$
$\therefore$ Slope $= 3$

(ii)
$$5x + 4y - 12 = 0$$
$$4y = -5x + 12$$
$$y = -\tfrac{5}{4}x + 3$$

$\downarrow$

Compare to $y = mx + c$
$\therefore$ Slope $= -\tfrac{5}{4}$

Method 2:

(i)
$$a = 3, \qquad b = -1$$
$$\text{slope} = -\frac{a}{b}$$
$$= -\frac{3}{-1}$$
$$= 3$$

(ii)
$$5x + 4y - 12 = 0$$
$$a = 5, \qquad b = 4$$
$$\text{slope} = -\frac{a}{b}$$
$$= -\frac{5}{4}$$

To prove whether or not two lines are parallel, do the following.

1. Find the slope of each line.
2. (i) If the slopes are the same, the lines are parallel.
   (ii) If the slopes are different, the lines are **not** parallel.

To prove whether or not two lines are perpendicular, do the following.

1. Find the slope of each line.
2. Multiply both slopes.
3. (i) If the answer in step 2 is −1, the lines are perpendicular.
   (ii) If the answer in step 2 is **not** −1, the lines are **not** perpendicular.

EXAMPLE 2

$l : 3x + 4y − 8 = 0$ and $k : 4x − 3y + 6 = 0$ are two lines. Prove that $l \perp k$.

Solution:

(i)
$$3x + 4y − 8 = 0$$
$$4y = −3x + 8$$
$$y = −\tfrac{3}{4}x + 4$$
slope of $l = −\tfrac{3}{4}$

(ii)
$$4x − 3y + 6 = 0$$
$$−3y = −4x − 6$$
$$3y = 4x + 6$$
$$y = \tfrac{4}{3}x + 2$$
slope of $k = \tfrac{4}{3}$

(slope of l) × (slope of k) = $−\tfrac{3}{4} \times \tfrac{4}{3} = −1$
$$\therefore l \perp k$$

Note: To get the slopes, we could have used $m = −\dfrac{a}{b}$ in each case.

Exercise 2.8

In questions 1–12, find the slope of each of the following lines.

1. $2x + y + 7 = 0$
2. $3x − y − 2 = 0$
3. $4x − 2y − 7 = 0$
4. $9x + 3y − 11 = 0$
5. $2x + 3y − 15 = 0$
6. $4x − 3y − 12 = 0$
7. $x + 4y − 3 = 0$
8. $x − 3y + 2 = 0$
9. $4x − 3y = 0$
10. $5x − 7y = 8$
11. $3x − 2y − 3 = 0$
12. $7x − 10y − 11 = 0$
13. $l : 5x − 2y − 10 = 0$ and $k : 2x + 5y − 15 = 0$ are two lines. Prove that $l \perp k$.
14. $l : 3x + 2y − 2 = 0$ and $k : 2x − 3y + 6 = 0$ are two lines. Prove that $l \perp k$.
15. $l : 3x + 4y − 11 = 0$ and $k : 6x + 8y − 5 = 0$ are two lines. Prove that $l \parallel k$.
16. If the line $3x + 2y − 10 = 0$ is parallel to the line $tx + 4y − 8 = 0$, find the value of t.
17. If the lines $5x − 4y − 20 = 0$ and $4x + ty − 6 = 0$ are perpendicular, find the value of t.

Equation of a line, parallel or perpendicular to a given line

In some questions we need to find the equation of a line containing a particular point that is parallel to, or perpendicular to, a given line.

When this happens, do the following.

1. Find the slope of the given line.
2. (i) If parallel, use the slope in step 1.
   (ii) If perpendicular, turn the slope in step 1 upside down and change the sign.
3. Use the slope in step 2 with the point in the formula:

$$(y - y_1) = m(x - x_1)$$

Remember: To find the equation of a line we need:

1. Slope, m.　　　　2. One point, (x_1, y_1).　　　　3. Formula, $(y - y_1) = m(x - x_1)$.

EXAMPLE

l is the line $5x - 3y - 2 = 0$. The line k contains the point $(3, -1)$ and $k \perp l$.
Find the equation of k.

Solution:
We have a point, $(3, -1)$. The slope is missing.

Step 1: Find the slope of l

$$5x - 3y - 2 = 0$$
$$-3y = -5x + 2$$
$$3y = 5x - 2$$
$$y = \tfrac{5}{3}x - \tfrac{2}{3}$$
$$\therefore \text{Slope of } l = \tfrac{5}{3}$$

Step 2: Find the slope of k perpendicular to l.
$$\therefore \text{Slope of } k = -\tfrac{3}{5}$$
(turn upside down and change sign)

Step 3: Containing $(3, -1)$ with slope $-\tfrac{3}{5}$

$$x_1 = 3, \quad y_1 = -1, \quad m = -\tfrac{3}{5}$$
$$(y - y_1) = m(x - x_1)$$
$$(y + 1) = -\tfrac{3}{5}(x - 3)$$
$$5(y + 1) = -3(x - 3)$$

(multiply both sides by 5)

$$5y + 5 = -3x + 9$$
$$3x + 5y + 5 - 9 = 0$$
$$3x + 5y - 4 = 0$$

The equation of the line k is $3x + 5y - 4 = 0$.

Exercise 2.9

1. Find the equation of the line containing $(2, 1)$ and parallel to $2x - y + 6 = 0$.

2. Find the equation of the line containing $(3, -2)$ and perpendicular to $3x - 2y + 8 = 0$.

3. Find the equation of the line containing $(-1, -4)$ and parallel to $5x + 4y - 3 = 0$.

4. Find the equation of the line containing $(-2, 5)$ and perpendicular to $4x - 3y - 1 = 0$.

5. l is the line $3x + 5y - 10 = 0$. The line k contains the point $(-2, 0)$ and $k \perp l$. Find the equation of k.

6. m is the line $x + 2y - 6 = 0$. The line l contains the point $(-3, -1)$ and $m \parallel l$. Find the equation of the line l.

7. $A(3, -6)$ and $B(-1, -2)$ are two points, C is the midpoint of $[AB]$ and k is the line $2x + 5y - 5 = 0$. The line l contains the point C and $l \perp k$. Find the equation of l.

Point of intersection of two lines

Use the method of solving simultaneous equations to find the point of intersection of two lines.

When the point of intersection contains whole numbers only

EXAMPLE

l is the line $2x - 5y - 9 = 0$ and k is the line $3x - 2y - 8 = 0$.
Find the coordinates of Q, the point of intersection of l and k.

Solution:
Write both equations in the form $ax + by = n$.

$2x - 5y = 9$	(l)	Put $y = -1$ into (l) or (k)
$3x - 2y = 8$	(k)	
		$2x - 5y = 9$ $\quad(l)$
$6x - 15y = 27$	$(l) \times 3$	$2x - 5(-1) = 9$
$-6x + 4y = -16$	$(k) \times -2$	$2x + 5 = 9$
		$2x = 4$
$-11y = 11$	(add)	$x = 2$
$11y = -11$		
$y = -1$		

$\therefore$ The coordinates of Q are $(2, -1)$.

When the point of intersection contains fractions

If the point of intersection contains fractions, the following is a very useful method.

Step 1: Remove the y terms and get a value for x.
Step 2: Remove the x terms and get a value for y.

Note: This method can be used even if the point of intersection contains whole numbers only.

EXAMPLE

$l : 6x + 3y - 11 = 0$ and $k : 5x + 2y - 8 = 0$ are two lines. $l \cap k = \{P\}$. Find the coordinates of P.

Solution:

Write both equations in the form $ax + by = n$.

Remove the y terms:

$6x + 3y = 11$	(l)
$5x + 2y = 8$	(k)
$12x + 6y = 22$	$(l) \times 2$
$-15x - 6y = -24$	$(k) \times -3$
$-3x = -2$	(add)
$3x = 2$	
$x = \frac{2}{3}$	

Remove the x terms:

$6x + 3y = 11$	(l)
$5x + 2y = 8$	(k)
$30x + 15y = 55$	$(l) \times 5$
$-30x - 12y = -48$	$(k) \times -6$
$3y = 7$	(add)
$y = \frac{7}{3}$	

$\therefore$ The coordinates of P are $\left(\frac{2}{3}, \frac{7}{3}\right)$.

Exercise 2.10

In questions 1–15, find the point of intersection of each of the following pairs of lines.

1. $2x + 3y - 7 = 0$
    $5x - 2y - 8 = 0$

2. $5x - 2y - 11 = 0$
    $3x - 4y - 1 = 0$

3. $3x - 2y - 3 = 0$
    $x + 4y - 1 = 0$

4. $4x - 3y + 25 = 0$
    $3x + 5y - 3 = 0$

5. $3x - y + 8 = 0$
    $x - 7y - 4 = 0$

6. $2x - 3y - 15 = 0$
    $5x - y - 5 = 0$

7. $x + 2y - 5 = 0$
    $2x - y = 0$

8. $x + 2y - 4 = 0$
    $4x - 5y - 29 = 0$

9. $5x + 2y + 1 = 0$
    $2x + 5y - 29 = 0$

Questions 10–15 have solutions that contain fractions.

10. $5x + 10y - 11 = 0$
    $2x + y - 2 = 0$

11. $3x - y - 6 = 0$
    $x - 7y - 12 = 0$

12. $x + 2y - 2 = 0$
    $2x - y - 2 = 0$

13. $2x - 3y + 2 = 0$
    $4x - y - 2 = 0$

14. $4x + 2y - 11 = 0$
    $3x - y - 7 = 0$

15. $3x + 3y - 20 = 0$
    $x + 2y - 10 = 0$

16. $l : x + 3y + 12 = 0$ and $k : 3x - 2y + 3 = 0$ are two lines. $l \cap k = \{P\}$.
    Find the coordinates of P.

17. $l : 5x - 4y - 6 = 0$ and $m : 2x - 3y - 8 = 0$ are two lines. $l \cap m = \{Q\}$.
    Find the coordinates of Q.

18. $l : 3x - 2y - 4 = 0$ and $k : 5x + 2y - 12 = 0$ are two lines. $l \cap k = \{A\}$.
    $m : x + 3y + 8 = 0$ and $n : 3x + 4y + 9 = 0$ are also two lines. $m \cap n = \{B\}$.
    Find the equation of the line AB.

Graphing lines

Lines in the form $ax + by = d$

To draw a line, only two points are needed. The easiest points to find are those where a line cuts the x- and y-axes.

This is known as the **intercept method**. We use the following facts.

$$\boxed{\text{On the } x\text{-axis, } y = 0. \quad \text{On the } y\text{-axis, } x = 0.}$$

To draw a line, do the following.

1. Let $y = 0$ and find x.
2. Let $x = 0$ and find y.
3. Plot these two points.
4. Draw the line through these points.

Note: Any two points on the line will do; it is not necessary to use the points where the line cuts the x- and y-axes.

EXAMPLE

Graph the line $3x - 2y - 12 = 0$.

Solution:

1. and 2. $3x - 2y = 12$

$y = 0$	$x = 0$
$3x = 12$	$-2y = 12$
$x = 4$	$2y = -12$
	$y = -6$
$(4, 0)$	$(0, -6)$

3. Plot the points $(4, 0)$ and $(0, -6)$.

4. Draw the line through these points.

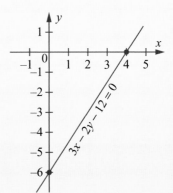

Lines in the form $ax + by + c = 0$

Arrange the equation into the form $ax + by = d$ and use the intercept method.

Lines in the form $y = mx + c$

Method 1: Arrange the equation in the form $ax + by = d$ and use the intercept method.

Method 2: Find two points by using two different values of x. One of these values should be zero. The other value will depend on the coefficient of x.

To draw a line, do the following.

1. Let $x = 0$ and find y.
2. Let $x = $ a different value and find y.
3. Plot these two points.
4. Draw the line through these points.

EXAMPLE 1

Graph the line $y = 2x - 1$.

Solution:

The coefficient of x is 2. As this is a whole number, you may choose **any** other value of x.

1. and 2.

$$y = 2x - 1$$

$x = 0$	$x = 2$
$y = 2(0) - 1$	$y = 2(2) - 1$
$y = -1$	$y = 3$
$(0, -1)$	$(2, 3)$

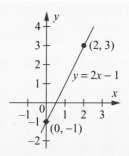

3. Plot the points $(0, -1)$ and $(2, 3)$.

4. Draw the line through these points.

EXAMPLE 2

Graph the line $y = -\frac{2}{3}x + 4$.

Solution:

The coefficient of x is $-\frac{2}{3}$. As this is a fraction, choose a
multiple of its denominator. As the denominator is 3, the x
value should be selected from 3, 6, 9, etc.

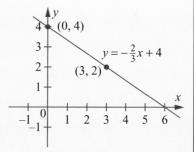

1. and 2.

$$y = -\frac{2}{3}x + 4$$

$x = 0$	$x = 3$
$y = -\frac{2}{3}(0) + 4$	$y = -\frac{2}{3}(3) + 4$
$y = -0 + 4$	$y = -2 + 4$
$y = 4$	$y = 2$
$(0, 4)$	$(3, 2)$

3. Plot the points $(0, 4)$ and $(3, 2)$.

4. Draw the line through these points.

Exercise 2.11

In questions 1–24, graph each of the following lines.

1. $2x + 3y - 6 = 0$
2. $x + y - 5 = 0$
3. $3x - 5y + 15 = 0$
4. $4x - y - 8 = 0$
5. $x - y - 3 = 0$
6. $2x - 5y - 10 = 0$
7. $4x + 3y - 24 = 0$
8. $x - 3y - 12 = 0$
9. $4x - 5y - 10 = 0$
10. $x - y - 6 = 0$
11. $3x - 2y + 12 = 0$
12. $x + 4y - 6 = 0$
13. $y = 3x + 2$
14. $y = x - 1$
15. $y = 5x - 2$
16. $y = -4x + 3$
17. $y = -2x + 5$
18. $y = -3x + 4$

19. $y = \frac{2}{3}x + 2$

20. $y = \frac{3}{4}x - 1$

21. $y = \frac{5}{3}x - 2$

22. $y = -\frac{4}{3}x + 3$

23. $y = -\frac{2}{5}x + 1$

24. $y = -\frac{5}{6}x + 3$

25. Draw the line $2x + 3y - 12 = 0$. Show **(i)** graphically and **(ii)** algebraically that the point $(3, 2)$ is on the line.

26. Where does the line $y = 4x - 7$ cross the y-axis?

27. If the line $y = -2x + c$ cuts the y-axis at $(0, 3)$, find the value of c.

28. Write down the equation of a line with slope 3 and which crosses the y-axis at $(0, 2)$.

29. Write down the equation of a line with slope $-\frac{2}{3}$ and which intercepts the y-axis at $(0, -3)$.

30. **(i)** Graph the following lines on the same axes and scales.
     (a) $2x + 3y = 6$ **(b)** $2x + 3y = 12$
     (ii) What do you notice about the lines?

31. **(i)** Graph the following lines on the same axes and scales.
     (a) $y = 2x - 2$ **(b)** $y = 2x + 1$ **(c)** $y = 2x + 3$
     (ii) What do you notice about the lines?
     (iii) Write down the equation of two other lines that match the others.

32. **(i)** Graph the following lines on the same axes and scales.
     (a) $y = -3x + 2$ **(b)** $y = x + 2$ **(c)** $y = 2x + 2$
     (ii) What do you notice about the lines?

33. **(i)** Graph the following lines on the same axes and scales.
     (a) $y = x + 3$ **(b)** $y = x + 1$ **(c)** $y = x + 5$
     (ii) What do you notice about the lines?
     (iii) Mark on your diagram where you think $y = x + 7$ should be.
     (iv) How could you check your answer?

Lines that contain the origin

If the constant in the equation of a line is zero, e.g. $3x - 5y = 0$ or $4x = 3y$, then the line will pass through the origin, $(0, 0)$. In this case the **intercept method** will not work.

To draw a line that contains the origin, $(0, 0)$, do the following.

1. Choose a suitable value for x and find the corresponding value for y (or vice versa).
2. Plot this point.
3. A line drawn through this point and the origin is the required line.

Note: A suitable value is to let x equal the number in front of y and then find the corresponding value for x (or vice versa).

EXAMPLE

Graph the line $3x + 4y = 0$.

Solution:

1. Let $x = 4$ (number in front of y).
$$3x + 4y = 0$$
$$3(4) + 4y = 0$$
$$12 + 4y = 0$$
$$4y = -12$$
$$y = -3$$

2. Plot the point $(4, -3)$.

3. Draw the line through the points $(4, -3)$ and $(0, 0)$.

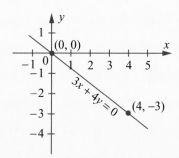

Exercise 2.12

Graph each of the following lines.

1. $3x - 2y = 0$
2. $x + y = 0$
3. $3x - y = 0$
4. $5x = 3y$
5. $2x - 5y = 0$
6. $x = 4y$
7. $y = 3x$
8. $4x - y = 0$
9. $3x - 4y = 0$
10. $6x - 5y = 0$
11. $x - y = 0$
12. $2y = 3x$

Lines parallel to the axes

Some lines are parallel to the x- or y-axis.

$x = 5$ is a line parallel to the y-axis through 5 on the x-axis.

$y = -3$ is a line parallel to the x-axis through -3 on the y-axis.

Note:

1. $y = 0$ is the equation of the x-axis.
2. $x = 0$ is the equation of the y-axis.

EXAMPLE

On the same axes and scales, graph the lines $x = 2$ and $y = -1$.

Solution:

(i) $x = 2$

Line parallel to the y-axis through 2 on the x-axis.

(ii) $y = -1$

Line parallel to the x-axis through -1 on the y-axis.

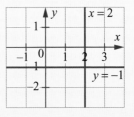

Exercise 2.13

In questions 1–12, graph each of the following lines.

1. $x = 4$
2. $y = 3$
3. $x = -2$
4. $y = -1$
5. $x + 3 = 0$
6. $y - 5 = 0$
7. $x = -5$
8. $y - 4 = 0$
9. $x - 7 = 0$
10. $x = -4$
11. $2x = 1$
12. $2y = 3$

13. $x - 4 = 0$ is the equation of the line l and $y + 2 = 0$ is the equation of the line k.

    (i) On the same axes and scales, graph the lines l and k.

    (ii) Write down the coordinates of Q, the point of intersection of l and k.

Area of a triangle

The area of a triangle with vertices $(0, 0)$, (x_1, y_1) and (x_2, y_2) is given by the formula:

$$\text{Area of triangle} = \tfrac{1}{2} \left| x_1 y_2 - x_2 y_1 \right|$$

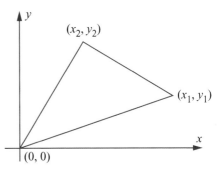

Notes:

1. The modulus symbol, $| \ |$, is included to make sure your answer is positive. Therefore, if the above formula gives a negative answer, simply ignore the negative sign, e.g. $\tfrac{1}{2} \left| -10 \right| = \tfrac{1}{2}(10) = 5$.

2. If none of the vertices is at the origin, simply select one of the vertices and map (move) it to the point $(0, 0)$ by a translation. Then apply the same translation to the other two vertices to get (x_1, y_1) and (x_2, y_2).

EXAMPLE 1

Find the area of the triangle with vertices (0, 0), (−2, 5) and (6, −3).

Solution:

(−2, 5) (6, −3)	Area of triangle $= \frac{1}{2}\lvert x_1 y_2 - x_2 y_1 \rvert$
(x_1, y_1) (x_2, y_2)	$= \frac{1}{2}\lvert (-2)(-3) - (6)(5) \rvert$
$x_1 = -2, y_1 = 5$ $x_2 = 6, y_2 = -3$	$= \frac{1}{2}\lvert -24 \rvert$
	$= 12$ sq. units

 EXAMPLE 2

Find the area of the triangle with vertices (−2, 4), (1, −4) and (2, −2).

Solution:

Map (move) the point (−2, 4) to (0, 0).
Rule: Add 2 to x, subtract 4 from y.

(−2, 4) (1, −4) (2, −2)
↓   ↓   ↓
(0, 0) (3, −8) (4, −6)
        (x_1, y_1) (x_2, y_2)
$x_1 = 3, y_1 = -8$ $x_2 = 4, y_2 = -6$

Area of triangle $= \frac{1}{2}\lvert x_1 y_2 - x_2 y_1 \rvert$

$= \frac{1}{2}\lvert (3)(-6) - (4)(-8) \rvert$

$= \frac{1}{2}\lvert -18 + 32 \rvert$

$= \frac{1}{2}\lvert 14 \rvert$

$= 7$ sq. units

Note: To find the area of a quadrilateral (four-sided figure), divide it into two triangles.

If the quadrilateral is a **parallelogram**, then the areas of both triangles are equal. Therefore, all that is needed is to find the area of one triangle and double it.

Exercise 2.14

In questions 1–10, find the area of each of the following triangles whose vertices are as follows.

1. (0, 0), (5, 2), (3, 4)
2. (0, 0), (10, 8), (3, 5)
3. (8, 7), (0, 0), (2, −3)
4. (6, −3), (−2, 4), (0, 0)
5. (5, 0), (1, 3), (6, 2)
6. (−5, −3), (1, 5), (−2, 1)

7. $(3, -2), (-5, 6), (7, -1)$

8. $(1, 3), (-4, 1), (5, -3)$

9. $(4, -5), (3, -2), (-4, -8)$

10. $(-1, -4), (2, -1), (-2, 3)$

In questions 11–14, find the area of the parallelogram whose vertices are as follows.

11. $(0, 0), (1, 3), (5, 5), (4, 2)$

12. $(5, 1), (3, 1), (5, 4), (7, 4)$

13. $(-2, 4), (2, 4), (2, 7), (-2, 7)$

14. $(-1, 3), (0, 2), (5, 4), (4, 5)$

In questions 15–18, find the area of the quadrilateral whose vertices are as follows.

15. $(1, 1), (1, 2), (9, 3), (6, 1)$

16. $(2, -4), (-2, 4), (-2, 2), (5, 5)$

17. $(5, -6), (5, -4), (0, 1), (-2, -9)$

18. $(-2, 2), (-5, -6), (8, -4), (9, 0)$

19. $A(-2, -5)$, $B(1, -3)$ and $C(4, -1)$ are the vertices of triangle ABC. By finding the area of triangle ABC, show that A, B and C are collinear (on the same line).

Exercise 2.15
(Revision of Exercises 2.1 to 2.14)

1. $A(-2, 4)$, $B(2, 2)$ and $C(5, 3)$ are three points. Find the following.

   (i) $|AB|$
   (ii) The coordinates of M, the midpoint of $[AB]$
   (iii) The area of triangle ABC
   (iv) The slope of AB
   (v) The equation of the line AB
   (vi) The equation of the line l through the point C and $l \perp AB$
   (vii) The coordinates of P, the point of intersection of the lines l and AB

2. (i) Verify that the point $(-2, -4)$ is on the line $2x - 5y - 16 = 0$.
   (ii) If $(k, -2)$ is also on the line $2x - 5y - 16 = 0$, find the value of k.

3. $A(2, -3)$, $B(5, 1)$ and $C(1, 4)$ are three points. Verify that $|\angle ABC| = 90°$.

4. The midpoint of the line segment $[AB]$ is $(1, -4)$.
   If the coordinates of A are $(-1, 3)$, find the coordinates of B.

5. The equation of the line k is $3x - 2y - 12 = 0$.
   k intersects the x-axis at A and the y-axis at B.

   (i) Find the coordinates of A and the coordinates of B.
   (ii) Graph the line k.
   (iii) Calculate the area of triangle AOB, where O is the origin.

6. (i) l is the line $x - 2y + 5 = 0$ and k is the line $3x + y - 6 = 0$.
        Find the coordinates of A, the point of intersection of l and k.
    (ii) l and k cut the x-axis at B and C, respectively. Find the coordinates of B and C.
    (iii) Find the area of triangle ABC.

7. (i) h is the line $3x + 2y - 4 = 0$. Verify that $C(2, -1)$ is on h.
    (ii) Points $A(-5, 1)$ and $B(1, 9)$ are on l. Find the following.

    (a) The equation of l
    (b) The coordinates of D, the point of intersection of h and l
    (c) The coordinates of the fourth point, M, of the parallelogram $DACM$
    (d) The area of $DACM$
    (e) The value of k if the point $(4, k)$ is on the line l

8. $l : x + 2y + 2 = 0$ and $k : 2x - y + 9 = 0$ are two lines.

    (i) Verify that $P(4, -3)$ is on l.
    (ii) Prove that $l \perp k$.
    (iii) Find the coordinates of Q, the point of intersection of l and k.
    (iv) Find the coordinates of R, the point where k cuts the y-axis.
    (v) Prove that $|PQ| = |QR|$.
    (vi) Calculate the area of triangle PQR.

9. l is the line $x - 2y + 5 = 0$.

    (i) Find the coordinates of the point R where l intersects the y-axis.
    (ii) Find the equation of the line m, which contains the point $P(\frac{5}{2}, 0)$ and is perpendicular to l.
    (iii) Calculate the coordinates of Q if $l \cap m = \{Q\}$.
    (iv) Calculate the area of the quadrilateral $OPQR$, where O is the origin.

10. $l : x + 2y - 11 = 0$ and $k : 2x - 5y + 5 = 0$ are two lines.

    (i) Verify that $A(1, 5)$ is on l.
    (ii) Find the coordinates of B if $l \cap k = \{B\}$.
    (iii) Is $l \perp k$? Give a reason for your answer.
    (iv) Find the equation of the line m, containing $C(6, 2)$, if $l \perp m$.
    (v) m meets the x-axis at D. Find the coordinates of D.
    (vi) Calculate the area of the quadrilateral $ABCD$.

11. k is the line $3x - y - 8 = 0$.

    (i) Verify that $(2, -2)$ is on k.
    (ii) Find the coordinates of the point where k crosses the y-axis.
    (iii) Find the equation of the line l containing the point $(-3, 3)$ if $k \perp l$.
    (iv) Find the coordinates of the point where l crosses the y-axis.

   (v) $k \cap l = \{P\}$. Find the coordinates of P.

   (vi) Find the area of the triangle formed by the lines l, k and the y-axis.

12. $P(1, 4)$, $Q(x, 9)$ and $R(2x, x)$ are three points.

   If $|PQ| = |QR|$, calculate the two possible values of x.

Transformations of the plane

Translation

A **translation** moves a point in a straight line.

Note: The translation $a \rightarrow b$ is usually written $\overrightarrow{ab}$.

EXAMPLE 1

$P(-2, 4)$ and $Q(1, -1)$ are two points. Find the image of the point $(3, -4)$ under the translation $\overrightarrow{PQ}$.

Solution:
Under the translation $\overrightarrow{PQ}$, $(-2, 4) \rightarrow (1, -1)$.
Rule: Add 3 to x, subtract 5 from y.
∴ $(3, -4) \rightarrow (3 + 3, -4 - 5) = (6, -9)$
∴ The image of $(3, -4)$ is $(6, -9)$.

Translations are useful in finding the missing coordinates of one of the vertices of a parallelogram when given the other three.

EXAMPLE 2

$A(1, -2)$, $B(-3, 1)$, $C(2, 3)$ and $D(x, y)$ are the vertices of a parallelogram $ABCD$. Find the coordinates of D.

Solution:
Make a rough diagram (keep cyclic order).
Since $ABCD$ is a parallelogram, $\overrightarrow{BC} = \overrightarrow{AD}$
(i.e. the movement from B to C is the same as the movement from A to D).

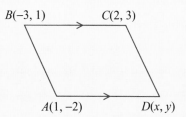

Find the rule that moves B to C, then apply this rule to A to find D.

$\overrightarrow{BC}$: $(-3, 1) \rightarrow (2, 3)$

Rule: Add 5 to x, add 2 to y.

$\overrightarrow{AD}$ $(1, -2) \rightarrow (1 + 5, -2 + 2) = (6, 0)$

$\therefore$ The coordinates of D are $(6, 0)$.

Note: By 'cyclic order' we mean that the points are taken in clockwise or anticlockwise order.

Central symmetry

Central symmetry is a reflection in a point. The image of a point under a central symmetry in another point can be found with a translation.

EXAMPLE

Find the image of the point $P(-1, 3)$ under the central symmetry in the point $Q(2, -1)$.

Solution:
Rough diagram:

$P(-1, 3)$ $\quad\quad\quad$ $Q(2, -1)$ $\quad\quad\quad$ $P'(5, -5)$

Translation from P to Q:

Rule: Add 3 to x, subtract 4 from y.

Apply this rule to Q to find the image of P.

$P(2, -1) \rightarrow (2 + 3, -1 - 4) = P'(5, -5)$

Therefore, the image of $P(-1, 3)$ under a central symmetry in $Q(2, -1)$ is $P'(5, -5)$.

Exercise 2.16

1. Find the image of $(3, 2)$ under the translation that maps $(5, 2) \rightarrow (7, 6)$.

2. Find the image of each of the following points under the translation that maps $(-3, 1) \rightarrow (-5, 4)$.
   (i) $(6, 2)$ $\quad\quad$ (ii) $(3, -1)$ $\quad\quad$ (iii) $(-4, -3)$ $\quad\quad$ (iv) $(-6, 0)$

3. (i) $A(1, -3)$ and $B(4, -5)$ are two points. Find the image of each point under the translation $\overrightarrow{AB}$.
   (a) $(4, -1)$ $\quad\quad$ (b) $(-2, 6)$ $\quad\quad$ (c) $(-5, -2)$ $\quad\quad$ (d) $(9, 5)$
   (ii) What is the image of $(1, 1)$ under the translation $\overrightarrow{BA}$?

4. Find the missing coordinates in each of the following parallelograms *PQRS*.

   (i) *P*(1, 1), *Q*(4, 1), *R*(4, 6), *S*(*x*, *y*)

   (ii) *P*(−2, −1), *Q*(2, −2), *R*(*x*, *y*), *S*(2, 3)

   (iii) *P*(−6, −3), *Q*(*x*, *y*), *R*(1, 5), *S*(−5, 1)

   (iv) *P*(*x*, *y*), *Q*(2, 0), *R*(−4, 3), *S*(−7, 2)

5. *A*(−2, −2), *B*(4, *k*), *C*(7, 2) and *D*(*h*, 1) are the coordinates of the parallelogram *ABCD*. Find the value of *h* and the value of *k*.

6. Find the image of the point (−1, 2) under the central symmetry in the point (2, −3).

7. Find the image of the point (4, 3) under the central symmetry in the point (−2, 5).

8. Find the image of the point (−4, 0) under the central symmetry in the point (3, −1).

9. *A*(2, −1) and *B*(4, −5) are two points. Find:

   (i) The image of *A* under a central symmetry in *B*

   (ii) The image of *B* under a central symmetry in *A*

10. *A*(1, 1), *B*(9, 2), *C*(*h*, *k*) and *D*(*p*, *q*) are the vertices of parallelogram *ABCD*. *X*(6, 3) is the point of intersection of the diagonals [*AC*] and [*BD*]. Find the coordinates of *C* and *D*.

11.   (i) *A*(2, 1) and *B*(*x*, *y*) are two points. The image of *A* under the central symmetry in *B* is (8, −3). Find the coordinates of *B*.

   (ii) (3, −1) is the image of (*p*, *q*) under the translation (3, −2) → (1, −3). Find (*p*, *q*).

Equation of a circle, centre (0, 0) and radius r

The diagram shows a circle with centre (0, 0), radius r and (x, y) is any point on the circle.
The distance between (0, 0) and (x, y) equals the radius, r.

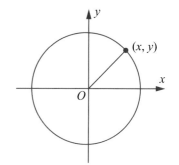

$$\therefore \sqrt{(x-0)^2 + (y-0)^2} = r \quad \text{(distance formula)}$$
$$\sqrt{x^2 + y^2} = r$$
$$x^2 + y^2 = r^2 \quad \text{(square both sides)}$$

Hence, $x^2 + y^2 = r^2$ is said to be the equation of the circle.

> Equation of a circle, centre (0, 0) and radius r, is
> $$x^2 + y^2 = r^2$$

Two quantities are needed to find the equation of a circle.

> **1.** Centre   **2.** Radius
> If the centre is (0, 0), the equation of the circle will be of the form $x^2 + y^2 = r^2$.

EXAMPLE 1

Find the equation of the circle k, of centre (0, 0), which has a radius of 6.

Solution:
Centre is (0, 0), therefore k is of the form $x^2 + y^2 = r^2$.
Substitute $r = 6$ into this equation:
$$x^2 + y^2 = 6^2$$
$$x^2 + y^2 = 36$$
$\therefore k$ is the circle $x^2 + y^2 = 36$.

EXAMPLE 2

Find the equation of the circle c whose centre is $(0, 0)$ and which contains the point $(3, -2)$.

Solution:
Centre $(0, 0)$, therefore c is of the form $x^2 + y^2 = r^2$.
The radius of c needs to be found.
The radius is the distance from $(0, 0)$ to $(3, -2)$.
Using the distance formula:

$$r = \sqrt{(3 - 0)^2 + (-2 - 0)^2}$$
$$= \sqrt{3^2 + (-2)^2}$$
$$= \sqrt{9 + 4} = \sqrt{13}$$
$$x^2 + y^2 = (\sqrt{13})^2$$
$$x^2 + y^2 = 13$$

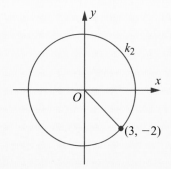

$\therefore$ c is the circle $x^2 + y^2 = 13$.
Alternatively, as the centre is $(0, 0)$, c is of the form $x^2 + y^2 = r^2$.
Thus, $x^2 + y^2 = (3)^2 + (-2)^2 = 9 + 4 = 13$
$\therefore$ c is the circle $x^2 + y^2 = 13$.

EXAMPLE 3

Find the radius of each of the following circles.
(i) $x^2 + y^2 = 49$ (ii) $x^2 + y^2 = 10$

Solution:
Compare each to $x^2 + y^2 = r^2$.

(i) $x^2 + y^2 = 49$
$\quad x^2 + y^2 = r^2$
$\qquad r^2 = 49$
$\qquad r = \sqrt{49} = 7$

(ii) $x^2 + y^2 = 10$
$\quad x^2 + y^2 = r^2$
$\qquad r^2 = 10$
$\qquad r = \sqrt{10}$

Note: Ignore negative values for a radius length.

EXAMPLE 4

The circle c has equation $x^2 + y^2 = 25$.

(i) Write down the centre and radius length of c.

(ii) Find the coordinates of the points where c intersects the x- and y-axes.

(iii) Draw a diagram of c.

Solution:

(i) $x^2 + y^2 = 25$

As the equation is in the form $x^2 + y^2 = r^2$, the centre is $(0, 0)$.

$$r^2 = 25$$
$$r = \sqrt{25} = 5$$

Thus, the radius length is 5.

(ii) $x^2 + y^2 = 25$

On the x-axis, $y = 0$

$$\therefore x^2 = 25$$
$$x = \pm\sqrt{25} = \pm 5$$

Thus, c intersects the x-axes at $(5, 0)$ and $(-5, 0)$.

On the y-axis, $x = 0$

$$\therefore y^2 = 25$$
$$y = \pm\sqrt{25} = \pm 5$$

Thus, c intersects the y-axes at $(0, 5)$ and $(0, -5)$.

(iii) Diagram of c

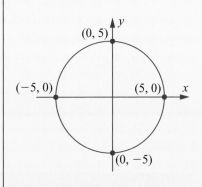

Note: When drawing a circle, the scales on the x- and y-axes must be the same.

Exercise 3.1

In questions 1–14, find the equation of each of the circles of centre $(0, 0)$ and:

1. Radius 2
2. Radius 3
3. Radius 1
4. Radius 10
5. Radius $\sqrt{5}$
6. Radius $\sqrt{13}$
7. Radius $\sqrt{17}$
8. Radius $\sqrt{23}$
9. Containing the point $(4, 3)$
10. Containing the point $(-3, -2)$
11. Containing the point $(1, -5)$
12. Containing the point $(0, -4)$
13. Containing the point $(1, -1)$
14. Containing the point $(-2, 5)$

In questions 15–20, write down the radius length of each of the following circles.

15. $x^2 + y^2 = 16$ 16. $x^2 + y^2 = 9$ 17. $x^2 + y^2 = 1$

18. $x^2 + y^2 = 13$ 19. $x^2 + y^2 = 5$ 20. $x^2 + y^2 = 29$

In questions 21–26, draw a graph of each of the circles and write down the coordinates where each circle intersects the x- and y-axes.

21. $x^2 + y^2 = 9$ 22. $x^2 + y^2 = 16$ 23. $x^2 + y^2 = 49$

24. $x^2 + y^2 = 64$ 25. $x^2 + y^2 = 25$ 26. $x^2 + y^2 = 100$

27. Find the equation of the circle that has the line segment joining $(3, -4)$ to $(-3, 4)$ as a diameter.

28. $A(6, 1)$ and $B(-6, -1)$ are two points. Find the equation of the circle with $[AB]$ as a diameter.

29. $(6, -3)$ is an extremity of a diameter of the circle $x^2 + y^2 = 45$. What are the coordinates of the other extremity of the same diameter?

30. What is the area of the circle $x^2 + y^2 = 40$? Leave your answer in terms of π.

31. Tom and Jerry are discussing the pattern of ripples caused by dropping a stone into a pond. They suggest that one of the following diagrams is correct.

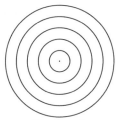

Diagram A

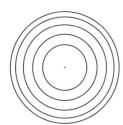

Diagram B

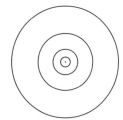

Diagram C

Match each diagram with one of these sets of circles.

Set 1	Set 2	Set 3
$x^2 + y^2 = 1$	$x^2 + y^2 = 1^2$	$x^2 + y^2 = 1^3$
$x^2 + y^2 = 2$	$x^2 + y^2 = 2^2$	$x^2 + y^2 = 2^3$
$x^2 + y^2 = 3$	$x^2 + y^2 = 3^2$	$x^2 + y^2 = 3^3$
$x^2 + y^2 = 4$	$x^2 + y^2 = 4^2$	$x^2 + y^2 = 4^3$
$x^2 + y^2 = 5$	$x^2 + y^2 = 5^2$	$x^2 + y^2 = 5^3$

Points inside, on or outside a circle 1

Method 1

To find whether a point is inside, on or outside a circle, calculate the distance from the centre, $(0, 0)$, to the point and compare this distance with the radius. Three cases arise.

 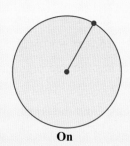 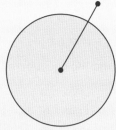

Inside	**On**	**Outside**

1. Distance from the centre to the point is **less** than the radius.

   ∴ Point is inside the circle.

2. Distance from the centre to the point is **equal** to the radius.

   ∴ Point is on the circle.

3. Distance from the centre to the point is **greater** than the radius.

   ∴ Point is outside the circle.

Method 2

If the coordinates of a point satisfy the equation of a circle, then the point is **on** the circle. Otherwise, the point is either **inside** or **outside** the circle. By substituting the coordinates into the equation of the circle, one of the following situations can arise.

1. $x^2 + y^2 < r^2$, the point is **inside** the circle.
2. $x^2 + y^2 = r^2$, the point is **on** the circle.
3. $x^2 + y^2 > r^2$, the point is **outside** the circle.

EXAMPLE 1

Determine whether the point $(3, 2)$ is inside, on or outside the circle $x^2 + y^2 = 10$.

Solution:
Using Method 1, the radius of the circle is $\sqrt{10}$.
Distance from centre, $(0, 0)$, to the point $(3, 2)$:

$$\sqrt{(3 - 0)^2 + (2 - 0)^2} = \sqrt{3^2 + 2^2} = \sqrt{9 + 4} = \sqrt{13}$$

Distance from the centre to the point is greater than the radius, i.e. $\sqrt{13} > \sqrt{10}$.
∴ The point $(3, 2)$ is outside the circle $x^2 + y^2 = 10$.

EXAMPLE 2

Determine whether the points $(4, -1)$, $(5, 2)$ and $(3, \sqrt{5})$ are inside, on or outside the circle $x^2 + y^2 = 17$.

Solution:

Using Method 2:

$x^2 + y^2 = 17 \Rightarrow r^2 = 17$ (by comparing with $x^2 + y^2 = r^2$)

Substitute $(4, -1)$: $x^2 + y^2 = 4^2 + (-1)^2 = 16 + 1 = 17$

$17 = 17$

$\therefore (4, -1)$ is on the circle.

Substitute $(5, 2)$: $x^2 + y^2 = 5^2 + 2^2 = 25 + 4 = 29$

$29 > 17$

$\therefore (5, 2)$ is outside the circle.

Substitute $(3, \sqrt{5})$: $x^2 + y^2 = 3^2 + (\sqrt{5})^2 = 9 + 5 = 14$

$14 < 17$

$\therefore (3, \sqrt{5})$ is inside the circle.

Exercise 3.2

In questions 1–12, determine whether the given point is inside, on or outside the given circle.

1. Point $(3, 1)$;   circle $x^2 + y^2 = 10$
2. Point $(4, 2)$;   circle $x^2 + y^2 = 17$
3. Point $(2, -1)$;   circle $x^2 + y^2 = 5$
4. Point $(-2, 1)$;   circle $x^2 + y^2 = 9$
5. Point $(7, -1)$;   circle $x^2 + y^2 = 50$
6. Point $(-5, 2)$;   circle $x^2 + y^2 = 29$
7. Point $(1, -9)$;   circle $x^2 + y^2 = 100$
8. Point $(0, -4)$;   circle $x^2 + y^2 = 16$
9. Point $(-2, -2)$;   circle $x^2 + y^2 = 9$
10. Point $(-5, 1)$;   circle $x^2 + y^2 = 25$
11. Point $\left(\frac{4}{5}, \frac{3}{5}\right)$;   circle $x^2 + y^2 = 1$
12. Point $(3, \sqrt{2})$;   circle $x^2 + y^2 = 11$

13. Show that the point $(3, 2)$ is on the circle $x^2 + y^2 = 13$ and hence draw a graph of the circle.

14. (i) Show that the point $(5, -5)$ is on the circle $k : x^2 + y^2 = 50$.

    (ii) Write down two points of the form $(-5, y)$ that are also on k.

15. The circle s has equation $x^2 + y^2 = 29$. The point $(5, p)$ lies on s. Find two real values of p.

16. A goat is tethered by a 9 m chain to the point $(0, 0)$ in a park. There are some primroses at $(8, -1)$, some tulips at $(-4, 2)$, some geraniums at $(0, 11)$ and some daisies at $(-3, 8)$. Are any of the flowers out of range of the goat?

Intersection of a line and a circle

To find the points where a line and a circle meet, the **method of substitution** between their equations is used.

The method involves the following three steps.

1. Get x or y on its own from the equation of the line.
   (Look carefully and select the variable that will make the working easier.)

2. Substitute for this same variable into the equation of the circle and solve the resultant quadratic equation.

3. Substitute separately the value(s) obtained in step 2 into the linear equation in step 1 to find the corresponding value(s) of the other variable.

Two points of intersection

EXAMPLE

Find the points of intersection of the line $x - 2y - 5 = 0$ and the circle $x^2 + y^2 = 10$.

Solution:

Line $x - 2y - 5 = 0$ and circle $x^2 + y^2 = 10$.

Step 1: $\quad x - 2y - 5 = 0$

$\qquad\qquad x = 2y + 5 \qquad$ (get x on its own from the line equation)

Step 2: Substitute $(2y + 5)$ for x into the equation of the circle.

$$x^2 + y^2 = 10$$
$$(2y + 5)^2 + y^2 = 10 \qquad \text{(substitute } (2y + 5) \text{ for } x)$$
$$4y^2 + 20y + 25 + y^2 = 10$$
$$5y^2 + 20y + 15 = 0 \qquad \text{(everything to the left)}$$
$$y^2 + 4y + 3 = 0 \qquad \text{(divide across by 5)}$$
$$(y + 3)(y + 1) = 0 \qquad \text{(factorise)}$$
$$y + 3 = 0 \text{ or } y + 1 = 0$$
$$y = -3 \text{ or } y = -1$$

These are the y coordinates.

Step 3: Substitute $y = -3$ and $y = -1$ separately into the equation of the line in step 1 to find the x coordinates.

$$x = 2y + 5 \qquad\qquad x = 2y + 5$$
$$y = -3 \qquad\qquad y = -1$$
$$x = 2(-3) + 5 \qquad\qquad x = 2(-1) + 5$$
$$= -6 + 5 \qquad\qquad = -2 + 5$$
$$x = -1 \qquad\qquad x = 3$$
$$\text{point } (-1, -3) \qquad\qquad \text{point } (3, -1)$$

Thus, the two points of intersection are $(-1, -3)$ and $(3, -1)$.

The diagram illustrates the situation.

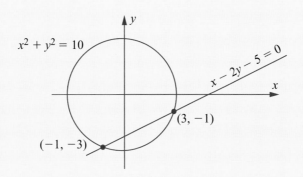

Exercise 3.3

In questions 1–10, find the points of intersection of the given line and circle in each case.

1. Line: $x - y = 3$;   circle: $x^2 + y^2 = 5$
2. Line: $x - y = 5$;   circle: $x^2 + y^2 = 17$
3. Line: $x - y + 7 = 0$;   circle: $x^2 + y^2 = 25$
4. Line: $x - 3y = 0$;   circle: $x^2 + y^2 = 10$
5. Line: $x + 2y - 5 = 0$;   circle: $x^2 + y^2 = 10$
6. Line: $x + 5y + 13 = 0$;   circle: $x^2 + y^2 = 13$
7. Line: $x + y + 1 = 0$;   circle: $x^2 + y^2 = 13$
8. Line: $2x + y - 10 = 0$;   circle: $x^2 + y^2 = 25$
9. Line: $x + 3y - 5 = 0$;   circle: $x^2 + y^2 = 5$
10. Line: $2x + y + 10 = 0$;   circle: $x^2 + y^2 = 40$

11. The line $x - 2y + 5 = 0$ cuts the circle $x^2 + y^2 = 25$ at A and B. Calculate $|AB|$.

12. The line $x + 3y - 5 = 0$ intersects the circle $x^2 + y^2 = 5$ at P and Q. Calculate $|PQ|$.

13. (i) The line l contains the point $(3, -1)$ and $(-1, -3)$. Find the equation of l.
    (ii) Find, algebraically, the points of intersection of l and the circle k, $x^2 + y^2 = 25$.
    (iii) Using the same axes and scales, graph l and k.

14. A plane is travelling along the line $x - y = -10$.
    Ahead lies a large cloud of ash from a volcanic eruption
    that can be represented by the circle $x^2 + y^2 = 52$.

    Note: Each unit represents 1 kilometre.

    (i) What is the centre and radius of the cloud?
    (ii) Find the coordinates of the points A and B.
    (iii) If it is considered unsafe to travel more than 10 km through such an ash cloud, should
    the plane alter its course?
    (iv) Find the midpoint, C, of $[AB]$.
    (v) The point C is the nearest point on the plane's path to the centre of the cloud. If it is
    considered unsafe to travel further than 1 km inward from the edge of the cloud, should
    the plane alter its course?

One point of intersection

Note: If there is only **one point of intersection** between a line and a circle, then the line is a **tangent** to the circle.

EXAMPLE

Find where the line $4x - y - 17 = 0$ cuts the circle $x^2 + y^2 = 17$ and investigate if this line is a tangent to the circle.

Solution:
Line $4x - y - 17 = 0$ and circle $x^2 + y^2 = 17$.

Step 1: $4x - y - 17 = 0$

$-y = -4x + 17$

$y = 4x - 17$ (get y on its own from the line equation)

Step 2: Substitute $(4x - 17)$ for y into the equation of the circle.

$$x^2 + y^2 = 17$$
$$x^2 + (4x - 17)^2 = 17 \qquad \text{(substitute } (4x - 17) \text{ for } y)$$
$$x^2 + 16x^2 - 136x + 289 = 17$$
$$17x^2 - 136x + 272 = 0 \qquad \text{(everything to the left)}$$
$$x^2 - 8y + 16 = 0 \qquad \text{(divide across by 17)}$$
$$(x - 4)(x - 4) = 0 \qquad \text{(factorise)}$$
$$x - 4 = 0 \text{ or } x - 4 = 0$$
$$x = 4$$

Step 3: Substitute $x = 4$ into the equation of the line in step 1 to find the y coordinates.

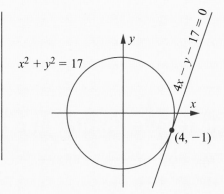

$$x = 4$$
$$y = 4x - 17$$
$$= 4(4) - 17$$
$$= 16 - 17$$
$$y = -1$$
$$\text{point } (4, -1)$$

$\therefore$ The line $4x - y - 17 = 0$ cuts the circle $x^2 + y^2 = 17$ at the point $(4, -1)$.

Since there is only **one point of contact** between the line and the circle, the line is a tangent to the circle.

The diagram illustrates the situation.

Exercise 3.4

In questions 1–8, verify that each line l is a tangent to the corresponding circle c in each of the following and find the coordinates of the point of tangency in each case.

1. $l : x - y - 2 = 0,$ $\quad c : x^2 + y^2 = 2$
2. $l : x - y - 4 = 0,$ $\quad c : x^2 + y^2 = 8$
3. $l : 2x - y - 5 = 0,$ $\quad c : x^2 + y^2 = 5$
4. $l : x - 3y - 10 = 0,$ $\quad c : x^2 + y^2 = 10$
5. $l : 3x + y - 10 = 0,$ $\quad c : x^2 + y^2 = 10$
6. $l : x - 4y - 17 = 0,$ $\quad c : x^2 + y^2 = 17$
7. $l : 5x - y - 26 = 0,$ $\quad c : x^2 + y^2 = 26$
8. $l : x + 7y - 50 = 0,$ $\quad c : x^2 + y^2 = 50$
9. (i) k is a circle with centre $(0, 0)$ and radius $\sqrt{5}$. Write down the equation of k.
   (ii) l is a line with equation $2x - y + 5 = 0$. Prove that l is a tangent to k and find the coordinates of the point of tangency.

10. As part of the opening ceremony of a sports event, an archer will fire a lit arrow at a balloon of gas, causing it to burst into flames.

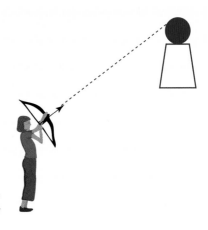

The arrow must **pass through** the balloon. If it misses, the effect will fail entirely, while if the arrow only nicks the balloon, it is unlikely that the gas will ignite despite bursting the balloon.

(i) If the balloon can be represented by the equation $x^2 + y^2 = 10$ and the path of the arrow by $x - y + 4 = 0$, how could you confirm mathematically that the arrow will burst the balloon?

(ii) Will the plan work? Show all your calculations.

General equation of a circle, centre (*h*, *k*) and radius *r*

On the right is a circle with centre (h, k), radius r and (x, y) is any point on the circle.

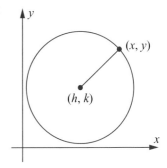

Distance between (h, k) and (x, y) equals the radius, r.

$$\therefore \sqrt{(x - h)^2 + (y - k)^2} = r \qquad \text{(distance formula)}$$
$$(x - h)^2 + (y - k)^2 = r^2 \qquad \text{(square both sides)}$$

Hence, $(x - h)^2 + (y - k)^2 = r^2$ is said to be the equation of the circle.

> The equation of a circle, centre (h, k) and radius r, is
> $$(x - h)^2 + (y - k)^2 = r^2.$$

Two quantities are needed to find the equation of a circle.

> **1.** Centre, (h, k) \qquad **2.** Radius, r
> Then use the formula $(x - h)^2 + (y - k)^2 = r^2$.

Note: If $(h, k) = (0, 0)$, the equation $(x - h)^2 + (y - k)^2 = r^2$ is reduced to $x^2 + y^2 = r^2$.

EXAMPLE 1

(i) Find the equation of the circle, centre (2, 3) and radius 5.

(ii) Find the centre and radius of the circle, $(x + 1)^2 + (y - 4)^2 = 36$.

Solution:

(i) Centre (2, 3), radius 5

$h = 2, k = 3, r = 5$

Equation of the circle is:

$(x - h)^2 + (y - k)^2 = r^2$

$(x - 2)^2 + (y - 3)^2 = 5^2$

$(x - 2)^2 + (y - 3)^2 = 25$

(ii) Compare exactly to:

$(x - h)^2 + (y - k)^2 = r^2$

$\downarrow \qquad \downarrow \qquad \downarrow$

$(x + 1)^2 + (y - 4)^2 = 36$

$\therefore h = -1, k = 4, r = 6$

Thus, centre $= (-1, 4)$ and radius $= 6$.

EXAMPLE 2

Find the equation of the circle that has the line segment from $A(-4, 3)$ to $B(2, -1)$ as a diameter.

Solution:

The **centre** and **radius** are needed.

The diagram on the right illustrates the situation.

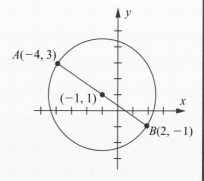

Centre

The centre is the midpoint of $[AB]$.

$$\text{Centre} = \left(\frac{-4 + 2}{2}, \frac{3 - 1}{2} \right) = \left(\frac{-2}{2}, \frac{2}{2} \right)$$

$$= (-1, 1) = (h, k)$$

Radius

The radius is the distance from the centre $(-1, 1)$ to either $(-4, 3)$ or $(2, -1)$.

Distance from $(-1, 1)$ to $(2, -1)$:

$$r = \sqrt{(2 + 1)^2 + (-1 - 1)^2} = \sqrt{3^2 + (-2)^2} = \sqrt{9 + 4} = \sqrt{13}$$

$$h = -1, k = 1, r = \sqrt{13}$$

Equation is $(x - h)^2 + (y - k)^2 = r^2$

$$(x + 1)^2 + (y - 1)^2 = (\sqrt{13})^2$$

$$(x + 1)^2 + (y - 1)^2 = 13$$

Exercise 3.5

In questions 1–10, find the equation of each circle with the given centre and radius.

1. Centre (2, 3) and radius 4
2. Centre (1, 4) and radius 5
3. Centre (2, −1) and radius 2
4. Centre (−5, 2) and radius 1
5. Centre (−4, −3) and radius $\sqrt{17}$
6. Centre (−3, 0) and radius $\sqrt{13}$
7. Centre (0, 2) and radius $\sqrt{5}$
8. Centre (−2, −6) and radius $\sqrt{29}$
9. Centre (−1, −1) and radius $\sqrt{10}$
10. Centre (−4, 2) and radius $\sqrt{12}$

In questions 11–16, find the equation of the circle with the following.

11. Centre (1, 2) and containing the point (2, 5)
12. Centre (2, −1) and containing the point (6, 4)
13. Centre (4, −3) and containing the point (0, 5)
14. Centre (−2, −5) and containing the point (3, 0)
15. Centre (1, −1) and containing the point (2, 4)
16. Centre (−4, −2) and containing the point (0, 0)

In questions 17–26, find the centre and radius of the circle.

17. $(x - 3)^2 + (y - 2)^2 = 16$
18. $(x + 4)^2 + (y + 5)^2 = 9$
19. $(x - 1)^2 + (y + 3)^2 = 25$
20. $(x - 3)^2 + (y - 5)^2 = 4$
21. $(x - 2)^2 + (y - 2)^2 = 49$
22. $(x - 8)^2 + (y - 7)^2 = 1$
23. $(x - 5)^2 + (y + 2)^2 = 25$
24. $(x - 1)^2 + (y + 5)^2 = 36$
25. $x^2 + (y - 2)^2 = 64$
26. $(x - 3)^2 + y^2 = 4$

27. $A(5, 2)$ and $B(1, 4)$ are two points. Find the equation of the circle with $[AB]$ as a diameter.

28. The end points of a diameter of a circle are $P(2, 4)$ and $G(-4, 0)$. Find the equation of the circle.

29. $A(-1, 5)$, $B(5, 13)$ and $C(-2, 12)$ are the vertices of triangle ABC.

    (i) Show that the triangle is right angled at C.
    (ii) Find the equation of the circle that passes through the points A, B and C.

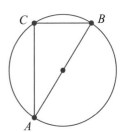

30. The circle c has equation $(x + 2)^2 + (y - 2)^2 = 13$. Find the coordinates of the points where c intersects the x- and y-axes.

31. The circle c has equation $(x - 5)^2 + (y - 3)^2 = 18$. c intersects the x-axis at P and Q. Find the coordinates of P and the coordinates of Q.

32. The end points of a diameter of a circle are $(2, 3)$ and $(-6, -1)$.

   (i) Find the equation of the circle.

   (ii) The circle cuts the y-axis at the points P and Q. Find $|PQ|$.

33. $A(3, 5)$ and $B(-1, -1)$ are the end points of a diameter of a circle k.

   (i) Find the centre and radius length of k.

   (ii) Find the equation of k.

   (iii) k intersects the x-axis at P and Q, $P < Q$. Find the coordinates of P and Q.

34. A manufacturer uses the following symbol for its products.

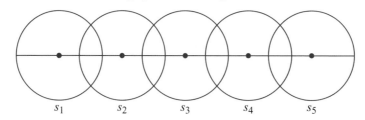

   s_1 s_2 s_3 s_4 s_5

   If the equation of s_1 is $x^2 + y^2 = 16$ and the equation of s_3 is $(x - 12)^2 + y^2 = 16$, find the equations of s_2, s_4 and s_5.

35. The circles $c_1 : x^2 + y^2 = 32$ and $c_2 : (x - 3)^2 + (y - 3)^2 = 1$ touch at the point $P(4, 4)$.

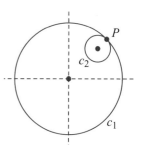

   (i) Write down the centre of c_1.

   (ii) Write down the centre of c_2.

   (iii) Find the equation of the line containing the two centre points.

   (iv) Show that the point of contact, P, is also on this line.

36. This pattern is being used on a tile. The equation of the middle circle is $x^2 + y^2 = 25$.

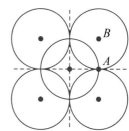

   (i) Write down the centre and radius length of the middle circle.

   (ii) Write down the coordinates of the point A.

   (iii) Write down the coordinates of the point B.

   (iv) Find the equations of the other circles.

37. A set of circles with a common point of contact $(0, 0)$ are shown. The radius of s_1 is 4 units and its centre is $A(4, 0)$.

   $|AB| = |BC| = |CD| = |DE|$.

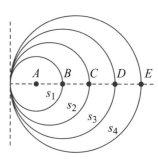

   (i) Find the equation of the circle s_1.

   (ii) Write down the coordinates of the point B.

   (iii) Write down the coordinates of the point C.

     (iv) What is the length of the diameter of the circle s_2?

     (v) What is the centre of s_2?

     (vi) Find the equation of s_2.

     (vii) Show that B is the centre of s_3.

     (viii) By finding the length of the diameter of s_4 or otherwise, find the equation of s_4.

Points inside, on or outside a circle 2

Method 1

To find whether a point is inside, on or outside a circle, calculate the distance from the centre, (h, k), to the point and compare this distance with the radius. Three cases arise.

 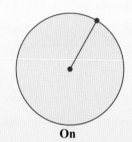 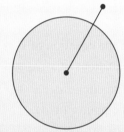

Inside	On	Outside
1. Distance from the centre to the point is **less** than the radius. ∴ Point is inside the circle.	**2.** Distance from the centre to the point is **equal** to the radius. ∴ Point is on the circle.	**3.** Distance from the centre to the point is **greater** than the radius. ∴ Point is outside the circle.

Method 2

If the coordinates of a point satisfy the equation of a circle, then the point is **on** the circle. Otherwise, the point is either **inside** or **outside** the circle. By substituting the coordinates into the equation of the circle, one of the following situations can arise:

1. $(x - h)^2 + (y - k)^2 < r^2$, the point is **inside** the circle.

2. $(x - h)^2 + (y - k)^2 = r^2$, the point is **on** the circle.

3. $(x - h)^2 + (y - k)^2 > r^2$, the point is **outside** the circle.

EXAMPLE

Determine if the points (5, 3), (−1, 4) and (−2, −3) are inside, on or outside the circle $(x - 3)^2 + (y - 2)^2 = 20$.

Solution:

$$(x - 3)^2 + (y - 2)^2 = 20 \qquad \text{(using Method 2)}$$

Substitute (5, 3): $(5 - 3)^2 + (3 - 2)^2 = (2)^2 + (1)^2 = 4 + 1 = 5 < 20$

$\therefore$ (5, −3) is **inside** the circle.

Substitute (−1, 4): $(-1 - 3)^2 + (4 - 2)^2 = (-4)^2 + (2)^2 = 16 + 4 = 20$

$\therefore$ (−1, 4) is **on** the circle.

Substitute (−2, −3): $(-2 - 3)^2 + (-3 - 2)^2 = (-5)^2 + (-5)^2 = 25 + 25 = 50 > 20$

$\therefore$ (−2, −3) is **outside** the circle.

Exercise 3.6

In questions 1−14, determine if the given point is inside, on or outside the given circle.

1. (4, −1); $(x + 3)^2 + (y - 2)^2 = 16$
2. (−1, 2); $(x - 2)^2 + (y + 3)^2 = 9$
3. (3, 2); $(x - 1)^2 + (y + 2)^2 = 49$
4. (−1, 5); $(x + 2)^2 + (y - 3)^2 = 36$
5. (3, −4); $(x + 1)^2 + (y + 4)^2 = 1$
6. (1, 2); $(x - 1)^2 + (y - 5)^2 = 4$
7. (6, −1); $(x - 2)^2 + (y + 4)^2 = 25$
8. (0, 0); $(x + 2)^2 + (y + 3)^2 = 64$
9. (−7, 0); $(x - 2)^2 + (y + 1)^2 = 100$
10. (−2, 1); $(x + 3)^2 + (y - 1)^2 = 16$
11. (−1, 4); $(x + 5)^2 + (y - 3)^2 = 13$
12. (4, 3); $(x - 2)^2 + (y + 1)^2 = 20$
13. (2, −4); $(x - 6)^2 + (y + 5)^2 = 17$
14. (1, −1); $(x + 1)^2 + (y - 2)^2 = 29$

15. The circle c has equation $(x + 1)^2 + (y + 1)^2 = 34$.
The point (−4, k) lies on c. Find the two real values of k.

16. The circle s has equation $(x - 4)^2 + (y - 2)^2 = 13$.
The point (p, 0) lies on s. Find the two real values of p.

Equation of a tangent to a circle at a given point

A tangent is perpendicular to the radius that joins the centre of a circle to the point of tangency.

This fact is used to find the slope of the tangent.

In the diagram on the right, the radius, r, is perpendicular to the tangent, t, at the point of tangency, P.

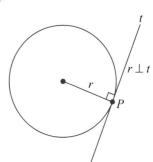

The equation of a tangent to a circle at a given point is found with the following steps.

1. Find the slope of the radius to the point of tangency.
2. Turn this slope upside down and change its sign. This gives the slope of the tangent.
3. Use the coordinates of the point of contact and the slope of the tangent at this point in the formula:

$$(y - y_1) = m(x - x_1)$$

This gives the equation of the tangent.

A diagram is often very useful.

EXAMPLE

Find the equation of the tangent to the circle $(x - 2)^2 + (y - 3)^2 = 25$ at the point $(5, 7)$ on the circle.

Solution:

$$(x - 2)^2 + (y - 3)^2 = 25$$
$$\text{Centre} = (2, 3)$$

Step 1:

Slope of radius, $r = \dfrac{7 - 3}{5 - 2} = \dfrac{4}{3}$

Step 2:

$\therefore$ Slope of tangent, $t = -\dfrac{3}{4}$

(turn upside down and change the sign)

Step 3: $x_1 = 5$ $\qquad y_1 = 7$ $\qquad m = -\dfrac{3}{4}$

$$(y - y_1) = m(x - x_1)$$
$$(y - 7) = -\tfrac{3}{4}(x - 5)$$
$$4(y - 7) = -3(x - 5)$$
$$4y - 28 = -3x + 15$$
$$3x + 4y - 28 - 15 = 0$$
$$3x + 4y - 43 = 0$$

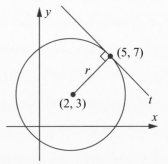

Diagram of the situation

Exercise 3.7

In questions 1–17, find the equation of the tangent to the given circle at the given point (make a rough diagram in each case).

1. Circle $x^2 + y^2 = 10$;   point $(3, 1)$
2. Circle $x^2 + y^2 = 5$;   point $(2, -1)$
3. Circle $x^2 + y^2 = 26$;   point $(-5, -1)$
4. Circle $x^2 + y^2 = 13$;   point $(-3, 2)$
5. Circle $x^2 + y^2 = 50$;   point $(-1, 7)$
6. Circle $x^2 + y^2 = 17$;   point $(-1, 4)$
7. Circle $x^2 + y^2 = 20$;   point $(4, 2)$
8. Circle $x^2 + y^2 = 29$;   point $(-5, -2)$
9. Circle $(x - 4)^2 + (y + 2)^2 = 13$;   point $(6, -5)$
10. Circle $(x - 2)^2 + (y - 2)^2 = 20$;   point $(-2, 0)$
11. Circle $(x - 4)^2 + (y + 3)^2 = 10$;   point $(7, -4)$
12. Circle $(x - 5)^2 + (y + 2)^2 = 85$;   point $(-1, 5)$
13. Circle $(x - 1)^2 + (y - 1)^2 = 2$;   point $(0, 0)$
14. Circle $(x + 3)^2 + y^2 = 25$;   point $(0, 4)$
15. Circle $x^2 + (y - 5)^2 = 29$;   point $(5, 3)$
16. Circle $(x - 2)^2 + (y + 4)^2 = 10$;   point $(3, -1)$
17. Circle $(x + 2)^2 + (y - 3)^2 = 29$;   point $(3, 5)$
18. Show that the point $(1, -3)$ is on the circle $(x + 2)^2 + (y - 1)^2 = 25$. Find the equation of the tangent to the circle at the point $(1, -3)$.
19. A car is parked on a hill as on the diagram. If the edge of one wheel can be represented by the equation $(x - 3)^2 + (y + 5)^2 = 20$ and the point of contact with this wheel and the hill is $(5, -9)$, find the equation of the line that represents the hill.

Transformations

Under a central symmetry, axial symmetry or translation, a circle will keep the same radius. Hence, all that is needed is to find the image of the centre under the particular transformation.

The equation of a circle under a transformation is found with the following steps.

1. Find the centre and radius of the given circle.
2. Find the image of the centre under the given transformation.
3. Use this new centre and the radius of the original circle in the equation $(x - h)^2 + (y - k)^2 = r^2$.

As before, a diagram is very useful.

EXAMPLE

Find the equation of the image of the circle $(x - 3)^2 + (y - 4)^2 = 4$ under the translation $(2, 2) \rightarrow (4, -5)$.

Solution:

Step 1: Centre = $(3, 4)$

Radius = $\sqrt{4} = 2$

Given circle has centre = $(3, 4)$ and radius 2.

Step 2: $(2, 2) \rightarrow (4, -5)$

Rule: Add 2 to x, subtract 7 from y.

Apply this translation to the centre, $(3, 4)$, of the given circle.

$\therefore (3, 4) \rightarrow (3 + 2, 4 - 7) = (5, -3)$

Thus, the image of the circle has centre $(5, -3)$ and radius 2.

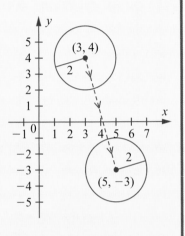

Step 3: $h = 5, k = -3, r = 2$

$(x - h)^2 + (y - k)^2 = r^2$

$(x - 5)^2 + (y + 3)^2 = 2^2$

$(x - 5)^2 + (y + 3)^2 = 4$

Exercise 3.8

1. Find the equation of the image of the circle $(x - 2)^2 + (y - 3)^2 = 20$ under the translation $(1, 1) \rightarrow (3, -4)$.

2. Find the equation of the image of the circle $(x - 5)^2 + (y + 4)^2 = 25$ under an axial symmetry in the y-axis.

3. Find the equation of the image of the circle $(x + 2)^2 + y^2 = 9$ under a central symmetry in the centre of the circle $(x - 1)^2 + (y + 2)^2 = 1$.

4. $A(3, -1)$ and $B(0, 4)$ are two points. Find the equation of the image of the circle $(x - 2)^2 + (y + 3)^2 = 9$ under the translation $\overrightarrow{AB}$.

5. The equation of the circle s is $(x - 5)^2 + (y + 6)^2 = 64$. Find the centre and radius of s. Find the equation of the image of s under an axial symmetry in the x-axis.

6. The circle $k : (x - 5)^2 + (y + 2)^2 = 36$ is the image of the circle c under an axial symmetry in the y-axis. Find the equation of c.

7. The equation of the circle c is $(x - 10)^2 + (y - 6)^2 = 20$.

    (i) Find the centre and radius of c.

    (ii) Verify that the point $S(6, 4)$ is on c.

    (iii) Find the equation of the tangent t to c at the point S.

    (iv) Find the coordinates of R, the point where t intersects the x-axis.

    (v) Find the equation of the circle k, the image of c under an axial symmetry in t.

    (vi) Find the coordinates of P and Q, the points where k intersects the x-axis.

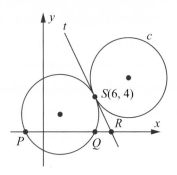

Right-angled triangles

In a right-angled triangle, special ratios exist between the angles and the lengths of the sides. We will look at three of these ratios.

Consider the right-angled triangle below with the acute angle θ.

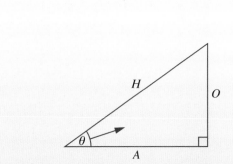

Ratios

$$\sin \theta = \frac{\text{Opposite}}{\text{Hypotenuse}} = \frac{O}{H}$$

$$\cos \theta = \frac{\text{Adjacent}}{\text{Hypotenuse}} = \frac{A}{H}$$

$$\tan \theta = \frac{\text{Opposite}}{\text{Adjacent}} = \frac{O}{A}$$

Memory aid: <u>O</u>, <u>H</u>ell, <u>A</u>nother <u>H</u>our <u>O</u>f <u>A</u>lgebra, <u>s</u>in, <u>c</u>os and <u>t</u>an.
Each trigonometric ratio links two sides and an angle in a right-angled triangle.

Notes:

1. The side opposite the right angle is called the **hypotenuse**, **H**. The side opposite the angle θ is called the **opposite**, **O**. The other side near the angle θ is called the **adjacent**, **A**.

2. If the lengths of any two sides are known, the third side can be found using Pythagoras' theorem: $A^2 + O^2 = H^2$, where A, O and H are the lengths of the sides.

3. The three angles of a triangle add up to $180°$.

4. Sin, cos and tan are short for sine, cosine and tangent, respectively.

5. The arrow points to the side opposite the angle under consideration.

6. θ is a Greek letter, pronounced 'theta', often used to indicate an angle.

We can write trigonometric ratios for the two acute angles in a right-angled triangle. Make sure you know which angle you are using and which sides are the opposite and adjacent (the hypotenuse is always opposite the right angle). A good idea is to draw an arrow from the angle under consideration to indicate the opposite side to the angle. If we are given one trigonometric ratio, we can find the other two trigonometric ratios by representing the situation with a right-angled triangle and using Pythagoras' theorem to find the missing side.

The following summary of right-angled triangles is also in the mathematical tables.

Right-angled triangle

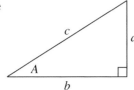

$$\sin A = \frac{a}{c} \qquad \cos A = \frac{b}{c} \qquad \tan A = \frac{a}{b}$$

Pythagoras' theorem $\qquad c^2 = a^2 + b^2$

Note: You should become familiar with the book of mathematical tables (approved for use in the state examinations).

EXAMPLE 1

$\sin \theta = \dfrac{5}{13}$, where $0° < \theta < 90°$.

   (i) Find, as fractions, the value of $\cos \theta$ and the value of $\tan \theta$.

  (ii) Show that $\cos^2 \theta + \sin^2 \theta = 1$.

 (iii) Find the measurement of angle θ, correct to the nearest degree.

Solution:

   (i) From the trigonometric ratio given, sketch a right-angled triangle to represent the situation and use Pythagoras' theorem to find the missing side.

Given: $\sin \theta = \dfrac{5}{13}$

Opposite = 5, hypotenuse = 13, let the adjacent = x.

$$x^2 + 5^2 = 13^2 \qquad \text{(Pythagoras' theorem)}$$
$$x^2 + 25 = 169$$
$$x^2 = 144$$
$$x = \sqrt{144} = 12$$
$$\cos \theta = \frac{A}{H} = \frac{12}{13}$$
$$\tan \theta = \frac{O}{A} = \frac{5}{12}$$

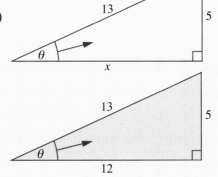

(ii) $\cos^2 \theta + \sin^2 \theta$

$= \left(\frac{12}{13}\right)^2 + \left(\frac{5}{13}\right)^2$

$= \frac{144}{169} + \frac{25}{169}$

$= \frac{169}{169} = 1$

(iii) Given: $\sin \theta = \frac{5}{13}$

$\theta = \sin^{-1} \frac{5}{13}$

$\theta = 22 \cdot 61986495°$

$\theta = 23°$ (nearest degree)

(▦ 2nd F sin 5 $a\frac{b}{c}$ 13 =)

Notes:

1. $\cos^2 \theta = (\cos \theta)^2$, $\sin^2 \theta = (\sin \theta)^2$ and $\tan^2 \theta = (\tan \theta)^2$

2. If $\frac{5}{13}$ is keyed in as 5 ÷ 13, then brackets must be used: ▦ 2nd F sin (5 ÷ 13) =

EXAMPLE 2

(i) By using Pythagoras' theorem, investigate if the angle marked B in the diagram is right angled.

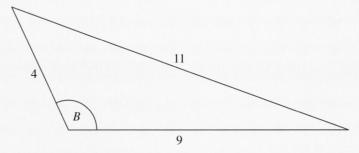

(ii) Can you conclude whether $B > 90°$ or $B < 90°$ from your work? Justify your conclusion.

Solution:

(i) **Pythagoras' theorem:**

$$(\text{hyp})^2 = (\text{opp})^2 + (\text{adj})^2$$
$$11^2 = 9^2 + 4^2$$
$$121 = 81 + 16$$

No, in fact $121 > 81 + 16$.

Hence, angle B is not right angled, since Pythagoras' theorem is not true in this case.

(ii) Notice that since $121 > 81 + 16$, we can conclude that angle $B > 90°$.

Exercise question

If $a^2 < b^2 + c^2$ in this triangle, which of the following statements are true?

(i) $A = 90°$ (ii) $A > 90°$ (iii) $A < 90°$

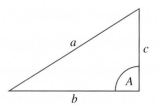

Exercise question

Assign values to a, b and c, the lengths of the sides, so that:

(i) $A = 90°$ (ii) $A < 90°$ (iii) $A > 90°$

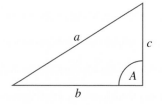

Note: $a = 10$, $b = 6$ and $c = 3$ does not form a triangle. Can you explain why?

Exercise 4.1

1. In each of the right-angled triangles **(i)**, **(ii)** and **(iii)**, the lengths of the sides are shown in the diagram and the angles are labelled. Complete the tables below, writing the answers as fractions (ratios).

(i)

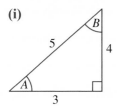

(ii)

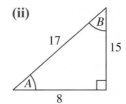

(iii)

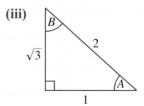

	sin A	cos A	tan A
(i)	$\frac{4}{5}$		
(ii)			$\frac{15}{8}$
(iii)			

	sin B	cos B	tan B
(i)			
(ii)			
(iii)		$\frac{\sqrt{3}}{2}$	

2. Evaluate each of the following.

   (i) $3^2 + 4^2 =$ (ii) $5^2 + 12^2 =$ (iii) $8^2 + 6^2 =$ (iv) $20^2 + 21^2 =$

   (v) $1^2 + 3^2 =$ (vi) $1^2 + (\sqrt{3})^2 =$ (vii) $5^2 - 3^2 =$ (viii) $13^2 - 12^2 =$

   (ix) $4^2 - 3^2 =$ (x) $2^2 - (\sqrt{3})^2 =$ (xi) $(\sqrt{13})^2 - 2^2 =$ (xii) $(\sqrt{5})^2 - 1^2 =$

3. Give two examples of right-angled triangles with:

   (i) All three sides of integer length, e.g. 5, 12, 13

   (ii) Two sides integer lengths and one side surd length, e.g. 4, 5, $\sqrt{41}$

4. Use Pythagoras' theorem to find x, the length of the missing side, in surd form where necessary. Express $\sin \theta$, $\cos \theta$ and $\tan \theta$ as simple fractions or as surd fractions in each of the following.

   (i)
   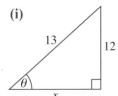

   (ii)
   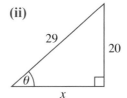

   (iii)
   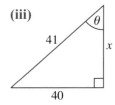

   (iv)
   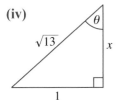

   (v)
   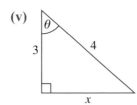

   (vi)
   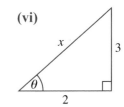

5. (i) From the diagram, if $\cos B = \frac{3}{5}$, label the angle B.

   (ii) Hence or otherwise, find the value of x.

   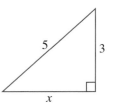

6. (i) Given that $\tan Q = \frac{c}{d}$, label angle Q in the diagram.

   (ii) Hence, express $\cos Q$ and $\sin Q$ as simple fractions.

   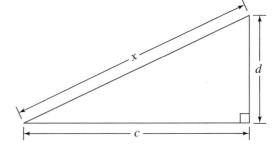

In questions 7–14, find the measure of the angle θ, where $0° < \theta < 90°$, correct to the nearest degree.

7. $\sin \theta = \dfrac{2}{3}$

8. $\cos \theta = \dfrac{4}{7}$

9. $\tan \theta = \dfrac{1}{8}$

10. $\sin \theta = 0{\cdot}3$

11. $\tan \theta = 2$

12. $\cos \theta = \dfrac{3}{5}$

13. $\sin \theta = \dfrac{7}{10}$

14. $\tan \theta = \dfrac{1}{\sqrt{10}}$

15. Using Pythagoras' theorem, investigate if the angle marked θ in each of the following diagrams equals 90°, is less than 90° or is greater than 90°. Justify your answers.

(i)

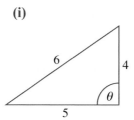

(ii)

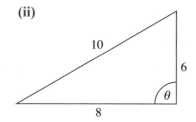

(iii)

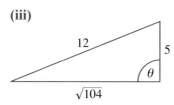

(iv)

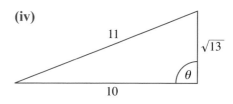

16. By Pythagoras' theorem, $a^2 = b^2 + c^2$ in the right-angled triangle below.

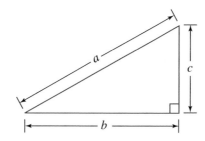

Hence or otherwise, in the triangle below, where angle A is obtuse, is $a^2 > b^2 + c^2$ or is $a^2 < b^2 + c^2$? Justify your answer.

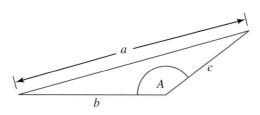

17. $\cos \theta = \frac{4}{5}$, where $0° < \theta < 90°$.

    (i) Find, as fractions, the value of $\sin \theta$ and the value of $\tan \theta$.

    (ii) Show that: **(a)** $\cos^2 \theta + \sin^2 \theta = 1$ **(b)** $\cos \theta + \sin \theta > \tan \theta$

    (iii) Find the measure of the angle θ, correct to the nearest degree.

18. $\tan A = \frac{8}{15}$, where $0° < A < 90°$.

    (i) Find, as fractions, the value of $\sin A$ and the value of $\cos A$.

    (ii) Show that $\cos A + \sin A > \tan A$.

    (iii) Find the measure of the angle A, correct to the nearest degree.

19. $\sin \theta = \frac{7}{25}$, where $0° < \theta < 90°$.

    (i) Find, as fractions, the value of $\cos \theta$ and the value of $\tan \theta$.

    (ii) Show that $\cos^2 \theta + \sin^2 \theta = 1$.

20. $29 \sin \theta = 21$, where $0° < \theta < 90°$.

    If $\tan \theta = \dfrac{21}{k}$, find the value of k, $k \in \mathbb{N}$.

21. The diagram shows a triangle with lengths of sides 3, 4 and 5.

    (i) Verify that $\dfrac{\sin \theta}{\cos \theta} = \tan \theta$.

    (ii) Evaluate $\sqrt{\dfrac{\sin \theta \tan \theta}{\cos \theta}}$.

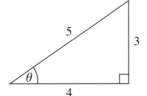

22. A vertical building on horizontal ground is 5 m tall. The building requires an outside support beam to prevent it from collapsing. The maximum amount of space to erect a support beam is 12 m to the left of the building.

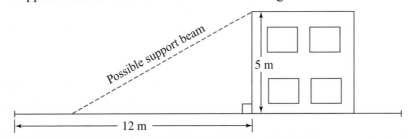

    (i) Using the diagram, calculate the maximum length the support beam can be.

    (ii) An engineer calculates that a support beam reaching up a height of 4 m on the building would be more effective. Find, correct to the nearest cm, the maximum length of this support beam.

    (iii) Further analysis indicates that the optimum (best) angle for the support beam is at 45° to the ground. Find the length of this support beam if the point of support is at 4 m high, as in **(ii)**.

    (iv) Give one reason why you think this mathematical model would be suitable or not in practice.

Notation

The diagram shows the usual notation for a triangle in trigonometry.

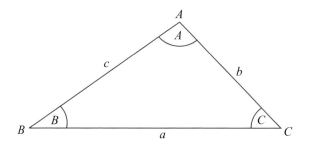

- Vertices: *A*, *B*, *C*.
- Angles: *A*, *B*, *C*.
- Length of sides: *a*, *b*, *c*.

> The lengths of the sides are denoted by a lower case letter and named after the angle they are opposite, i.e. *a* is opposite angle *A*, *b* is opposite angle *B* and *c* is opposite angle *C*.

Using the terminology, we also have the following:

$$A = |\angle BAC| \quad B = |\angle ABC| \quad C = |\angle ACB|$$
$$a = |BC| \qquad b = |AC| \qquad c = |AB|$$

Solving right-angled triangles

We can use a trigonometric ratio to calculate the length of a side in a right-angled triangle if we know the length of one side and one angle (other than the right angle). We can also find the size of an angle in a right-angled triangle if we know the lengths of two of its sides.

Summary of which trigonometric ratio to choose linking the given sides and angles:

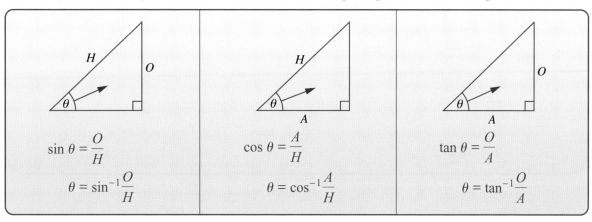

EXAMPLE

In the diagram, $PR \perp QS, |\angle PQR| = 34°, |QR| = 15$ and $|RS| = 8$.

(i) Calculate $|PR|$, correct to two decimal places.

(ii) Hence, calculate $|\angle PSR|$, correct to the nearest degree.

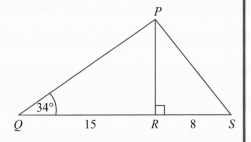

Solution:

Split the diagram into two right-angled triangles.

(i) We require the opposite and know the adjacent.

Therefore, use the tan ratio.

$$\tan \theta = \frac{\text{Opposite}}{\text{Adjacent}}$$

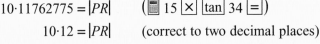

$\tan 34° = \dfrac{|PR|}{15}$ (put in known values)

$15 \tan 34° = |PR|$ (multiply both sides by 15)

$10 \cdot 11762775 = |PR|$ ($\boxed{\text{📱}}$ 15 $\boxed{\times}$ $\boxed{\tan}$ 34 $\boxed{=}$)

$10 \cdot 12 = |PR|$ (correct to two decimal places)

(ii) We know the opposite, from part (i), and the adjacent.

Therefore, use the tan ratio.

$S = |\angle PSR|$

$\tan \theta = \dfrac{\text{Opposite}}{\text{Adjacent}}$

$\tan S = \dfrac{10 \cdot 12}{8}$ (put in known values)

$S = \tan^{-1}\left(\dfrac{10 \cdot 12}{8}\right)$

$S = 51 \cdot 67314168°$ ($\boxed{\text{📱}}$ $\boxed{\text{2nd F}}$ $\boxed{\tan}$ $\boxed{(}$ $10 \cdot 12$ $\boxed{\div}$ 8 $\boxed{)}$ $\boxed{=}$)

$\therefore |\angle PSR| = 52°$ (correct to the nearest degree)

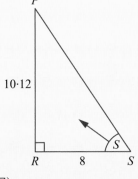

Note: In part (ii), the question uses the word '**hence**'. Therefore, we must use the value $|PR| = 10 \cdot 12$.

Exercise 4.2

In questions 1–6, calculate, to the nearest degree, the angles marked with a letter.

1.

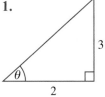

2.

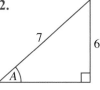

3.

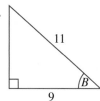

4.

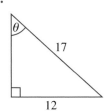

5.

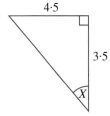

6.

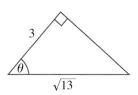

In questions 7–9, calculate the length of the sides marked with a letter, correct to two decimal places.

7.

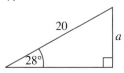

8.

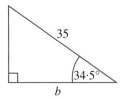

9.

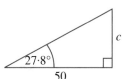

10. In triangle ABC, $|\angle ABC| = 90°$, $|AB| = 2$ and $|BC| = 1·5$. Find:

    (i) $|AC|$

    (ii) $|\angle BAC|$, correct to the nearest degree

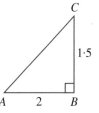

11. In the diagram, $XW \perp YZ$, $|XY| = 10$, $|\angle XYW| = 30°$ and $|WZ| = \frac{2}{5}|XY|$. Calculate:

    (i) $|XW|$ **(ii)** $|\angle WXZ|$, correct to the nearest degree

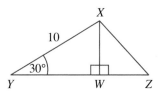

12. In the diagram, $|AB| = 16$ cm and $|\angle ABC| = 90°$. The point D is on $[BC]$. $|BD| = 30$ cm and $|AD| = |DC|$. Find:

    (i) $|AD|$ **(ii)** $|BC|$

    (iii) $|\angle ACB|$, correct to the nearest degree

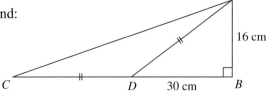

Practical applications

Many practical problems in navigation, surveying, engineering and geography involve solving a triangle. In this section we will restrict the problems to those that involve right-angled triangles. When solving practical problems using trigonometry in this section, represent each situation with a right-angled triangle.

Mark on your triangle the angles and lengths you know and label what you need to calculate, using the correct ratio to link the angle or length required with the known angle or length.

Angles of elevation, depression and compass directions

Angle of elevation
The **angle of elevation** of an object as seen by an observer is the angle between the horizontal line from the object to the observer's eye (upwards from the horizontal).

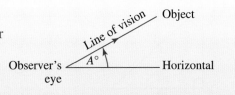

$A°$ = Angle of elevation of object

Angle of depression
If the object is below the level of the observer, the angle between the horizontal and the observer's line of vision is called the **angle of depression** (downwards from the horizontal).

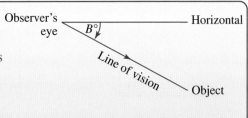

$B°$ = Angle of depression of object

Note: An angle of elevation has an equal angle of depression. The angle of elevation from A to B is equal to the angle of depression from B to A. The angles are alternate angles, as the horizontal lines are parallel.

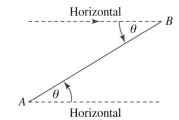

A note on clinometers:

A clinometer is a device use to measure angles of elevation and/or angles of depression.

Q. Who might use a clinometer?

A. Motorway construction engineers, movie production engineers, forestry engineers and secondary school maths students in Ireland!

There are many different types of clinometer. A very simple type looks like this:

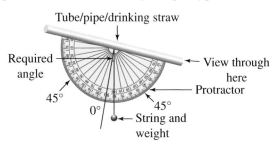

Tube/pipe/drinking straw

Required angle

View through here

Protractor

45°

0° 45°

String and weight

Compass directions

The direction of a point is stated as a number of degrees east or west of north and south.

- *A* is N 60° E
- *B* is N 40° W
- *C* is S 45° W (or SW)
- *D* is S 70° E

Note: N 60° E means start at north and turn 60° towards east.

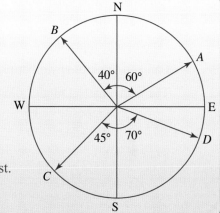

Mathematical modelling

When solving a problem, factors that have a negligible effect are often ignored. This has the advantage of simplifying the problem without sacrificing too much accuracy. This simplified problem is referred to as a **mathematical model** for the real situation.

EXAMPLE 1

On the seafront at Bray, the beach slopes down at a constant angle of 9° to the horizontal. Cian is 1·7 m tall. How far can he walk out to sea before the water just covers his head?

Solution:

Represent Cian and his height by a straight line.

Consider that as Cian walks out to sea, his body (and head!) is at a right angle to the surface of the water.

'The beach slopes down at a constant angle' allows us to ignore rocks, etc. underfoot.

Can you think of any other physical issues the mathematical model eliminates?

The mathematical model allows us to arrive at the diagram:

$$\tan 9° = \frac{\text{Opposite}}{\text{Adjacent}} = \frac{1·7}{y}$$

$$y \tan 9° = 1·7$$

$$y = \frac{1·7}{\tan 9°} = \frac{1·7}{0·15838} = 10·733 \text{ m}$$

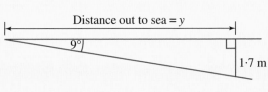

EXAMPLE 2

The diagram shows a ladder, 8 m in length, which leans against a vertical wall on level ground. The ladder makes an angle of 58° with the ground. Calculate the distance from the point where the ladder meets the ground to the wall, correct to two decimal places.

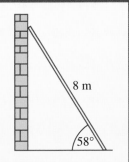

Solution:

Represent the situation with a right-angled triangle. Let d represent the distance from the point where the ladder meets the ground to the wall.

We know the hypotenuse and require the adjacent. Therefore, use the cos ratio.

$$\cos \theta = \frac{\text{Adjacent}}{\text{Hypotenuse}}$$

$\cos 58° = \dfrac{d}{8}$ (put in known values)

$8 \cos 58° = d$ (multiply both sides by 8)

$4 \cdot 239354114 = d$ ($\boxed{}$ 8 $\boxed{\times}$ $\boxed{\cos}$ 58 $\boxed{=}$)

$4 \cdot 24 = d$ (correct to two decimal places)

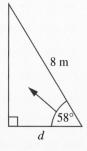

Therefore, the distance from the point where the ladder meets the ground to the wall is $4 \cdot 24$ m (correct to two decimal places).

EXAMPLE 3

Lisa wishes to measure the height of a particular tree in her local park. She brings a tape, a homemade clinometer and her brother Bart.

$a = $ Distance from ground to eye
$b = $ Distance from Bart to tree

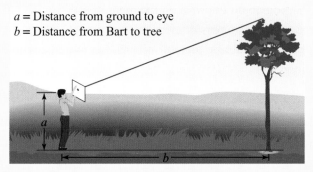

With Bart operating the clinometer by looking through the straw/tube at the top of the tree, Lisa reads the angle of elevation, E.

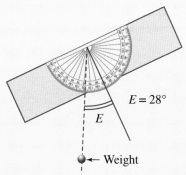

$E = 28°$

E

← Weight

Using the tape, she measures the distance from Bart to the tree, $b = 27\cdot4$ m, and Bart's height to eye level, $a = 1\cdot32$ m. How does she calculate the approximate height of the tree?

Solution:

Lisa uses a mathematical model to describe the situation.

Lisa assumes the tree is at right angles to the ground.

$$\tan 28 = \frac{\text{Opposite}}{\text{Adjacent}} = \frac{x}{27\cdot4}$$

$$27\cdot4 \tan 28 = x$$
$$14\cdot5688 = x$$

Height of the tree $= 14\cdot5688 + 1\cdot32 = 15\cdot8888$

Lisa might claim the height of the tree is approximately $15\cdot89$ m or $15\cdot9$ m or 16 m. Which do you think is best and why?

Exercise

1. Select a suitable tree, pole or high building in your area and find its height using the method followed by Lisa and Bart.

   Note: Be very mindful of motorised traffic if doing this project near a road. It is best to work in teams of two.

2. Suggest how you could improve on the method used by Lisa and Bart.

3. Name three possible sources of error in your work.

4. The internet is a valuable source of information to assist with the construction of a suitable clinometer.

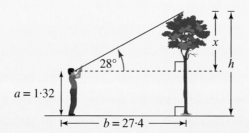

Exercise 4.3

1. From a point 12 m from the bottom of a wall, the angle of elevation to the top of the wall is 22°. Calculate the height of the wall, correct to two decimal places.

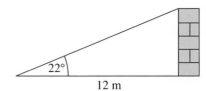

2. When the angle of elevation of the sun is 15°, an upright flagpole casts a shadow of length 18 m. Calculate the height of the pole, correct to one decimal place.

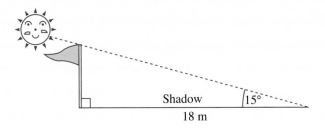

Shadow
18 m
15°

3. The distance of the point *P*, the top of a wall, from the point *Q* on level ground is 24 m. The angle of elevation of the point *P* from the point *Q* is 29°.

   Calculate the height *h* of the wall, correct to two decimal places.

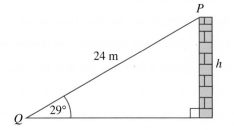

4. A ladder of length 3·7 m rests against a vertical wall so that the base of the ladder is 1·2 m from the wall.
   (i) Find the vertical height that the ladder reaches on the wall.
   (ii) Find the measure of the angle, *θ*, that the ladder makes with the horizontal, correct to the nearest degree.

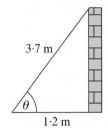

5. A girl is flying a kite. The length of string from her hand to the top of the kite is 60 m.

   The string, which is being held 1 m above the ground, makes an angle of elevation of 50° with the horizontal.
   (i) Calculate the height of the kite above the ground, correct to the nearest metre.
   (ii) Describe how the angle of elevation might be measured.

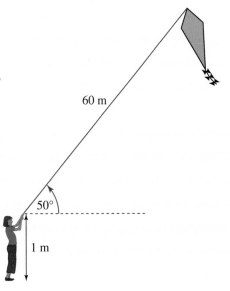

6. From a boat at sea, the angle of elevation to the top of a vertical cliff 200 m above sea level is 14°. After the boat has sailed directly towards the cliff, the angle of elevation of the cliff is found to be 28°. How far did the boat sail towards the cliff, correct to the nearest metre?

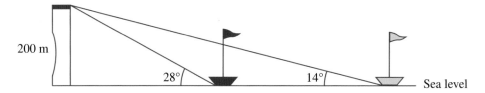

7. When a person stands on level ground at a point 100 m from the foot of a vertical cliff, the angle of elevation of the top of the cliff is 40°.

    (i) Calculate the height of the cliff, correct to the nearest metre.

    (ii) If the person moves to a different point on level ground, 244 m from the foot of the cliff, what will the measure of the angle of elevation be then? Give your answer correct to the nearest degree.

8. Anne is swinging on a wooden garden swing. The seat, *S*, is held in position by two ropes, all of length 3 m. Her total angle of swing is 110° (55° each way).

    (i) What is the difference in height of the seat at the lowest and highest point in her swing? Give your answer to the nearest cm.

    (ii) In your solution, explain how you think the mathematical model below is arrived at.

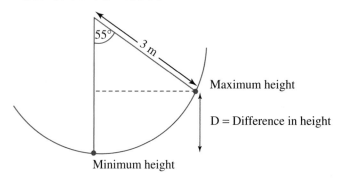

    Do you think the mathematical model is accurate? Justify your answer.

9. Copy the diagram and indicate the following directions on it.

    (i) N 20° E

    (ii) S 60° W

    (iii) S 50° E

    (iv) N 70° W

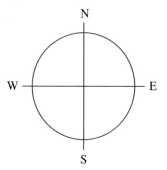

10. Two ships, P and Q, leave a harbour H at the same time. P, the faster ship, sails in a direction S 70° E at 31 km/h. Q sails in the direction S 20° W at x km/h. After two hours' sailing, the ships are 61 km apart. Calculate the distance travelled by ship Q.

11. Two ships, X and Y, left a harbour o at the same time. X travelled due north at 20 km/h while Y travelled in the direction N 60° E. After one hour, Y was directly east of X. Calculate:

    (i) The distance travelled by Y

    (ii) The distance between the ships, correct to the nearest km

12. (i) On leaving a port P, a fishing boat sails in the direction S 30° E for 3 hours at 10 km/h, as shown. What distance has the boat then sailed?

    (ii) The boat next sails in the direction N 60° E at 10 km/h until it is due east of the port P. Calculate how far the boat is from the port P.

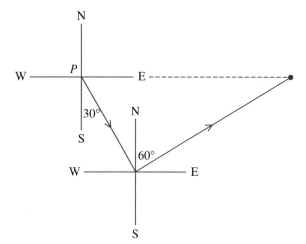

    (iii) Write a note on the mathematical model used here. Do you think the length of the boat is important? Justify your answer.

Solving non-right-angled triangles

Area of a triangle

Area of triangle $ABC = \frac{1}{2}ab \sin C = \frac{1}{2}ac \sin B = \frac{1}{2}bc \sin A$

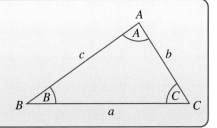

Note: See the mathematical tables for area of a triangle $= \frac{1}{2}ab \sin C$.

To use this formula to find the area of a triangle, we need the length of two sides **and** the size of the angle between these sides.

Area of triangle $= \frac{1}{2}$(length of side) × (length of side)
$\qquad\qquad$ × (sine of the angle between these sides)

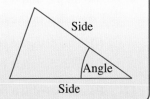

EXAMPLE 1

In triangle ABC, $|AB| = 3$ cm, $|BC| = 10$ cm and $|\angle ABC| = 62°$. Calculate the area of triangle ABC, correct to one decimal place.

Solution:
Let $B = |\angle ABC| = 62°$
$\qquad a = |BC| = 10$
and $c = |AB| = 3$.
Area $\triangle ABC = \frac{1}{2}ac \sin B$

$\qquad\qquad = \frac{1}{2}(10)(3) \sin 62$

$\qquad\qquad = 13\cdot24421389$

$\qquad\qquad = 13\cdot2$ cm^2

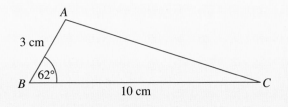

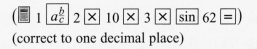

($\boxed{1}$ $\boxed{a\frac{b}{c}}$ 2 $\boxed{\times}$ 10 $\boxed{\times}$ 3 $\boxed{\times}$ $\boxed{\sin}$ 62 $\boxed{=}$)
(correct to one decimal place)

In some questions, we are given an equation in disguise.

EXAMPLE 2

In triangle ABC, $|BC| = 25$ m and $|AC| = 14$ m.

If the area of triangle ABC is 65 m², find $|\angle ACB|$, correct to one decimal place.

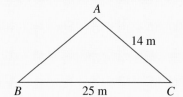

Solution:

Let $C = |\angle ACB|$, $a = |BC|$ and $b = |AC|$.

Equation given in disguise:

Area of triangle $ABC = 65$ m²

$$\tfrac{1}{2}ab \sin C = 65$$

$$\tfrac{1}{2}(25)(14) \sin C = 65 \qquad \text{(put in known values)}$$

$$175 \sin C = 65$$

$$\sin C = \tfrac{65}{175} \qquad \text{(divide both sides by 175)}$$

$$\sin C = \tfrac{13}{35} \qquad \left(\tfrac{65}{175} = \tfrac{13}{35}\right)$$

$$C = \sin^{-1} \tfrac{13}{35}$$

$$C = 21 \cdot 80374799° \qquad (\boxed{\text{⬚}}\ \boxed{\text{2nd F}}\ \boxed{\sin}\ 13\ \boxed{a\frac{b}{c}}\ 35\ \boxed{=})$$

$$\therefore |\angle ACB| = 21 \cdot 8° \qquad \text{(correct to one decimal place)}$$

Note: Another method to find the area of triangle ABC:

$$\text{Area } \triangle ABC = \sqrt{s(s-a)(s-b)(s-c)}$$

$$\text{where } s = \frac{a+b+c}{2}$$

This formula is in the mathematical tables booklet.

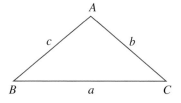

EXAMPLE 3

Dora has a flowerbed in her garden. The bed is triangular in shape with dimensions as shown.

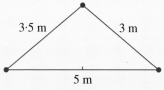

(i) Find the area of the flowerbed, correct to two decimal places.

(ii) Dora applies fertilizer on the flowerbed at the rate of 135 g per metre once a week for nine weeks. The fertilizer comes in 1 kg bags. Find the minimum number of bags Dora requires to complete the job.

Solution:

(i) Let $a = 5$, $b = 3$ and $c = 3\cdot5$

and use area $\triangle = \sqrt{s(s-a)(s-b)(s-c)}$

where $s = \dfrac{5 + 3 + 3\cdot5}{2} = 5\cdot75$.

$$\begin{aligned}
\text{Area } \triangle &= \sqrt{(5\cdot75)(5\cdot75 - 5)(5\cdot75 - 3)(5\cdot75 - 3\cdot5)} \\
&= \sqrt{(5\cdot75)(0\cdot75)(2\cdot75)(2\cdot25)} \\
&= \sqrt{26\cdot68359 \ldots} = 5\cdot1656 \ldots
\end{aligned}$$

Answer $= 5\cdot17 \text{ m}^2$

(ii) $135 \times 5\cdot17 \times 9 = 6281\cdot55$

or

$135 \times 5\cdot1656 \ldots \times 9 = 6276\cdot2240 \ldots$

Either way, the minimum she requires is 7 bags $= 7,000$ g.

Exercise 4.4

In questions 1–9, find, correct to two decimal places, the area of each of the following triangles, where the lengths of the sides are in centimetres.

1.

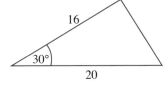

2.

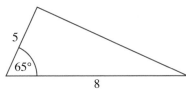

3.

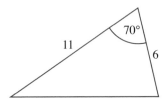

4.

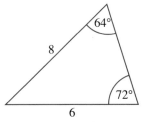

5.

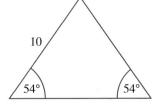

6.

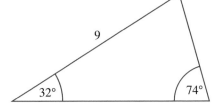

7.

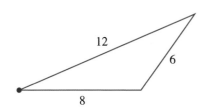

8.

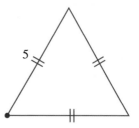

9.

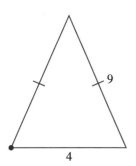

For questions 10–14, a rough diagram may help. Where relevant, give all answers correct to two decimal places.

10. In triangle PQR, $|PR| = 8$ m, $|PQ| = 7$ m and $|\angle QPR| = 54°$. Calculate the area of triangle PQR.

11. In triangle ABC, $|BC| = 8$ cm, $|AC| = 10$ cm and $|\angle ACB| = 48°$. Calculate the area of triangle ABC.

12. In triangle XYZ, $|XY| = 14$ cm, $|XZ| = 9$ cm and $|YZ| = 11$ cm. Calculate the area of triangle XYZ.

13. In triangle PQR, $|QR| = 6$ m, $|PR| = 16$ m, $|\angle RPQ| = 40°$ and $|\angle PQR| = 30°$. Calculate the area of triangle PQR.

14. In triangle ABC, $|AC| = 14$ cm, $|\angle ABC| = 70°$ and $|\angle BAC| = 40°$. Calculate the area of triangle ABC.

15. The diagram shows the quadrilateral $PQSR$.

    $QP \perp PR$, $|PQ| = 2·4$ cm, $|PR| = 1·8$ cm, $|RS| = 2$ cm and $|\angle QRS| = 70°$. Calculate:

    (i) $|QR|$

    (ii) The area of triangle PQR

    (iii) The area of $PQSR$, correct to two decimal places

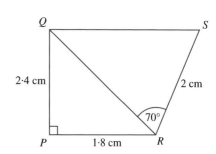

16. The diagram shows the quadrilateral *ABCD*.
$|AD| = 7$ m, $|AB| = 4$ m, $|BD| = 9$ m, $|CD| = 7.2$ m
and $|\angle BDC| = 78°$. Calculate:

   (i) The area of triangle *ABD*, correct to one
       decimal place

   (ii) The area of *ABCD*, correct to one decimal
        place

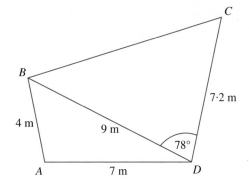

17. *OPQ* is a sector of a circle with a radius of 10 cm and $|\angle POQ| = 36°$.

   (i) Taking $\pi = 3.14$, calculate the area of the sector *OPQ*.

   (ii) Calculate, correct to one decimal place:

      (a) The area of triangle *OPQ*

      (b) The area of the shaded segment

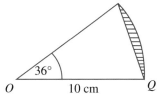

18. In triangle *PQR*, $|PQ| = 8$ cm and $|\angle PQR| = 30°$.
If the area of triangle $PQR = 48$ cm^2, calculate $|QR|$.

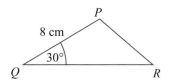

19.   (i) Calculate $\sin 34°$ correct to two decimal places.

   (ii) In triangle *ABC*, $|AB| = 20$ m and $|\angle BAC| = 34°$. If the
       area of triangle $ABC = 145.6$ m^2, find $|AC|$, using the
       value of $\sin 34°$ obtained in part (i).

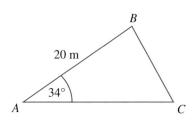

20. In triangle *PQR*, $|PR| = 14$ m and $|QR| = 10$ m. If the area of
triangle *PQR* is 45 m^2, calculate $|\angle PRQ|$, correct to the nearest
degree.

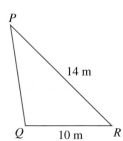

Sine rule

In any triangle ABC:

$$\frac{a}{\sin A} = \frac{b}{\sin B} = \frac{c}{\sin C}$$

or $\quad \dfrac{\sin A}{a} = \dfrac{\sin B}{b} = \dfrac{\sin C}{c}$

(The first form is given in the mathematical tables.)

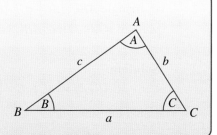

This is known as the **sine rule** and it applies to any triangle, including a right-angled triangle.

The sine rule can be used to:

1. Find an unknown side, a. Using the sine rule, we need two angles and one side. 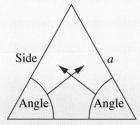 If we know two angles we can calculate the third angle, as the three angles add up to $180°$.	2. Find an unknown angle, $A°$. Using the sine rule, we need two sides and the size of one angle opposite one of these sides. 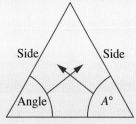 The unknown angle, $A°$, must be opposite a known side.

The sine rule connects each side with the angle opposite in a triangle.

Notes: 1. In practice we put only two fractions equal to each other. For example:

$$\frac{a}{\sin A} = \frac{b}{\sin B}$$

2. Put the required quantity, side or angle on the top of the first fraction.

To find a, use $\quad \dfrac{a}{\sin A} = \dfrac{b}{\sin B}$

To find B, use $\quad \dfrac{\sin B}{b} = \dfrac{\sin A}{a}$

EXAMPLE 1

In triangle ABC, $|AC| = 7$, $|\angle ABC| = 30°$ and $|\angle ACB| = 80°$. Find $|AB|$, correct to the nearest integer.

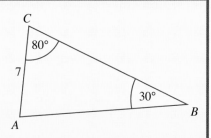

Solution:

Let $c = |AB|$, $b = |AC|$, $B = |\angle ABC|$ and $C = |\angle ACB|$.

Using the sine rule:

$$\frac{c}{\sin C} = \frac{b}{\sin B} \qquad (c \text{ is missing, so put that first})$$

$$\frac{c}{\sin 80°} = \frac{7}{\sin 30°} \qquad (\text{put in known values})$$

$$c = \frac{7 \sin 80°}{\sin 30°} \qquad (\text{multiply both sides by } \sin 80°)$$

$$c = 13 \cdot 78730854 \qquad (\boxed{\text{📱}}\; 7\; \boxed{\times}\; \boxed{\sin}\; 80\; \boxed{\div}\; \boxed{\sin}\; 30\; \boxed{=})$$

$$\therefore |AB| = 14 \qquad (\text{correct to the nearest integer})$$

EXAMPLE 2

In triangle PQR, $|QR| = 10$ m, $|PR| = 8$ m and $|\angle PQR| = 42°$.
Find $|\angle QPR|$, correct to the nearest degree.

Solution:

Let $p = |QR|$, $q = |PR|$, $Q = |\angle PQR|$ and $P = |\angle QPR|$.

Using the sine rule:

$$\frac{\sin P}{p} = \frac{\sin Q}{q} \qquad (P \text{ is missing, so put that first})$$

$$\frac{\sin P}{10} = \frac{\sin 42°}{8} \qquad (\text{put in known values})$$

$$\sin P = \frac{10 \sin 42°}{8} \qquad (\text{multiply both sides by } 10)$$

$$P = \sin^{-1}\left(\frac{10 \sin 42°}{8}\right)$$

$$P = 56 \cdot 76328432 \qquad (\boxed{\text{📱}}\; \boxed{\text{2nd F}}\; \boxed{\sin}\; \boxed{(\!(}\; 10\; \boxed{\times}\; \boxed{\sin}\; 42\; \boxed{\div}\; 8\; \boxed{)}\; \boxed{=})$$

$$\therefore |\angle QPR| = 57° \qquad (\text{correct to the nearest degree})$$

Exercise 4.5

In questions 1–6, find the value of a correct to two decimal places and find the value of A correct to the nearest degree.

1.
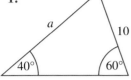

2.
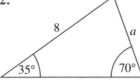

3.
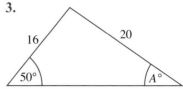

4.
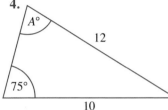

5.
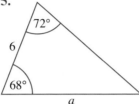

6.
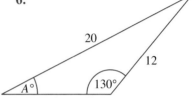

7. In triangle PQR, $|QR| = 7$ cm, $|\angle QPR| = 30°$ and $|\angle PQR| = 84°$.
    Calculate:
    (i) $|PR|$ correct to the nearest integer
    (ii) $|PQ|$ correct to the nearest integer

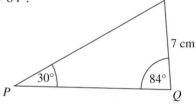

8. In triangle PQR, $|PR| = 10$ cm, $|\angle QPR| = 70°$ and $|\angle PQR| = 45°$.
    (i) Find $|\angle PRQ|$.
    Calculate the following, correct to one decimal place.
    (ii) $|QR|$
    (iii) $|PQ|$

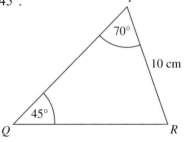

9. In triangle ABC, $|AC| = 4$ cm, $|AB| = 6$ cm and $|\angle ACB| = 37°$.
    (i) Calculate $|\angle ABC|$, correct to the nearest degree.
    (ii) Calculate $|BC|$, correct to the nearest centimetre.

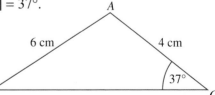

10. In the diagram, $PQ \perp QR$, $|PQ| = 8$ m and $|QR| = 15$ m.

    (i) Find $|PR|$.

    Given $|PS| = |PR|$ and $|\angle PSR| = 65°$:

    (ii) Find $|\angle SPR|$

    (iii) Find the area of triangle *PRS*, correct to the nearest m^2

    (iv) Find $|SR|$, correct to two decimal places

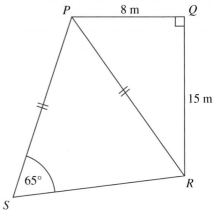

11. In the diagram, $PQ \perp SQ$, $|SR| = 60$ m, $|\angle PSR| = 42°$ and $|\angle PRQ| = 65°$.

    (i) Calculate $|\angle SPR|$.

    (ii) Calculate $|PR|$, correct to the nearest metre.

    (iii) Hence or otherwise, calculate $|PQ|$ correct to the nearest metre.

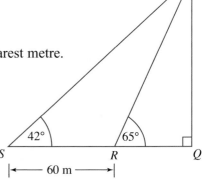

Cosine rule

In any triangle *abc*:

$$a^2 = b^2 + c^2 - 2bc \cos A$$
or $b^2 = a^2 + c^2 - 2ac \cos B$
or $c^2 = a^2 + b^2 - 2ab \cos C$

(The first form is given in the mathematical tables.)

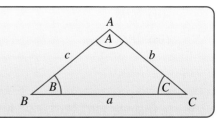

This is known as the **cosine rule** and it applies to any triangle, including a right-angled triangle.

The cosine rule can be used to:

1. Find the length of the third side, a, of a triangle when given the lengths of the other two sides and the angle contained between these sides.

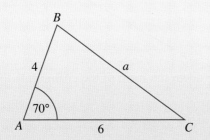

2. Find the measure of an angle, A, of a triangle when given the lengths of the three sides.

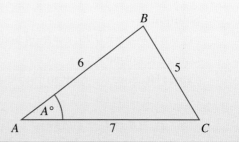

Note: In 1 and 2 above, the sine rule would not work.

If the unknown angle is between 90° and 180°, its cosine is negative.

For example, $\cos 120° = -\frac{1}{2}$.

The largest angle of a triangle is opposite the largest side and the smallest angle is opposite the shortest side. There can be only one obtuse angle in a triangle.

EXAMPLE 1

In triangle ABC, $|BC| = 16$ cm, $|AC| = 12$ cm and $|\angle ACB| = 43°$. Calculate $|AB|$, correct to two decimal places.

Solution:
Let $c = |AB|$, $a = |BC|$, $b = |AC|$ and $C = |\angle ACB|$.

Using the cosine rule:

(Note: Because we want to find c, write down the form of the cosine rule that has c^2 on its own)

$c^2 = a^2 + b^2 - 2ab \cos C$
$c^2 = (16)^2 + (12)^2 - 2(16)(12) \cos 43°$ (put in known values)
$c^2 = 256 + 144 - 2(16)(12)(0{\cdot}7313537016)$
$c^2 = 119{\cdot}1601786$
$c = \sqrt{119{\cdot}1601786}$
$c = 10{\cdot}91605142$
$|AB| = 10{\cdot}92$ cm   (correct to two decimal places)

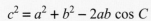

EXAMPLE 2

In triangle PQR, $|QR| = 3$ cm, $|PR| = 5$ cm and $|PQ| = 7$ cm.
Calculate $|\angle QPR|$, correct to the nearest degree.

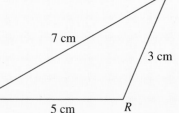

Solution:
Let $p = |QR|$, $q = |PR|$, $r = |PQ|$ and $P = |\angle QPR|$.
Using the cosine rule:
(**Note:** Because we want to find the angle P, write down the form of the cosine rule that contains $\cos P$)

$$p^2 = q^2 + r^2 - 2qr \cos P$$
$$3^2 = 5^2 + 7^2 - 2(5)(7) \cos P \qquad (p = 3,\ q = 5,\ r = 7)$$
$$9 = 25 + 49 - 70 \cos P$$
$$9 = 74 - 70 \cos P$$
$$70 \cos P = 65$$
$$\cos P = \tfrac{65}{70} \qquad \text{(divide both sides by 70)}$$
$$\cos P = \tfrac{13}{14} \qquad \left(\tfrac{65}{70} = \tfrac{13}{14}\right)$$
$$P = \cos^{-1} \tfrac{13}{14}$$
$$P = 21 \cdot 7867893 \qquad (\boxed{}\ \boxed{\text{2nd F}}\ \boxed{\cos}\ 13\ \boxed{a\tfrac{b}{c}}\ 14\ \boxed{=})$$
$$|\angle QPR| = 22° \qquad \text{(correct to the nearest degree)}$$

Exercise 4.6

In questions 1–6, use the cosine rule to calculate the following in the triangles below: (i) a, correct to two decimal places or (ii) A, correct to the nearest degree.

1.

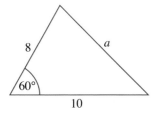

2.

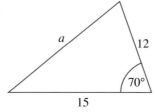

3.

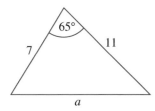

4.

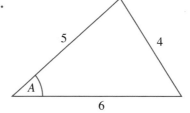

5.

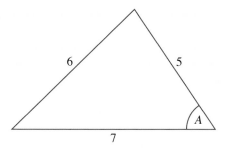

6.

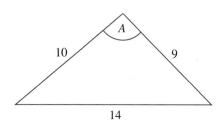

7. In triangle ABC, $|AB| = 7$ cm, $|AC| = 4$ cm and $|BC| = 9$ cm.
Calculate the measure of the greatest angle, correct to
one decimal place.

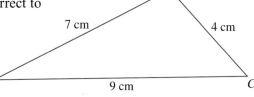

8. In triangle XYZ, $|XY| = 6$ cm, $|XZ| = 8$ cm
and $|YZ| = 4$ cm. Calculate the measure of the
smallest angle, correct to the nearest degree.

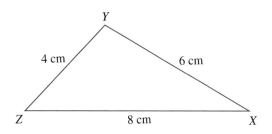

9. In the diagram, $|AB| = 5$ cm, $|AC| = 3$ cm, $|BD| = 8$ cm,
$|CD| = 4$ cm and $|\angle BAC| = 120°$.

   (i) Calculate $|BC|$.

   (ii) Find the measure of $|\angle BDC|$, correct to the
nearest degree.

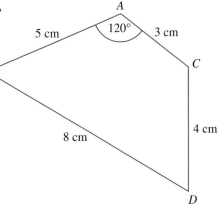

Practical applications and more difficult problems

EXAMPLE 1

Two ships, A and B, leave a port C at noon. A is travelling due east and B is travelling E $56°$ S. Calculate, to the nearest kilometre, the distance between A and B when A is 6 km from C and B is 9 km from C.

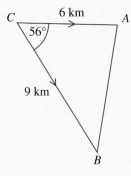

Solution:

Let $c = |AB|$, $b = |AC|$, $a = |BC|$ and $C = |\angle ACB|$.

We have two sides and the included angle.

$\therefore$ Use the cosine rule.

$c^2 = a^2 + b^2 - 2bc \cos C$

$c^2 = 9^2 + 6^2 - 2(9)(6) \cos 56°$ (put in known values)

$c^2 = 81 + 36 - 108(0 \cdot 559192903)$ ($\cos 56° = 0 \cdot 559192903$)

$c^2 = 117 - 60 \cdot 39283357$

$c^2 = 56 \cdot 60716643$

$c = \sqrt{56 \cdot 60716643}$

$c = 7 \cdot 523773417$

$\therefore |AB| = 8$ km   (correct to the nearest km)

In more advanced problems, it is usual that one or more preliminary steps are necessary before the required side or angle is found. In many cases, two triangles are linked. It is good practice in these cases to redraw the situation so as to have two separate triangles. As a general rule, if you cannot use the sine rule, then use the cosine rule and vice versa.

EXAMPLE 2

In the diagram, $|PQ| = 6$ cm, $|PR| = 5$ cm, $|QR| = 4$ cm and $|\angle PSR| = 22°$. Calculate the following correct to one decimal place.

(i) $|\angle QPR|$ (ii) $|RS|$

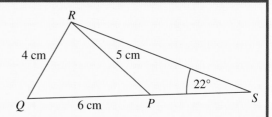

Solution:

(i) Two triangles are linked. Therefore, redraw the two triangles separately.

Question: Which of the two triangles do we begin with, and why?

Answer: We begin with the triangle on the left-hand side in the diagram because we require three pieces of information in a triangle to successfully use the sine or cosine rule.

Hence, we consider triangle PQR.

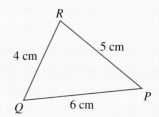

Let $p = |QR|$
$q = |PR|$
$r = |PQ|$
and $P = |\angle QPR|$

We use the cosine rule to calculate P.

$$p^2 = q^2 + r^2 - 2qr \cos P$$
$$4^2 = 5^2 + 6^2 - 2(5)(6) \cos P \quad \text{(put in known values)}$$
$$16 = 25 + 36 - 60 \cos P$$
$$60 \cos P = 45$$
$$\cos P = \tfrac{45}{60} \quad \text{(divide both sides by 60)}$$
$$\cos P = \tfrac{3}{4} \quad \left(\tfrac{45}{60} = \tfrac{3}{4}\right)$$
$$P = \cos^{-1} \tfrac{3}{4}$$
$$P = 41 \cdot 40962211 \quad \left(\boxed{\text{2nd F}} \; \boxed{\cos} \; 3 \; \boxed{a\tfrac{b}{c}} \; 14 \; \boxed{=} \right)$$
$$\therefore |\angle QPR| = 41 \cdot 4° \quad \text{(correct to one decimal price)}$$

(ii) Now $|\angle RPS| = 180° - 41 \cdot 4°$
$|\angle RPS| = 138 \cdot 6°$

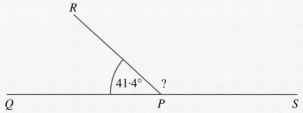

Consider triangle *PRS*.

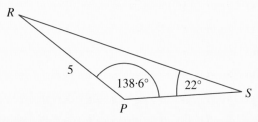

Let $p = |RS|$
$s = |PR|$
$P = |\angle RPS|$
and $S = |\angle RSP|$

We now use the sine rule to find *p*.

$$\frac{p}{\sin P} = \frac{s}{\sin S}$$

$$\frac{p}{\sin 138 \cdot 6°} = \frac{5}{\sin 22°}$$ (put in known values)

$$p = \frac{5 \sin 138 \cdot 6°}{\sin 22°}$$ (multiply both sides by $\sin 138 \cdot 6°$)

$$p = 8 \cdot 826751543$$ (⌨ 5 ✕ sin 138·6 ÷ sin 22 =)

$$\therefore |RS| = 8 \cdot 8 \text{ cm}$$ (correct to one decimal place)

Exercise 4.7

1. A boat sets sail from a harbour, *H*, and travels 7 km due north to a marker buoy, *B*. At *B* the boat turns W 20° S and travels a further 8 km before stopping at *X*. Calculate the straight line distance from *H* to *X*, correct to two decimal places.

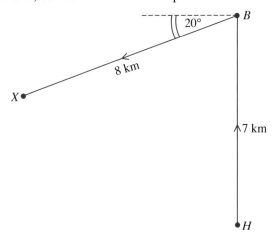

2. Use the sine rule to show that triangle ABC is an impossible triangle.

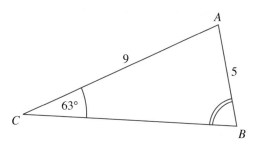

3. A snooker player cues the white (W) ball onto the cushion to rebound and hit the red (R) ball, as shown in the diagram. The white ball travels 85 cm before being deflected 88° by the cushion. It then travels 30 cm before hitting the red ball. The white ball then returns in a straight line to its original position. Find the total distance travelled by the white ball, correct to the nearest centimetre.

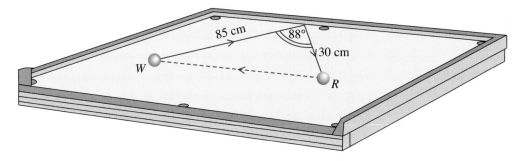

4. A garden, $PQRS$, is in the shape of a quadrilateral with $SP \perp PQ$, $|PQ| = 22\cdot5$ m, $|PS| = 12$ m, $|SR| = 18$ m and $|\angle QSR| = 42°$. Calculate the following.

   (i) $|QS|$
   (ii) $|RQ|$, correct to the nearest metre
   (iii) The area of the garden correct to the nearest m^2

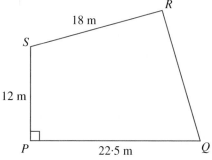

5. The goal posts on a soccer field are 8 m apart. A player kicks for a goal when he is 30 m from one post and 25 m from the other.

   Find the angle opposite the goal line, measured from both goal posts to where the ball is positioned, correct to the nearest degree.

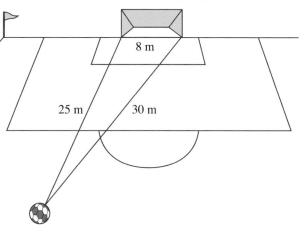

6. The third hole on a golf course is 470 m from the tee. A ball is driven from the tee a distance of 260 m. However, the drive is 10° off the line to the hole, as shown.

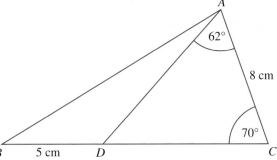

How far from the hole is the ball, correct to the nearest m?

7. *ABC* is a triangle and *D* is a point on [*BC*], as shown. |*BD*| = 5 cm, |*AC*| = 8 cm, |∠*ACD*| = 70° and |∠*DAC*| = 62°.
   Find the following correct to one decimal place.
   (i) |*DC*|
   (ii) The area of triangle *ABC*

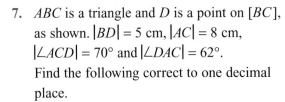

8. Nina is an engineer. She is asked to design a ramp for mountain bike enthusiasts. The site for the ramp is level but sloped, as in the diagram.

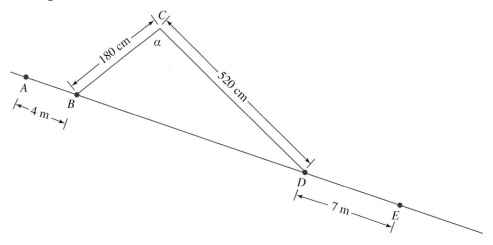

For health and safety reasons, |*AB*| = 4 m, |*DE*| = 7 m and α ≥ 96°.

For the ramp to meet the bikers' specifications, α ≤ 108°, |*BC*| = 180 cm and |*CD*| = 520 cm.

In order for Nina to meet the requirements, find:
   (i) The maximum |*AE*| correct to the nearest centimetre
   (ii) The minimum |*AE*| correct to the nearest centimetre
   (iii) Comment on the difference between the maximum and minimum |*AE*|. Would Nina favour case (i) over case (ii)? Justify your answer.

9. Erin has been kayaking on a river and has arrived at a point on the southern riverbank. However, she wants to get out on the northern side. There are only two possible landing points that she can see. One is slightly upstream from where she is now and one is farther downstream. Because of the current, Erin can paddle faster towards the downstream landing point than the upstream one.

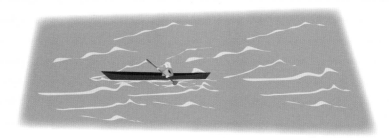

The situation is shown in the diagram below. The banks of the river are parallel. Erin's position is marked D, the upstream landing point is A and the downstream landing point is B. The angles from D to A and from D to B are as shown. The distance from B to A is 92 m.

If she travels in a straight line to A, Erin can go at 0·9 m/s, and if she travels in a straight line to B she can go at 2·8 m/s.

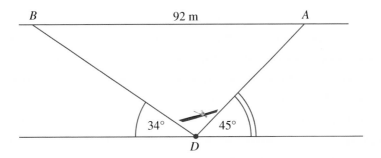

(i) Find the distance from D to A and from D to B. Give your answers correct to the nearest metre.

(ii) Find the time it will take to cross by each route. Give your answers correct to the nearest second.

(iii) Erin is late and wants to get home as fast as possible. Give one reason why she might not choose the faster of the two routes across the river.

10. The photograph shows the Dockland building in Hamburg, Germany.

The diagram below is a side view of the building. It is a parallelogram.

The parallelogram is 29 m high. The top and bottom edges are 88 m long.

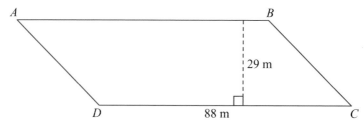

(i) Find the area of this side of the building.

(ii) If $|BD| = |AD|$, find $|BC|$.

(iii) The lines BC and AD are parallel. Find the distance between these parallel lines.

11. Two ships, H and K, set sail from a port, P, at the same time. H sails N 25° W at a steady speed. K sails N 55° E at a speed of 30 km/h. After two hours' sailing, H is directly west of K.

Calculate:

(i) The distance between the ships after two hours, correct to one decimal place

(ii) The average speed of ship H, correct to the nearest km/h

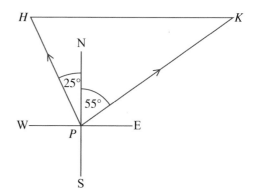

12. A ship, Q, is 37 km from a port, P.
The direction of Q from P is N 45° E.
A second ship, R, is 53 km from P.
The direction of R from Q is S 75° E.

Calculate:

(i) $|\angle QRP|$, correct to one decimal place

(ii) $|QR|$, correct to two decimal places

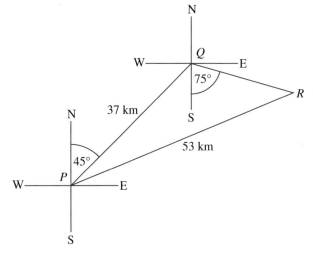

13. (i) A surveyor wishes to measure the height of a church. Measuring the angle of elevation, she finds that the angle increases from 30° to 40° after walking 25 m towards the church. What is the height of the church correct to the nearest metre?

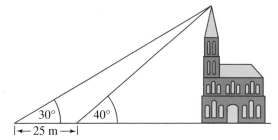

(ii) Name an instrument the surveyor could use to measure the angles of elevation.

(iii) Describe how that instrument is used to obtain one of the angles.

14. The vertices A, B and C of triangle ABC have coordinates $(2, 0) = A$, $(5, 1) = B$ and $(3, 7) = C$.

(i) Plot the points on a graph.

(ii) (a) Using the formula for length of a line segment $\sqrt{(x_2 - x_1)^2 + (y_2 - y_1)^2}$ from coordinate geometry, show that $|AB| = \sqrt{10}$.

(b) Hence, find $|BC|$ and $|AC|$ in surd form.

(iii) By using the cosine rule or otherwise, calculate $|\angle CAB|$ correct to the nearest degree.

(iv) Is the solution using the cosine rule the quickest/best solution to part (iii)? Justify your answer.

15. The diagram shows triangle ABC.

    $|AB| = x$ cm, $|AC| = x + 3$ cm, $|BC| = 2x + 1$ cm
    and $x > 1$. The angle at A is $60°$.

    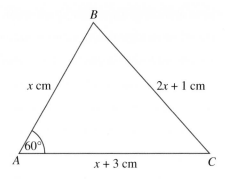

    (i) Use the cosine rule to show that x must satisfy
    the equation $3x^2 + x - 8 = 0$.

    (ii) Solve $3x^2 + x - 8 = 0$ to find the value of x,
    correct to one decimal place. Why is there only
    one value for x and not two values?

16. A school sports day includes a combined foot and swim race. The course is indicated in red.

    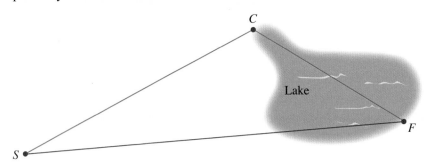

    Note: Diagram is not to scale.

    C and F are two trees on the edge of a lake and S is a large rock some distance from it.

    The race committee finds that the land distance $|CS| = 1,800$ m and also measures
    $|\angle CSF| = 23°$ and $|\angle SCF| = 105°$.

    (i) Calculate $|CF|$, the swim distance, correct to the nearest metre.

    (ii) The race consists of running from S to C and swimming from C to F. Find the total
    length of the race, correct to the nearest metre.

    (iii) Name an instrument they might have used to find $|CS|$ and describe how it was used.

    (iv) Name an instrument the committee might use to measure the angles $\angle CSF$ and $\angle SCF$.
    Hence, describe how the angles are measured.

    Hint 1: A clinometer is no use here.

    Hint 2:

    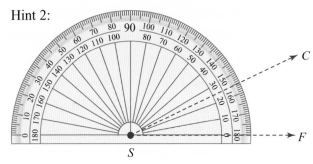

Special angles: 45°, 30° and 60°

There are three special angles whose sine, cosine and tangent ratios can be expressed as simple fractions or surds.

$$\sin 45° = \frac{1}{\sqrt{2}}$$

$$\cos 45° = \frac{1}{\sqrt{2}}$$

$$\tan 45° = 1$$

$$\sin 60° = \frac{\sqrt{3}}{2} \qquad \sin 30° = \frac{1}{2}$$

$$\cos 60° = \frac{1}{2} \qquad \cos 30° = \frac{\sqrt{3}}{2}$$

$$\tan 60° = \sqrt{3} \qquad \tan 30° = \frac{1}{\sqrt{3}}$$

These ratios can be used instead of a calculator.

These ratios are tabulated in the mathematical tables. The tables use both degrees and radians.

The tables use the fact that:

$$\pi \text{ radians} = 180°$$

Thus:

| $\frac{\pi}{2}$ radians = 90° | $\frac{\pi}{3}$ radians = 60° | $\frac{\pi}{4}$ radians = 45° | $\frac{\pi}{6}$ radians = 30° |

EXAMPLE

Without using a calculator, find the value of:

(i) $\tan 45° + \sin 30°$ (ii) $\sin^2 60° + \cos^2 45°$

Solution:

(i) $\tan 45° + \sin 30°$

$$= 1 + \tfrac{1}{2}$$

$$= \tfrac{3}{2}$$

(ii) $\sin^2 60° + \cos^2 45°$

$$= \left(\frac{\sqrt{3}}{2}\right)^2 + \left(\frac{1}{\sqrt{2}}\right)^2$$

$$= \tfrac{3}{4} + \tfrac{1}{2} = \tfrac{5}{4}$$

Note: $\sin^2 A = (\sin A)^2$, $\cos^2 A = (\cos A)^2$ and $\tan^2 A = (\tan A)^2$.

Exercise 4.8

1. **Complete the following tables (without using a calculator).**

   (i)

A	30°	45°	60°
$\cos A$			
$\sin A$		$\dfrac{1}{\sqrt{2}}$	
$\tan A$			
$\cos^2 A$			
$\sin^2 A$			
$\tan^2 A$		1	

(ii)

B	0	$\dfrac{\pi}{2}$	$\dfrac{\pi}{3}$	π	$\dfrac{3\pi}{2}$	2π
$\cos B$						
$\sin B$						
$\cos^2 B$						
$\sin^2 B$						

Without using a calculator, evaluate questions 2–13 exactly.

2. $\cos 60° + \sin 30°$

3. $\cos^2 45° + \sin 30°$

4. $1 + \tan^2 60°$

5. $\cos^2 45° + \tan 45°$

6. $\tan 45° - \tan^2 30°$

7. $2 \cos 30° \sin 60°$

8. $1 - \cos^2 30°$

9. $\cos^3 60° + \cos^2 45°$

10. $3 \tan^2 30° - 2 \cos 60°$

11. $\cos \dfrac{\pi}{3} + \cos \pi$

12. $\sin \dfrac{3\pi}{2} + \sin \dfrac{\pi}{6}$

13. $\tan \pi + \tan \dfrac{\pi}{3}$

14. Find the value of $\tan 90°$. Comment on your answer.

15. Verify that: **(i)** $\dfrac{1 + \tan 60° \tan 30°}{\cos^2 45°} = 4$ **(ii)** $\tan^2 30° \sin^2 60° = \frac{1}{4}$

16. If $A = 30°$, verify that:

     (i) $\sin 2A = 2 \sin A \cos A$ **(ii)** $\cos 2A = \cos^2 A - \sin^2 A$

17. If $\theta = 60°$, verify that:

     (i) $\cos^2 \theta + \sin^2 \theta = 1$ **(ii)** $\dfrac{\sin \theta}{\cos \theta} = \tan \theta$

Unit circle

The unit circle has its centre at the origin (0, 0) and the length
of the radius is 1.

Take any point $p(x, y)$ on the circle, making an angle of θ at
the centre.

$\cos \theta = \dfrac{x}{1} = x$

$\sin \theta = \dfrac{y}{1} = y$

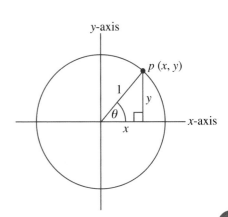

145

$$\tan \theta = \frac{y}{x} = \frac{\sin \theta}{\cos \theta}$$

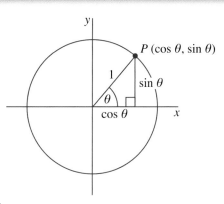

This important result indicates that the coordinates of any point on the unit circle can be represented by $P(\cos \theta, \sin \theta)$, where θ is any angle.

As the point P rotates, θ changes. These definitions of $\cos \theta$ and $\sin \theta$ in terms of the coordinates of a point rotating around the unit circle apply for **all** values of the angle $\theta°$.

Memory aid: (Christian name, surname) = $(\cos \theta, \sin \theta) = (x, y)$.

Note: Using Pythagoras' theorem, $\cos^2 \theta + \sin^2 \theta = 1$. (See the result on page 13 of the maths tables.)

Values of sin, cos and tan for 0°, 90°, 180°, 270° and 360°

Both of the diagrams below represent the unit circle, but using two different notations to describe any point P on the circle.

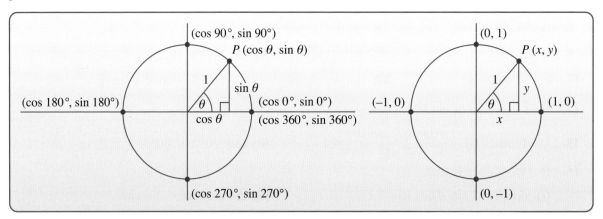

By comparing corresponding points on both unit circles, the values of sin, cos and tan for 0°, 90°, 180°, 270° and 360° can be read directly.

$(\cos 0°, \sin 0°) = (\cos 360°, \sin 360°) = (1, 0)$	$(\cos 90°, \sin 90°) = (0, 1)$
$\cos 0° = \cos 360° = 1$	$\cos 90° = 0$
$\sin 0° = \sin 360° = 0$	$\sin 90° = 1$
$\tan 0° = \tan 360° = \frac{0}{1} = 0$	$\tan 90° = \frac{1}{0}$ (undefined)
$(\cos 180°, \sin 180°) = (-1, 0)$	$(\cos 270°, \sin 270°) = (0, -1)$
$\cos 180° = -1$	$\cos 270° = 0$
$\sin 180° = 0$	$\sin 270° = -1$
$\tan 180° = \frac{0}{-1} = 0$	$\tan 270° = \frac{-1}{0}$ (undefined)

Note: Division by zero is undefined.

EXAMPLE

(i) Find the value of A for which $\cos A = -1$, $0° \leq A \leq 360°$.

(ii) If $0° \leq A \leq 360°$, find the value of A for which $\sin A = 1$.

(iii) If $0° \leq A \leq 360°$, find the values of A for which $\cos A = 0$.

(iv) Evaluate $\sin^2 270°$.

Solution:

Draw the unit circle.

Remember: (Christian name, surname) $= (\cos \theta, \sin \theta) = (x, y)$.

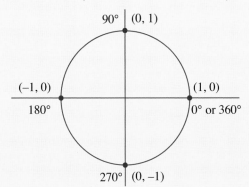

(i) $\cos A = -1$
$A = 180°$

(ii) $\sin A = 1$
$A = 90°$

(iii) $\cos A = 0$
$A = 90°$ or $270°$

(iv) $\sin^2 270°$
$= (\sin 270°)^2$
$= (-1)^2 = 1$

Exercise 4.9

Evaluate questions 1–14.

1. $\cos 90°$
2. $\sin 180°$
3. $\cos 0°$
4. $\sin 90°$
5. $\cos 180°$
6. $\sin 270°$
7. $\sin 360°$
8. $\cos 270°$
9. $\tan 180°$
10. $\dfrac{2 \cos 180°}{\sin 90°}$
11. $\dfrac{3 \sin 270°}{\cos^2 180°}$
12. $\dfrac{\sin^2 270° + \cos^2 180°}{2 \cos 0°}$
13. $\sin 180° \cos 90° + \cos 180° \sin 90°$
14. $(\sin 90° - \cos 180°)^2$

In questions 15–21, solve for A, where $0° \leq A \leq 360°$.

15. $\cos A = 1$
16. $\sin A = 1$
17. $\sin A = -1$
18. $\cos A = -1$
19. $\cos A = 0$
20. $\sin A = 0$
21. $\tan A = 0$

22. If $\cos A = 0$, find the two values of $\sin A$ when $0° \leq A \leq 360°$.

Trigonometric ratios for angles between 0° and 360°

The *x*- and *y*-axes divide the plane into four quadrants.
Consider the unit circle on the right:

$$\cos \theta = x \qquad \sin \theta = y$$

$$\tan \theta = \frac{\sin \theta}{\cos \theta} = \frac{y}{x}$$

By examining the signs of *x* and *y* in the four quadrants, the
signs of sin *θ*, cos *θ* and tan *θ* for any value of *θ* can be found.

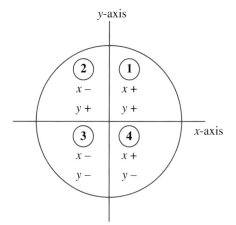

Summary of signs

- **1st quadrant:** sin, cos and tan are all positive.
- **2nd quadrant:** sin is positive, cos and tan are negative.
- **3rd quadrant:** tan is positive, sin and cos are negative.
- **4th quadrant:** cos is positive, sin and tan are negative.

A useful memory aid, *CAST*, in the diagram on the right, shows the ratios
that are positive for the angles between 0° and 360°.

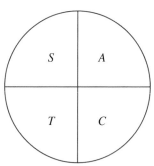

Method for finding the trigonometric ratio for any angle between 0° and 360°:

1. Draw a rough diagram of the angle.

2. Determine in which quadrant the angle lies and use $\left(\frac{S|A}{T|C}\right)$ to find its sign.

3. Find its **related** angle (the acute angle to the nearest horizontal).

4. Use the trigonometric ratio of the related angle with the sign in step 2.

EXAMPLE

Find sin 240°, leaving your answer in surd form.

Solution:
Surd form, ∴ you cannot use a calculator.

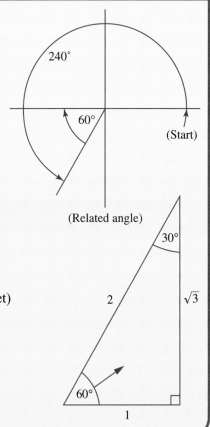

240°

60°

(Start)

1. The diagram shows the angle 240°.
2. 240° is in the 3rd quadrant, sin is negative in the 3rd quadrant.
3. Related angle is 60°.
4. ∴ sin 240°

   $$= -\sin 60°$$

   $$= -\frac{\sqrt{3}}{2}$$

   (or use the tables in the mathematical tables booklet)

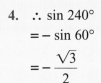

S	A
T	C

(Related angle)

30°

2   √3

60°

1

Exercise 4.10

Without using a calculator, evaluate questions 1–12 exactly.

1. cos 120°
2. sin 150°
3. tan 240°
4. sin 210°
5. tan 135°
6. cos 135°
7. sin 300°
8. tan 210°
9. sin 315°
10. tan 330°
11. cos 150°
12. cos 225°

Solving trigonometric equations

Between 0° and 360° there may be two angles with the same trigonometric ratios. For example, $\cos 120° = -\frac{1}{2}$ and $\cos 240° = -\frac{1}{2}$.

To solve a trigonometric equation, do the following.

1. Ignore the sign and calculate the related angle.
2. From the sign of the given ratio, decide in which quadrants the angles lie.
3. Using a rough diagram, state the angles between 0° and 360°.

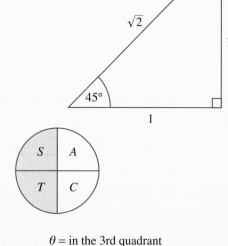

EXAMPLE

If $\cos \theta = -\dfrac{1}{\sqrt{2}}$, find two values of θ between 0° and 360°.

Solution:

1. Find the related angle (ignore the sign).

   If $\cos \theta = \dfrac{1}{\sqrt{2}}$,

   $\theta = 45°$

   The related angle is 45°.

   (🖩 2nd F cos ((1 ÷ √ 2)) =)

2. cos is negative in the 2nd and 3rd quadrants.

3. Rough diagram:

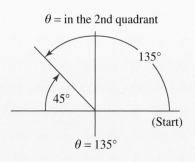

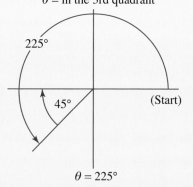

Thus, if $\cos \theta = -\dfrac{1}{\sqrt{2}}$, $\theta = 135°, 225°$.

Exercise 4.11

In questions 1–21, find all the values of θ between $0°$ and $360°$ if:

1. $\sin \theta = \dfrac{1}{2}$

2. $\sin \theta = \dfrac{\sqrt{3}}{2}$

3. $\tan \theta = \dfrac{1}{\sqrt{3}}$

4. $\cos \theta = \dfrac{1}{2}$

5. $\sin \theta = \dfrac{1}{\sqrt{2}}$

6. $\tan \theta = \sqrt{3}$

7. $\tan \theta = 1$

8. $\cos \theta = \dfrac{\sqrt{3}}{2}$

9. $\sin \theta = -\dfrac{\sqrt{3}}{2}$

10. $\cos \theta = -\dfrac{\sqrt{3}}{2}$

11. $\sin \theta = -\dfrac{1}{\sqrt{2}}$

12. $\tan \theta = -\dfrac{1}{\sqrt{3}}$

13. $\sin \theta = -\dfrac{1}{2}$

14. $\tan \theta = -\sqrt{3}$

15. $\cos \theta = \dfrac{1}{\sqrt{2}}$

In questions 16–21, give your answers correct to the nearest degree.

16. $\sin \theta = 0\cdot 4$

17. $\cos \theta = 0\cdot 12$

18. $\tan \theta = 1\cdot 6$

19. $\cos \theta = -\dfrac{4}{5}$

20. $\tan \theta = -\dfrac{8}{15}$

21. $\sin \theta = -\dfrac{2}{3}$

Operations

The result of an operation is called an **outcome**.

For example, if we throw a die, one possible outcome is 5.

If we throw a die there are six possible outcomes: 1, 2, 3, 4, 5 or 6.

Fundamental principle of counting 1

> Suppose one operation has m possible outcomes and that a second operation has n outcomes. The number of possible outcomes when performing the first operation **followed by** the second operation is $m \times n$.

Performing one operation **and** another operation means we **multiply** the number of possible outcomes.

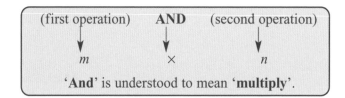

Note: We assume that the outcome of one operation does not affect the number of possible outcomes of the other operation.

The fundamental principle of counting 1 can be extended to three or more operations.

Fundamental principle of counting 2

> Suppose one operation has m possible outcomes and that a second operation has n outcomes. Then the number of possible outcomes of the first operation **or** the second operation is given by $m + n$.

Performing one operation **or** another operation means we **add** the number of possible outcomes.

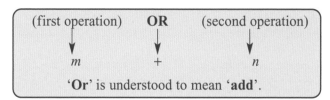

Note: We assume it is not possible for both operations to occur. In other words, there is no overlap of the two operations.

The fundamental principle 2 can be extended to three or more operations, as long as none of the operations overlap.

Permutations

> A **permutation** is an arrangement of a number of objects in a definite order.

Consider the three letters P, Q and R. If these letters are written down in a row, there are six different possible arrangements:

$$PQR \text{ or } PRQ \text{ or } QPR \text{ or } QRP \text{ or } RPQ \text{ or } RQP$$

The first letter can be written down in three ways, the second letter can then be written down in two ways and the third letter can be written down in only one way.

Thus the three operations can be performed in $\boxed{3} \times \boxed{2} \times \boxed{1} = 6$ ways.

The boxes are an aid in helping to fill in the number of ways each choice can be made at each position.

In an arrangement, or permutation, the order of the objects chosen is important.

EXAMPLE 1

(i) If a fair six-sided die is thrown and a coin is tossed, how many different outcomes are possible?

(ii) Write out all the possible outcomes.

Solution:

(i) Represent each operation with an empty box: Die   Coin $\square \times \square$

    1. There are six possible outcomes for a die: 1, 2, 3, 4, 5 or 6.

    2. There are two possible outcomes for a coin: H or T.

    Hence, the number of different outcomes $= \boxed{6} \times \boxed{2} = 12$.

(ii)

	1	2	3	4	5	6
T	•	•	•	•	•	•
H	•	•	•	•	•	•

$(1, H), (2, H), (3, H), (4, H), (5, H), (6, H)$
$(1, T), (2, T), (3, T), (4, T), (5, T), (6, T)$

Note: It can help to write down one possible outcome above the box.

                                  Die   Coin

One possible outcome: 5 T

Number of outcomes: $\boxed{6} \times \boxed{2} = 12$

This method is very useful when trying to decide the number of possible outcomes at a particular stage, especially when certain choices are restricted, such as in a question where the number must be even or where the word must begin with the letter K.

EXAMPLE 2

In a cinema complex, a customer in the VIP theatre has three choices of snack: popcorn, nachos or candyfloss. The customer also has three choices of drink: water, cola or wine. The customer can choose one snack and one drink.

  (i) Write down all the different selections possible.
 (ii) How many different selections are possible?
(iii) If your class went on a school trip to that VIP theatre, which selection(s) in your opinion would be (a) most popular (b) least popular? Justify your opinions.

Solution:
  (i) The possible selections are:

Nachos and wine	Popcorn and wine	Candyfloss and wine
Nachos and cola	Popcorn and cola	Candyfloss and cola
Nachos and water	Popcorn and water	Candyfloss and water

Note: We call such a list, with all outcomes, the sample space.

 (ii) **Using the fundamental principle of counting 1**
Choices for snack   multiplied by   choices for drink

$$\boxed{3} \qquad \times \qquad \boxed{3} = 9$$

Note: The word 'and' indicates multiply.

An alternative method is to construct a two-way table where we can see all the possible selections.

	Wine	Cola	Water
Nachos			
Popcorn			
Candyfloss			

Note: There are nine blank boxes in the table above. This confirms our previous answer.

(iii) Since popcorn is considered a traditional cinema snack, I think popcorn would be the most popular snack choice. I feel candyfloss would be the least popular snack choice for secondary school students. Candyfloss might be more popular with primary school students.

Given that a majority of secondary students are under 18 years old and that drinking alcohol on a school trip would not be permitted, I think the drinks choice would be split 50:50 between water and cola.

Note: In a justify/discuss type of question, there are no correct or incorrect answers. If you can back up your opinion with a logical statement, you are answering the question correctly.

EXAMPLE 3

Write down all the different arrangements that can be made from these cards, taking two cards at a time if no card can be repeated. Hence or otherwise, how many such arrangements are possible?

Solution:

For questions taking two cards at a time we can use a two-way table.

	K♣	Q♣	J♣	10♣
K♣		KQ	KJ	K10
Q♣	QK		QJ	Q10
J♣	JK	JQ		J10
10♣	10K	10Q	10J	

Note 1: We might conclude there are (4 × 4 =) 16 possible arrangements. However, we are not allowed to repeat a card in this question.

Note 2: To answer the question, it's best to complete each box and shade in the boxes that are not allowed.

Note 3: Some candidates would by-pass the two-way table and simply write down all arrangements. That would also be correct.

Finally, how many such arrangements are possible?

Method 1

Count the relevant boxes in the table or count your list. Answer = 12.

Method 2

Use the fundamental principle of counting 1.

We have four choices for the first card and three choices for the second card.

$$\boxed{4} \times \boxed{3} = 12$$

EXAMPLE 4

Raffle tickets are each labelled with a digit from {1, 2, 3, 4, 5, 6, 7, 8, 9} followed by a letter from the English alphabet {A, B, C, D, . . . X, Y, Z} (for example, 1A, 2A, 3A).

 (i) How many different raffle tickets can be formed?

(ii) Would this amount of tickets be suitable for a raffle in your class? Justify your answer.

Solution:

(i) 1A 2A   3A   4A   5A   6A   7A   8A   9A

  1B 2B   3B   4B   . . .

  1C 2C   . . .

  1D . . .

  1E . . .

  1F . . .

  :
  :

The total number of outcomes (sample space) is too great to write out here.

The total number of different tickets is given as follows.

Choose one digit from nine digits and choose one letter from 26 letters.

$$\boxed{9} \times \boxed{26} = 234$$

(ii) Would 234 tickets be suitable for a raffle in your class?

A majority of classes would have from 25 to 30 students.

If every student from a class of 30 bought exactly one ticket each, then out of 234 tickets, 30 are sold.

This means 30 tickets sold with (234 − 30 =) 204 unsold tickets.

Might some teachers buy tickets? Let's say 10 teachers buy two tickets each. That gives (20 × 2 =) 40 more tickets sold.

Now out of 234 tickets (30 + 40 =) 70 tickets are sold.

This means 70 tickets sold with (234 − 70 =) 164 unsold tickets.

The above figures would justify the statement that 234 tickets would be far too many for a class raffle. You might come to a different conclusion if all class members bought 10 tickets.

EXAMPLE 5

A team plays three matches. The team's result in each match is a win (W) or a draw (D) or a loss (L). Write down all the possible arrangements of the team's results for the three matches.

Solution:
Arrange the letters W, D, L, with repetition of letters allowed.

All the same	WWW	DDD	LLL
Two wins	WWD / WWL	WDW / WLW	DWW / LWW
Two draws	DDW / DDL	DWD / DLD	WDD / LDD
Two losses	LLW / LLD	LWL / LDL	WLL / DLL
All different	WLD WDL	DLW DWL	LWD LDW

Exercise 5.1

1. Write down all the different arrangements that can be made from the letters B, K, Q if no letter can be repeated and taking two letters at a time.

2. Write down all the different arrangements that can be made from the letters B, K, Q taking two letters at a time when repetition is allowed.

3. Write down all the different arrangements that can be made from the digits 6, 7, 8, 9 if no digit can be repeated and taking three digits at a time.

4. Write down all the different arrangements that can be made from the digits 6, 7, 8, 9 taking three digits at a time when repetition is allowed.

5. Use the fundamental principle of counting to verify your answers in questions 1, 2, 3 and 4.

6. How many different arrangements using all the letters of the word SEAT can be made that:
    (i) Begin with the letter T   (ii) Begin with the letter A
    (iii) Begin with the letter E   (iv) Begin with the letter S
    (v) Hence or otherwise, find the number of arrangements with no restriction.

7. How many different arrangements, taking three letters at a time, can be made from the word TAKE if:
    (i) The first letter must be E
    (ii) The first letter must be A
    (iii) The first letter must be a vowel

8. Four children, Abigail, Barack, Cal and David, are to be seated in a row on a bench.
    (i) If Barack must sit on the left-hand side, write down all six different arrangements.
    (ii) If Barack must sit on the left-hand side and Cal on the right-hand side, write down all possible arrangements.
    (iii) How many different arrangements are possible if there are no restrictions on seating?
    (iv) If Cal and David must always sit together, write down at least two such arrangements. Hence or otherwise, find the total number of different arrangements where Cal and David sit together.

9. The Widget Corporation operates a factory in the Midlands. There are 210 people employed in the factory, 80% of whom drive to work. A new car park, with entrance and exit barriers, is constructed for the exclusive use of the employees. Each employee who drives to work is given a different code to access and leave the car park. The code is made up of three letters from the word 'widget'.
    (i) Find how many different codes can be made:
        (a) If no letter is repeated
        (b) If letter repetition is allowed
    (ii) Which of (a) and (b) is more suitable for the situation? Justify your opinion.

10. **(i)** A number plate is to consist of three letters of the English alphabet and two digits. If no letter or digit can be repeated and 0 can never be used as the first digit, how many different plates can be manufactured?

BAT 45

(an example)

   (ii) A number plate is to consist of three digits and two letters of the English alphabet. If no letter or digit can be repeated and 0 can never be used as the first digit, how many different plates can be manufactured?

402 QB

(an example)

   (iii) The Ministry of Transport in a certain country decides to introduce a new type of number plate for motor vehicle registration. It is expected that there will be on average 86,000 new vehicle registrations in that country each year for the next five years. Which of **(i)** and/or **(ii)** above do you think would meet the needs of that Ministry of Transport? Justify your answer.

11. A personal identification number (PIN) for a credit card verification machine consists of four digits.

   (i) Write down the smallest PIN number.

   (ii) Write down the largest PIN number.

   (iii) How many four-digit PIN numbers can be formed?

   (iv) A bank issues 185,904 of its customers a credit card. Can the bank supply a different four-digit PIN number to each of those customers? Justify your answer.

Exercise:

Find out the reality of the four-digit PIN system that Visa uses for its customers. In particular, how many Visa cards are issued in Ireland, Europe and worldwide? What are the implications for a four-digit PIN and why does it work?

Factorials including practical applications

> The product of all the positive whole numbers from n down to 1 is called **factorial n** and is denoted by $n!$.
>
> Thus, $n! = n(n-1)(n-2)\ldots \times 3 \times 2 \times 1$.

The shorthand used is to write an exclamation mark after the number.

For example:

$$1! = 1$$
$$2! = 2 \times 1 = 2$$
$$3! = 3 \times 2 \times 1 = 6$$
$$4! = 4 \times 3 \times 2 \times 1 = 12$$
$$5! = 5 \times 4 \times 3 \times 2 \times 1 = 120$$

As you can see, the values of the factorial increase in size at a very fast rate, e.g. $10! = 3,628,800$.

Note: $10! = 10 \times 9! = 10 \times 9 \times 8!$ (and so on) $n! = n(n-1)! = n(n-1)(n-2)!$ (and so on)
$$7 \times 6! = 7!$$ $$(n+1)n! = (n+1)!$$

EXAMPLE 1

Evaluate:

(i) $\dfrac{9!}{6!}$ (ii) $4! + 2 \times 3!$

Solution:

(i) $\dfrac{9!}{6!}$

Method 1:

$$\frac{9!}{6!} = \frac{9 \times 8 \times 7 \times \cancel{6} \times \cancel{5} \times \cancel{4} \times \cancel{3} \times \cancel{2} \times \cancel{1}}{\cancel{6} \times \cancel{5} \times \cancel{4} \times \cancel{3} \times \cancel{2} \times \cancel{1}}$$

$$= 9 \times 8 \times 7$$
$$= 504$$

($\boxed{}\ 9\ \boxed{n!}\ \boxed{\div}\ 6\ \boxed{n!}\ \boxed{=}$)

Method 2:

$$\frac{9!}{6!} = \frac{9 \times 8 \times 7 \times 6!}{6!}$$

$$= 9 \times 8 \times 7$$
$$= 504$$

(Start with the larger factorial and work down to the smaller factorial.)

(ii) $4! + 2 \times 3!$

$4! = 4 \times 3 \times 2 \times 1 = 24$

$3! = 3 \times 2 \times 1 = 6$

$\therefore \quad 4! + 2 \times 3! = 24 + 2 \times 6 = 24 + 12 = 36$

EXAMPLE 2

A student has five reference books, one each on Maths, Geography, Art, History and Economics. The books are to be placed in a row on a shelf.

  (i) How many arrangements are possible?

 (ii) How many arrangements have the Art book in the middle?

(iii) How many arrangements have the Art book on the left-hand end and the Maths book on the right-hand end?

Solution:

  (i)

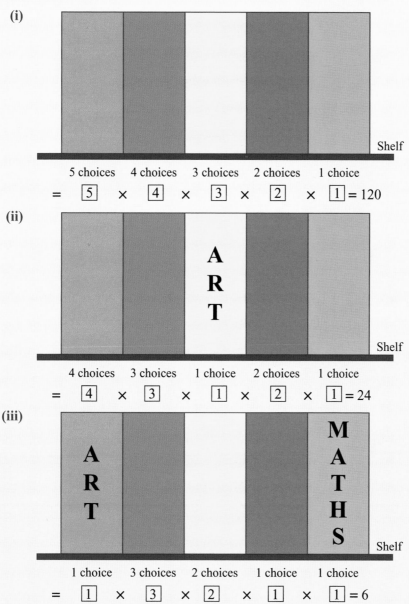

         5 choices   4 choices   3 choices   2 choices   1 choice

  =   5 × 4 × 3 × 2 × 1 = 120

 (ii)

         4 choices   3 choices   1 choice   2 choices   1 choice

  =   4 × 3 × 1 × 2 × 1 = 24

(iii)

         1 choice   3 choices   2 choices   1 choice   1 choice

  =   1 × 3 × 2 × 1 × 1 = 6

EXAMPLE 3

(i) A person is asked to select a four-digit number from the digits 1, 2, 3, 4 and each digit can be used only once. How many different selections can be made?

(ii) A person is asked to select a five-digit number from the digits 1, 2, 3, 4, 5 and each digit can be used only once. How many different selections can be made?

(iii) From a group of 109 people, one person is chosen at random. Investigate which of (i) or (ii) above would be best suited to do this. Justify your answer.

Solution:

(i) ☐ and ☐ and ☐ and ☐

Put one of the four digits in each box.

4 choices × 3 choices × 2 choices × 1 choice = 24 selections = 4!

(ii) ☐ and ☐ and ☐ and ☐ and ☐

Put one of the five digits in each box.

5 choices × 4 choices × 3 choices × 2 choices × 1 choice = 120 selections = 5!

(iii) You might consider the question to be somewhat vague. If so, you should mention that in your solution.

The word 'investigate' in this case means to find out something.

(i) Has 24 selections
(ii) Has 120 selections

You could decide to give each of the group of 109 people one of the selections found.

(i) 24 selections would not be enough to share out between 109 people.
(ii) 120 selections would give each person a different selection.

∴ I conclude (ii) is best suited.

The justification is given above.

Special note:

If your answers to (i) and (ii) are different to 24 and 120, do your own investigation with your answers. Make your own conclusion and justification.

For part (iii) you will get full marks provided your answer makes sense.

Exercise 5.2

Evaluate each of the following for questions 1–18.

1. 5!
2. 6!
3. 8!
4. 9!
5. 12!

6. $\dfrac{6!}{4!}$
7. $\dfrac{8!}{5!}$
8. $\dfrac{10!}{6!}$
9. $\dfrac{8!}{2! \times 6!}$
10. $\dfrac{10!}{3! \times 7!}$

11. $(4!)^2$
12. $(2! + 3!)^2$
13. $(5! - 3!)^2$
14. $5 \times 4! + 3 \times 2!$

15. $4.5! - 5.4!$
16. $\dfrac{6!}{(3!)^2}$
17. $\dfrac{6! - 4!}{3!}$
18. $\dfrac{15!}{4! \times 11!} - \dfrac{9!}{2! \times 7!}$

19. If $k(5!) = 7!$, find the value of k.

20. By letting $n = 6$, verify that:

(i) $\dfrac{(n + 1)!}{n!} = n + 1$ (ii) $\dfrac{(n + 1)!}{n + 1} = n!$ (iii) $\dfrac{(n + 1)!}{(n - 1)!} = n^2 + n$

21. Four identical laboratories are situated side by side in a straight corridor. The school principal wishes to designate a laboratory for each of Physics, Biology, Chemistry and Science.

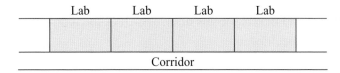

(i) How many different arrangements can the principal make?

(ii) How many different arrangements can be made if the science laboratory can only be at either end?

22. A TV show has a programme with seven acts. The director of the programme must decide the order in which the acts perform.

(i) How many arrangements are possible?

(ii) How many arrangements are possible if one particular act must always be the second to perform?

23. Eight horses run in a race. All horses finish the race and no two horses finish the race at the same time.

(i) In how many different orders can the eight horses finish the race?

(ii) There are two very slow horses in the race. They always finish last and second last. In how many different orders can the eight horses now finish the race?

24. Sheldon has five symbols he uses in his research.

    The symbols are ξ, α, ϵ, γ and ϕ.

    How many different arrangements can Sheldon make taking all five symbols

    (i) with no restriction

    (ii) ϵ always first and ξ always last

    (iii) if α and ϕ can never be together.

25. One suspect and eight other members of the public are taking part in a Police identification parade.

    (i) In how many different ways may the nine people be arranged in a straight line?

    (ii) If they are assigned an order at random in how many of the parades is the suspect either first or last in line

26. A football club in a town with approximately 9,000 inhabitants decides to run a weekly fundraiser every Saturday evening, the Blotto. The Blotto draw consists of seven cards numbered 1 to 7 that are placed in a bag. The seven cards are drawn one by one without replacement and noted until all seven cards are drawn. This seven-digit number is the winning combination.

    (i) How many different combinations are possible?

    (ii) Each week the club sells about 2,200 tickets for this draw. Which of the following would it be better for the club to change the draw to?

    (a) Six cards numbered 1 to 6 and draw all six cards for the winning selection

    (b) Eight cards numbered 1 to 8 and draw all eight cards for the winning selection

    (c) Stay with the existing method

    Justify your answer.

27. Five coloured beads, 1 red, 1 blue, 1 white, 1 green and 1 yellow are to be threaded onto a circular wire as in diagram.

    Given that $5! = 120$ is not the number of different ways the five beads can be arranged find the correct number of different arrangements by investigation. Explain your answer.

Probability

Probability involves the study of the laws of chance. It is a measure of the chance, or likelihood, of something happening.

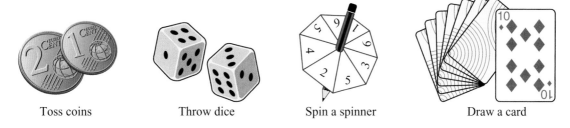

| Toss coins | Throw dice | Spin a spinner | Draw a card |

If you carry out an operation, or experiment, using coins, dice, spinners or cards, then each toss, throw, spin or draw is called a **trial**.

The possible things that can happen from a trial are called **outcomes**. The outcomes of interest are called an **event**. In other words, an event is the set of successful outcomes.

For example, if you throw a die and you are interested in the probability of throwing an even number, then the event is 2, 4, 6 – the successful outcomes.

If E is an event, then $P(E)$ stands for the probability that the event occurs. $P(E)$ is read as 'the probability of E'.

Definition

> The measure of the probability of an event, E, is given by:
>
> $$P(E) = \frac{\text{Number of successful outcomes}}{\text{Number of possible outcomes}}$$

The probability of an event is a number between 0 and 1, including 0 and 1.

$$0 \le P(E) \le 1$$

The value of $P(E)$ can be given as a fraction, decimal or percentage.

Note: $P(E) = 0$ means that an event is **impossible**.
$P(E) = 1$ means that an event is **certain**.

The chance of an event happening can be shown on a **probability scale**:

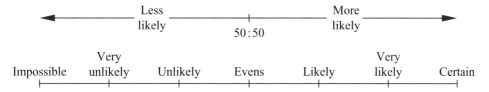

The probabilities of some events are shown on the probability scale below.

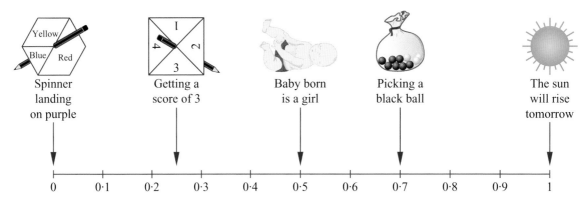

| Spinner landing on purple | Getting a score of 3 | Baby born is a girl | Picking a black ball | The sun will rise tomorrow |

Probabilities should always be written as fractions, decimals or percentages.

Note: $\frac{1}{2} = 0\cdot5 = 50:50 = \text{evens} = 50\%$

Exercise 5.3

1. Describe each of the following events as certain, impossible, unlikely likely or very likely.
    (i) The sun will rise tomorrow
    (ii) A shamrock will be displayed on St Patrick's Day
    (iii) Today is everyone's birthday
    (iv) Trains will run on time all week
    (v) You will win the state lottery once in your lifetime
    (vi) Visiting the moon will be a tourist activity by 2100

2. There are seven labels on the probability scale below.

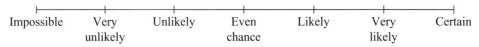

| Impossible | Very unlikely | Unlikely | Even chance | Likely | Very likely | Certain |

    Which of these labels best describes the likelihood of each of these events occurring?
    (i) The New Zealand cricket team will win the Sam Maguire Cup
    (ii) It will snow somewhere in Ireland next winter
    (iii) If a letter is selected from the English alphabet, it will be a vowel
    (iv) A phone number from the phone book is even
    (v) You will have an exam in the next four weeks
    (vi) Polar bears will survive in the Arctic despite global warming

3. The events *P*, *Q*, *R*, *S*, *T* have probabilities as shown on this probability scale.

0   1

P   *Q*   *R*   *S*   *T*

   (i) Which event is the **most likely** to take place?

  (ii) Which event is the **most unlikely** to take place?

 (iii) Which event is **more likely than not** to take place?

4. The events *W*, *X*, *Y*, *Z* are listed below.

   W: You will live to be at least 65 years old

   X: You will live to be at least 75 years old

   Y: You will live to be at least 85 years old

   Z: You will live to be at least 100 years old

   Make an estimate of the probability of each event and place it on a probability scale.

5. The probability of four events have been marked on a probability scale.

   Event *P*: A person is over 4 metres tall

   Event *Q*: Getting a score less than 7 on one roll of a die

   Event *R*: A coin lands tails up

   Event *S*: Pick a number greater than 1 from 1, 2, 3 and 4

   Label the arrows with the letters *P*, *Q*, *R* and *S* to show the event they represent.

6. The probability scale shows the probabilities of the events *A*, *B*, *C*, *D*, *E*. Which of the five events:

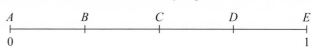

   (i) Has an even chance of happening

  (ii) Is impossible

 (iii) Is certain to happen

 (iv) Is unlikely to happen

  (v) Is very likely to happen

EXAMPLE 1

An unbiased six-sided die is thrown once. Find the probability that the number obtained is:

(i) 2   **(ii)** Odd   **(iii)** Greater than 4

Solution:

When an unbiased die is thrown there are six possible outcomes: 1, 2, 3, 4, 5 or 6.

(i) There is only one 2.

$$\therefore P(2) = \tfrac{1}{6}$$

(ii) There are three odd numbers, 1, 3 and 5.

$$\therefore P(\text{odd number}) = \tfrac{3}{6} = \tfrac{1}{2}$$

(iii) There are two numbers greater than 4: they are 5 and 6.

$$\therefore P(\text{number greater than 4}) = \tfrac{2}{6} = \tfrac{1}{3}$$

A pack of cards consists of 52 cards divided into four suits: clubs (black), diamonds (red), hearts (red) and spades (black). Each suit consists of 13 cards bearing the following values: 2, 3, 4, 5, 6, 7, 8, 9, 10, jack, queen, king and ace. The jack, queen and king are called picture cards.

The total number of outcomes if one card is picked is 52.

Note: The phrase 'drawn at random' means each object is **equally likely** to be picked. 'Unbiased' means 'fair'.

EXAMPLE 2

A card is drawn at random from a normal pack of 52 playing cards.

What is the probability that the card will be:

(i) An ace   **(ii)** A spade   **(iii)** Black   **(iv)** Odd numbered

Solution:

(i) $P(\text{ace}) = \dfrac{\text{Number of aces}}{\text{Number of cards}} = \dfrac{4}{52} = \dfrac{1}{13}$

(ii) $P(\text{spade}) = \dfrac{\text{Number of spades}}{\text{Number of cards}} = \dfrac{13}{52} = \dfrac{1}{4}$

(iii) $P(\text{black card}) = \dfrac{\text{Number of black cards}}{\text{Number of cards}} = \dfrac{26}{52} = \dfrac{1}{2}$

(iv) Each suit has four odd numbers: 3, 5, 7 and 9. There are four suits. Therefore, there are 16 cards with an odd number.

$$P(\text{odd-numbered card}) = \dfrac{\text{Number of cards with an odd number}}{\text{Number of cards}} = \dfrac{16}{52} = \dfrac{4}{13}$$

Note: If you stated an ace was an odd number, then the answer would be $\dfrac{20}{52} = \dfrac{5}{13}$. This would also be correct.

EXAMPLE 3

A complete suit of 13 hearts is added to a normal pack of 52 playing cards. A card is selected at random. What is the probability that the card will be:

(i) A ten of diamonds	(ii) A ten of hearts	(iii) Black
(iv) Red	(v) A spade	(vi) An ace

Solution:

Note: 13 hearts + 52-card deck = 65 cards

(i) $P(\text{a ten of diamonds}) = \dfrac{1}{65}$

(ii) $P(\text{a ten of hearts}) = \dfrac{1 + 1}{65} = \dfrac{2}{65}$ because an extra ten of hearts was added

(iii) $P(\text{black}) = \dfrac{26}{65} = \dfrac{2}{5}$

(iv) $P(\text{red}) = \dfrac{26 + 13}{65} = \dfrac{39}{65} = \dfrac{3}{5}$

(v) $P(\text{a spade}) = \dfrac{13}{65} = \dfrac{1}{5}$

(vi) $P(\text{an ace}) = \dfrac{4 + 1}{65} = \dfrac{5}{65} = \dfrac{1}{13}$

EXAMPLE 4

In a class, there are 21 boys and 15 girls. Three boys and five girls wear glasses. A pupil is picked at random from the class.

(i) What is the probability that the pupil is a boy?

(ii) What is the probability that the pupil wears glasses?

(iii) What is the probability that the pupil is a boy who wears glasses?

(iv) A girl is picked at random from the class. What is the probability that she wears glasses?

(v) A pupil wearing glasses is picked at random from the class. What is the probability that it is a boy?

(vi) Given that the class exactly represents the entire school of 972 pupils, how many boys in the school wear glasses?

(vii) A pupil from the school is selected at random. Find the probability that the student is a boy.

Solution:

It is good practice to represent the information in a two-way table (including the totals for each column and row).

There are $21 + 15 = 36$ pupils in the class.

	Boy	Girl	Total
Does not wear glasses	18	10	28
Wears glasses	3	5	8
Total	21	15	36

(i) $P(\text{boy}) = \dfrac{\text{Number of boys}}{\text{Number of pupils in the class}} = \dfrac{21}{36} = \dfrac{7}{12}$

(ii) $P(\text{pupil wears glasses}) = \dfrac{\text{Number of pupils who wear glasses}}{\text{Number of pupils in the class}} = \dfrac{8}{36} = \dfrac{2}{9}$

(iii) $P(\text{boy who wears glasses}) = \dfrac{\text{Number of boys who wear glasses}}{\text{Number of pupils in the class}} = \dfrac{3}{36} = \dfrac{1}{12}$

(iv) We are certain that the pupil picked is a girl. There are 15 girls in the class and five of these wear glasses.

$P(\text{when a girl is picked, she wears glasses})$

$= \dfrac{\text{Number of girls in the class who wear glasses}}{\text{Number of girls in the class}} = \dfrac{5}{15} = \dfrac{1}{3}$

(v) We are certain that the pupil picked wears glasses. There are eight pupils who wear glasses and three of these pupils are boys.

$$P(\text{when a pupil who wears glasses is picked, the pupil is a boy})$$

$$= \frac{\text{Number of boys in the class who wear glasses}}{\text{Number of pupils in the class who wear glasses}} = \frac{3}{8}$$

(vi) From **(iii)** $\frac{1}{12}$ of students in the class are boys who wear glasses.

$\therefore \frac{1}{12}(972) = 81$ students in the school are boys who wear glasses.

(vii) This could be considered as a trick question.

From **(i)** $\frac{7}{12}$ of the class are boys.

$\therefore \frac{7}{12}$ of the school are boys, since the class exactly represents the school.

Exercise 5.4

1. A box contains 36 coloured balls. Twelve are red, fifteen are blue, three are yellow and the rest are white. One ball is selected at random from the box. Calculate the probability of selecting a:

    (i) Red ball **(ii)** Blue ball **(iii)** Yellow ball **(iv)** White ball

2. **(i)** What is the probability of getting a 3 on each of these spinners?

    (a) 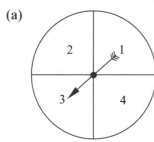 **(b)** 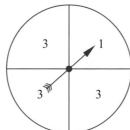 **(c)**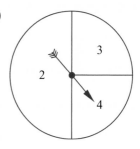

    (ii) What is the probability of getting a 2 or a 3 on spinner **(c)**?

    Exercise: Make a spinner yourself with five equal sections. Construct a question similar to parts **(i)** and **(ii)**.

3. From a class of 40 students with 25 boys, one student is chosen at random to read a poem. What is the probability that a girl is chosen?

4. In a raffle, a total of 500 tickets are sold. A girl bought 25 tickets. What is the chance of her winning the only prize?

5. The pie chart shows the sports played by people in a club. One person is selected at random from the club. Find the probability that the person selected plays:

   (i) Soccer (ii) Hurling (iii) Golf

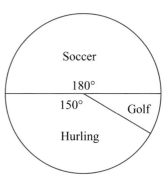

6. (i) Two hundred eggs were classified according to size (large or medium) and colour (brown or white). The results are given in the following table.

	Brown	White
Large	40	80
Medium	32	48

   An egg is chosen at random. What is the probability that it is:

   (a) A white egg (b) A brown egg (c) A large brown egg (d) A medium white egg

   (ii) Label the probability of each event with the letters A, B, C and D, respectively. Indicate the position of A, B, C and D on the probability scale.

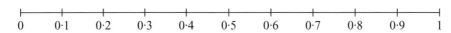

7. (i) One hundred and fifty students sitting an examination were grouped according to age (16, 17 or 18) and gender (female or male). The results are given in the following table.

	Age 16	Age 17	Age 18
Female	30	18	12
Male	60	27	3

   One student is chosen at random. What is the probability that the student is:

   (a) Male (b) A 16-year-old female (c) Younger than 18 (d) Older than 19

   (ii) Label the probability of each event with the letters P, Q, R and S, respectively. Indicate the position of P, Q, R and S on the probability scale.

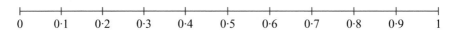

8. (i) A fair spinner has eight sides, as shown. The sides are labelled A, B, B, C, C, C, C and F. The spinner is spun once. What is the probability that the spinner lands on:

   (a) A   (b) B   (c) C

   (ii) By replacing the letters A and F on the spinner, describe how to make the fair spinner behave like a fair coin.

9. A card is drawn at random from a normal pack of 52 playing cards. What is the probability that the card will be:

   (i) The nine of spades   (ii) A red card   (iii) A club
   (iv) A king   (v) A picture card   (vi) A black picture card
   (vii) An even number   (viii) Not a queen   (ix) A joker

10. Two complete suits, one of spades and one of clubs, are added to a normal pack of 52 playing cards. What is the probability that a card drawn at random will be:

   (i) The nine of spades   (ii) A red card   (iii) A club
   (iv) A king   (v) A picture card   (vi) A black picture card
   (vii) An even number   (viii) Not a queen   (ix) A joker

11. A fair six-sided die is thrown 120 times. How many times would you expect the die to land on six?

12. One thousand tickets are sold in a raffle. There is only one prize. How many tickets does a person need to buy to have exactly one chance in five (i.e. $\frac{1}{5}$) of winning?

13. (i) A bag contains three red, three green and four blue discs. A disc is selected at random from the bag. What is the probability of selecting a blue disc?

   (ii) The selected disc is to be put back into the bag, plus a certain number of red discs. This causes the probability of selecting a red disc to equal $\frac{1}{2}$. Find the number of extra red discs that were placed in the bag.

14. A game consists of spinning an arrow on a square board.

   The board contains the letters A, B, C and D. The board is designed so that when the arrow stops spinning, it can only point at one letter.

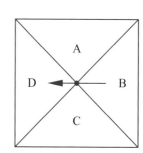

   The arrow is biased in favour of D so that the letter D is twice as likely as the letter A. The letters A, B and C are equally likely. Find the probability of:

   (i) The arrowing pointing to letter A   (ii) The arrowing pointing to letter D

15. **(i)** Frank has accidently put two old batteries back into his bag that also contains eight new batteries. He randomly picks out one battery from the bag. What is the probability that the battery selected is:

(a) A new battery **(b)** An old battery?

Represent each answer on the probability scale.

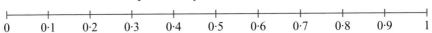

(ii) How many batteries should he take out to be certain that at least one is new?

16. To play a game, you spin the pointer. You win the prize on which the pointer lands. Martin has one spin.

(i) Which prize is Martin most likely to win?

(ii) Explain your answer to part **(i)**.

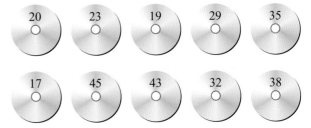

Copy the scale below.

Sheila has one spin. On the scale, mark the following.

(iii) *P*, the probability that Sheila will win €10.

(iv) *H*, the probability that Sheila will win €20.

17. There are 10 numbered discs in a bag. Claire selects one disc from the bag. What is the probability that Claire selects a disc that has:

(i) 2 on it **(ii)** No 2 on it

(iii) A 2 and a 3 on it

(iv) A 2 or a 3 on it

20 23 19 29 35

17 45 43 32 38

18.

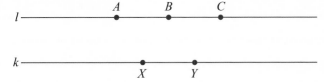

k and l are distinct parallel lines. A, B, C are points on l and X, Y are points on k.

(i) How many different triangles can be constructed using three of the named points as vertices?

(ii) Find the probability that the point B is used when constructing a triangle.

19. On a TV game show, a player spins a wheel that is fixed to a wall.

It spins freely around its centre point. Its rim is divided equally into 12 regions.

Three of the regions are coloured blue, each representing a prize of €3,000 for the player.

Two of the regions are coloured green, each representing a prize of €10,000 for the player.

Seven are coloured grey, each representing a prize of €1,000 for the player.

When the wheel stops, an arrow fixed to the wall points to one of the regions. All the regions are equally likely to stop at the arrow. The colour of the region decides the amount the player wins.

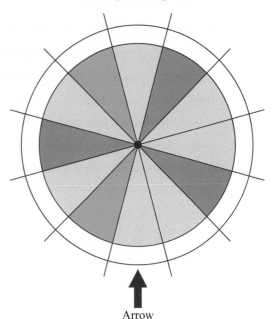

Arrow

(i) Find the probability that the player wins:
   (a) €1,000   (b) €10,000

(ii) The TV station accountant calculates that the average payout for one spin per show is €3,000. Describe how the accountant arrived at this amount.

(iii) Hence or otherwise, how much prize money should the TV station expect to pay out if the show runs once a week for 15 weeks and the wheel is spun once per show? Comment on your answer.

20. The points P, Q, R and S lie on a circle.

   (i) If these points are used as vertices, how many different triangles can be formed?

   (ii) If one such triangle is constructed at random, what is the probability that it contains the side $[PQ]$?

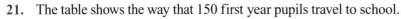

21. The table shows the way that 150 first year pupils travel to school.

   (i) A first year pupil is chosen at random. What is the probability that the pupil:

   (a) Is a boy   (b) Walks to school

   (c) Does not use the train

   (d) Is a girl who travels by bus

   (e) Is a boy who travels by train

	Walk	Bus	Car	Train	Bike
Boy	15	10	7	30	8
Girl	20	24	8	12	16

   (ii) A first year student who travels by bike is chosen at random. What is the probability that the pupil is a boy?

   (iii) A girl from first year is chosen at random. What is the probability that she:

   (a) Walks to school   (b) Does not travel by car

   (iv) If the number of girls in each category is doubled, find the total number of pupils now in first year. Hence, find the new probability that the pupil:

   (a) Is a boy   (b) Walks to school   (c) Does not use the train

22. A box contains 20 blue counters and 30 green counters. Each counter is numbered with an even or odd number. Five of the blue and 20 of the green counters are odd.

	Even	Odd	Total
Blue			20
Green			
Total			50

   (i) Complete the table opposite.

   (ii) One of the counters is chosen at random. What is the probability that the counter is:

   (a) Blue   (b) Green   (c) Blue and even   (d) Green and odd

   (iii) A green counter is chosen at random. What is the probability that it is odd?

   (iv) An odd-numbered counter is chosen at random. What is the probability that it is blue?

23. There are 80 members in a club, 32 male and 48 female. Four of the males and eight of the females wear glasses. A club member is selected at random.

   (i) What is the probability that the club member is a:

   (a) Male   (b) Female   (c) Person wearing glasses

   (d) Female not wearing glasses   (e) Male wearing glasses

   (ii) A male from the club is selected at random. What is the probability that he wears glasses?

   (iii) A member who wears glasses is selected at random.

   (a) What is the probability that it is a female?

   (b) All members who wear glasses resign from the club. What is the probability that a club member now selected at random is male?

Combining two events – Bernoulli trials

There are many situations where we have to consider two outcomes. In these situations, all the possible outcomes, called the **sample space**, can be listed in a sample space diagram (often called a **two-way table**).

EXAMPLE 1

A fair coin is tossed and an unbiased six-sided die is thrown. Calculate the probability of obtaining a tail and the number 3.

Solution:

Represent the situation with a sample space diagram and indicate a successful outcome with a dot.

Sample space diagram

		1	2	3	4	5	6
	T			•			
Coin	H						

Die

$P(\text{tail and the number 3}) = \frac{1}{12}$

Note: The word '**and**' indicates that we only count the outcomes where both a tail and the number 3 occur together.

We can consider this example as an experiment of tossing a coin and throwing a die.

If getting a tail and a 3 is regarded as a success, then any other result is a failure.

If a toss and throw are together regarded as a trial, then:
- For each trial there are two possible outcomes: success or failure.
- The probability of success (T, 3) is the same for each trial.
- Each trial is independent of the outcomes of other trials (one has no effect on the other).

Such experiments with repeated trials are known as **Bernoulli trials**, after James Bernoulli (1654–1705). He was the most outstanding member of a family of mathematicians from Switzerland.

In the experiment above, if we get (T, 3) for the first time on the third trial, we say that 'the first success occurs on the third trial'.

In our course, we shall only deal with problems that involve a maximum of three Bernoulli trials.

EXAMPLE 2

In a game, two fair six-sided dice are thrown, one red and the other black.

 (i) How many outcomes are possible?

 (ii) If the scores are added together, calculate the probability that the sum of the scores is:

    (a) Less than 6   (b) 7   (c) Greater than 10

 (iii) Using a sample space diagram or otherwise, find the average score expected for an outcome of this game.

Solution: Represent the situation with a sample space diagram.

Sample space diagram

6	7	8	9	10	11	12
5	6	7	8	9	10	11
4	5	6	7	8	9	10
3	4	5	6	7	8	9
2	3	4	5	6	7	8
1	2	3	4	5	6	7
	1	2	3	4	5	6

Black die (vertical label), Red die (horizontal label)

 (i) There are $6 \times 6 = 36$ possible outcomes.

 (ii) (a) $P(\text{sum less than 6}) = \frac{10}{36} = \frac{5}{18}$

    (b) $P(\text{sum is 7}) = \frac{6}{36} = \frac{1}{6}$

    (c) $P(\text{greater than 10}) = \frac{3}{36} = \frac{1}{12}$

 (iii) To find the average expected score (or mean expected score), we could add up all 36 outcomes in the sample space diagram and divide the total by 36.

Refer to the sample space diagram and add the six rows.

$$7 + 8 + 9 + 10 + 11 + 12 = 57$$
$$6 + 7 + 8 + 9 + 10 + 11 = 51$$
$$5 + 6 + 7 + 8 + 9 + 10 = 45$$
$$4 + 5 + 6 + 7 + 8 + 9 = 39$$
$$3 + 4 + 5 + 6 + 7 + 8 = 33$$
$$2 + 3 + 4 + 5 + 6 + 7 = 27$$

Then add the six results above.

$$57 + 51 + 45 + 39 + 33 + 27 = 252$$

Finally, the (average) expected score $= \frac{252}{36} = 7$.

Note 1: The expected score is not always a whole number.

Note 2: The expected score is not always one of the original outcomes.

EXAMPLE 3

A bag contains three red and two yellow discs only. When a disc is drawn from the bag, it is returned before the next draw. What is the probability that two draws will yield both discs the same colour?

Solution:
Make a sample space diagram. Let R stand for a red disc and Y stand for a yellow disc.

Sample space diagram

Second selection					
Y				●	●
Y				●	●
R	●	●	●		
R	●	●	●		
R	●	●	●		
	R	R	R	Y	Y

First selection

There are 25 possible outcomes (five for the first draw and five for the second draw).
The dots indicate where the colours are the same, successful outcome, either two reds or two yellows.
There are 13 dots. P(both discs the same colour) $= \frac{13}{25}$.

Exercise 5.5

1. Two fair six-sided dice are thrown, one red and the other black. Calculate the probability that:

    (i) The outcomes are the same on each die

    (ii) The sum of the outcomes is 9

    (iii) The sum of the outcomes is greater than or equal to 5

    (iv) The sum of the outcomes is divisible by 3

    (v) The sum of the outcomes is 6 or 10

    (vi) The product of the outcomes is 12

    (vii) The outcome on the red die is exactly three more than the outcome on the black die

2. Two unbiased five-sided spinners are labelled with the numbers 1, 2, 3, 4, 5. An experiment consists of spinning them together and the score is calculated by subtracting the smaller number from the larger number. When the numbers are equal, the score is 0.

    (i) Copy and complete the following sample space diagram to show all the possible scores.

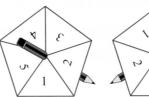
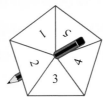

		Number on second spinner				
		1	2	3	4	5
Number on first spinner	1	0				
	2					3
	3					
	4		2			
	5					

(ii) Calculate the probability of a score of:

    (a) 0   **(b)** 5   **(c)** 3 or more

(iii) Consider the case where both spinners are relabelled with the numbers 5, 6, 7, 8, 9. As before, the score is calculated by subtracting the smaller number from the larger number.

    Construct a sample space diagram (two-way table) to show all the possible scores.

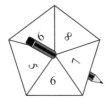 

    Calculate the probability of a score of:

    (a) 0   **(b)** 5   **(c)** 3 or more

(iv) By comparing the results in the two-way tables for both experiments or otherwise, what conclusion can be drawn?

3. **(i)** A game is played with two fair spinners, as shown. Both are spun at the same time and the outcomes are added to get a score. How many different scores are possible?

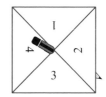 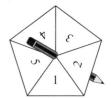

    (ii) Calculate the probability of a score:

        (a) Of 4   **(b)** Of 6

        (c) Greater than 6   **(d)** Less than or equal to 5

    (iii) Using a sample space diagram or otherwise, find the average score expected for an outcome of this game. Comment on your answer.

4. These number cards are shuffled and put into a row.

Lily picks one card at random and does not replace it. She then picks a second card.

If the first card drawn was a 2, find the probability that Lily selects an even number with her second selection.

5. **(i)** A game consists of spinning an unbiased five-sided spinner that can land on *A, B, C, D* or *E* and throwing an unbiased six-sided die. List all possible outcomes of the game, that is, of spinning the spinner and throwing the die.

(ii) Find the probability that in any one game the outcome will be:

(a) An *A* and a 6

(b) A *C* and an odd number

(c) A *B* and an even number or a *D* and an odd number

(d) An *E* and a number greater than 4 or an *A* and a number less than or equal to 2

(iii) A director of a TV game show decides to use this game as part of a weekly show.
If the contestant spins the spinner with outcome A, they are guaranteed to win €4,000.
The other letters win nothing.

If the contestant throws the die with outcome 6, they are guaranteed to win €5,000. The
other numbers win nothing.

However, an outcome of A **and** 6 wins a total of €18,000. Find the probability that a
contestant wins:

(a) €18,000

(b) €5,000

(c) €4,000

(d) Nothing

6. A bag contains five discs numbered 1, 2, 3, 4 and 5. A disc is drawn from the bag and not
replaced. Then a second disc is drawn from the bag.

(i) How many outcomes are possible?

(ii) Calculate the probability that:

(a) The sum of the outcomes is less than 5

(b) One outcome is exactly 3 greater than the other

(c) The difference between the outcomes is 2

(iii) Find the expected score for the sum of the two numbers drawn. Comment on your answer.

Estimating probabilities from experiments

Elaina suspects that a six-sided die is biased. In an experiment, she throws the die 300 times. She
records the results after 60, 120, 180, 240 and 300 throws. Her results are shown in the following table.

Number of throws	Score					
	1	2	3	4	5	6
60	8	11	13	11	7	10
120	19	23	25	19	15	19
180	31	32	35	27	25	30
240	40	44	44	36	36	40
300	50	53	52	45	51	49

Elaina **expects** each number to have an equal probability if the die is fair, i.e. $P(3) = \frac{1}{6} = 0{\cdot}1667$ correct to four decimal places.

As the number of throws increases, the number of threes divided by the number of throws is $\frac{13}{60}$, $\frac{25}{120}$, $\frac{35}{180}$, $\frac{44}{240}$, $\frac{52}{300}$ = 0·2167, 0·2083, 0·1944, 0.1833, 0.1733.

When Elaina compares her expected probability of $\frac{1}{6} = 0.1667$, she could reasonably conclude the die is fair.

As the number of throws increases, the number of threes divided by the number of throws gets closer to $\frac{1}{6} = 0{\cdot}1667$.

The values $\frac{13}{60}$, $\frac{25}{120}$, $\frac{35}{180}$, $\frac{44}{240}$, $\frac{52}{300}$ are called the relative frequencies. The more throws (trials) made, the more accurate the **relative frequency**.

The relative frequency gives an estimate that an event will happen.

Hence, to estimate the probability that an event will occur by carrying out an experiment or survey is given by the following formula:

$$\text{Relative frequency} = \frac{\text{Number of successful trials}}{\text{Total number of trials}}$$

Expected frequency

EXAMPLE 1

Elaina throws her fair six-sided die a total of 1,200 times. Find the expected number of times the number 3 would appear.

Solution:

If the die is fair, then the probability of a score of 3 would be $\frac{1}{6}$.

Then multiply 1,200 throws by $\frac{1}{6}$.

Thus, the expected number of threes would be $1{,}200 \times \frac{1}{6} = 200$.

Expected frequency = (probability)(number of trials)

EXAMPLE 2

This spinner is biased.

The probability that the spinner will land on each of the numbers 1 to 5 is given in the table below.

Number	1	2	3	4	5
Probability	0.25	0.2	0.25	0.15	B

(i) Write down the value of B.

(ii) If the spinner is spun 200 times, how many fives would you expect?

Solution:

(i) Since one of the numbers from 1 to 5 must appear, the sum of all the probabilities is 1.

$\therefore\ 0\cdot25 + 0\cdot2 + 0\cdot25 + 0\cdot15 + B = 1$

$0\cdot85 + B = 1$

$B = 0\cdot15$

(ii) Expected number of fives

= expected frequency × number of trials

$= 0\cdot15 \times 200 = 30$

Exercise 5.6

1. If a fair coin is tossed 250 times, how many tails would you expect to get?

2. Teddy thinks his coin is biased. He tosses it 100 times and gets 63 heads.

   (i) What is the experimental probability of getting a head with this coin?

   (ii) In 100 tosses, what is the expected value if the coin was fair?

   (iii) Is Teddy's coin biased? Justify your answer

3. One ball is selected at random from the bag shown and then replaced. This procedure is repeated 300 times. How many times would you expect to select:

   (i) A blue ball

   (ii) A white ball

4. A spinner with 10 equal sectors is spun 150 times.

   How often would you expect to spin:

   (i) An E

   (ii) A W

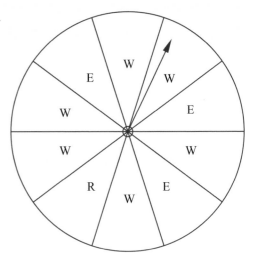

5. Joan wants to find out if a six-sided die is biased. She throws the die 600 times.

   The results are as follows.

Number on die	1	2	3	4	5	6
Frequency	56	84	110	130	105	115

   (i) For this die, calculate the experimental probability of obtaining a 4.

   (ii) For a fair die, calculate the probability of scoring a 4.

   (iii) Do your answers suggest that Joan's die is fair? Justify your answer.

6. Hugh and Brendan play 35 games of chess. Hugh wins 20 of these games.

   (i) Find the probability that Hugh wins the next game.

   (ii) They play another series of 14 games. How many of these games would you expect Hugh to win?

7. The probability that a biased spinner will land on each of the numbers 1 to 5 is given in the following table.

Number	1	2	3	4	5
Probability	W	0.2	0.1	0.3	0.1

   (i) Calculate the value of W.

   (ii) Hence, find the probability that on one spin the result will be a number less than 3.

   (iii) If the spinner is spun 800 times, estimate the number of times it will show:

   (a) A 2   (b) An odd number

8. **(i)** Nia, Nell and Tara each rolled a different die 180 times.
   Only one of the dice was fair. Whose was it? Explain your answer.

   (ii) Whose die is the most biased? Explain your answer.

Number	Nia	Nell	Tara
1	14	29	60
2	35	31	26
3	39	32	28
4	22	28	27
5	38	27	26
6	32	33	13

9. Red and green spinners were each spun 48 times.
   Each spinner has three sides indicating scores of 1, 2 and 3.

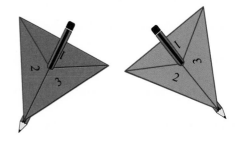

The bar chart shows the results.

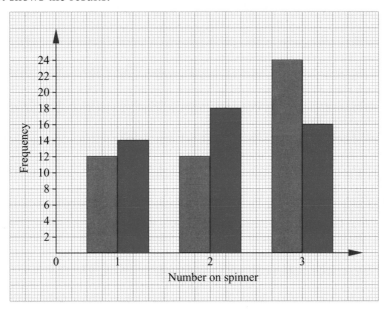

One spinner is fair and the other is unfair. Which spinner do you think is fair? Justify your answer.

10. Four Las Vegas casino managers have an initial meeting to consider a new type of six-sided die. To use it at their casinos, it must be perfectly fair. At the meeting they each throw the die a number of times and record the results.

Casino name	Number of throws	Results					
		1	2	3	4	5	6
Bellagio	60	12	8	11	9	7	13
Mirage	90	12	19	14	15	19	11
Luxor	30	4	6	5	5	7	3
Hard Rock	180	22	40	31	27	35	25

   (i) Which casino's results are most likely to give the best estimate of the probability of getting each number? Justify your answer.

  (ii) Make a table by adding together all four results. Use your table to decide whether you think the die is biased or fair. Explain your answer.

 (iii) Use your results to work out the probability of a score of 6. Comment on your answer.

 (iv) In your view, how should the casino managers proceed?

11. (i) Bill has a six-sided die with sides numbered 1, 1, 1, 1, 2, 2. He throws the die eight times and gets a score of 1 twice. Bill thinks the die is not fair. Do you agree with Bill? Explain your answer

   (ii) Bill has another six-sided die with sides numbered 4, 5, 5, 6, 6, 6. He throws the die 450 times. The results are as follows.

Score	4	5	6
Frequency	69	147	234

      (a) What do you think is the experimental (relative) frequency of throwing a 6?

      (b) Do you think the die is fair? Justify your answer.

12. A biased five-sided spinner has sides labelled 1, 2, 3, 4 and 5. The probability that the spinner will land on each of the numbers 1, 3 and 5 are given in the table.

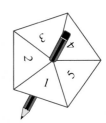

Number	1	2	3	4	5
Probability	0·3	X	0·15	X	0·35

(i) The probability that the spinner will land on 2 is equal to the probability that it will land on 4. Calculate the value of X.

(ii) Ronan spins the spinner 120 times. Estimate the number of times:

(a) It will land on 5

(b) It will land on 2

Show your work.

13. A TV game show plans to finish with the winner spinning a wheel. The wheel is fixed to a wall. It's divided equally into seven regions and the winning amounts are shown on the wheel in euro. The winner will receive the amount the arrow points to when the wheel stops.

The game show director suspects the wheel is not very fair, as some amounts seem to come more often than others.

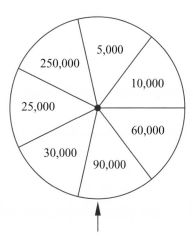

She spun the wheel 140 times and recorded the results. The results are shown in the table.

Amount won, in €1,000s	5	10	25	30	60	90	250
Number of times	7	19	17	8	29	42	18

(i) How many times would the director expect each number to occur if the wheel was fair?

(ii) Work out the experimental probability of spinning:

(a) €5,000

(b) €90,000

(iii) Do you think the director would conclude the wheel was fair? Justify your answer

Addition rule (OR)

The probability that two events, A or B, can happen is given by:

$$P(A \text{ or } B) = P(A) + P(B) - P(A \text{ and } B)$$

(removes double counting)

It is often called the **or rule**. It is important to remember that $P(A$ or $B)$ means A occurs or B occurs or both occur. By subtracting $P(A$ and $B)$, the possibility of double counting is removed.

Mutually exclusive events

Outcomes are **mutually exclusive** if they cannot happen at the same time.

If A and B are two events that cannot happen at the same time, then $A \cap B = \{\ \}$.

This removes the possibility of double counting.

Thus, if A and B are mutually exclusive events, we have:

$P(A \text{ or } B) = P(A) + P(B)$.

Probability of an event not happening

If E is any event, then 'not E' is the event that E does not occur. Clearly, E and not E cannot occur at the same time. Either E or not E must occur. Thus, we have the following relationship between the probabilities of E and not E:

$$P(E) + P(\text{not } E) = 1$$
$$\text{or}$$
$$P(\text{not } E) = 1 - P(E)$$

EXAMPLE 1

A fair spinner with 10 sides, numbered 1 to 10, is spun.
What is the probability of it landing on a number divisible by 2 or 3?

Solution:

The possible outcomes are 1, 2, 3, 4, 5, 6, 7, 8, 9 or 10.

Numbers divisible by 2 are 2, 4, 6, 8 or 10. $\therefore P(\text{number divisible by 2}) = \frac{5}{10}$

Numbers divisible by 3 are 3, 6 or 9. $\therefore P(\text{number divisible by 3}) = \frac{3}{10}$

Number divisible by 2 and 3 is 6. $\therefore P(\text{number divisible by 2 and 3}) = \frac{1}{10}$

$\quad P(\text{number divisible by 2 or 3})$

$= P(\text{number divisible by 2}) + P(\text{number divisible by 3}) - P(\text{number divisible by 2 and 3})$

$= \frac{5}{10} + \frac{3}{10} - \frac{1}{10}$ (removes the double counting of the number 6)

$= \frac{7}{10}$

The number 6 is common to both events. If the probabilities are added, then the number 6 would have been counted twice.

An alternative to using the rule is to write down all the successful outcomes and not include any twice.

$$P(\text{number divisible by 2 or 3}) = P(2 \text{ or } 3 \text{ or } 4 \text{ or } 6 \text{ or } 8 \text{ or } 9 \text{ or } 10) = \frac{7}{10}$$

(6 included only once)

EXAMPLE 2

A single card is drawn at random from a pack of 52. What is the probability that it is a king or a spade? What is the probability that it is not a king or spade?

Solution:

The pack contains 52 cards.

There are four kings in the pack. $\qquad \therefore P(\text{king}) = \frac{4}{52}$

There are 13 spades in the pack. $\qquad \therefore P(\text{spade}) = \frac{13}{52}$

One card is both a king and a spade. $\qquad \therefore P(\text{king and a spade}) = \frac{1}{52}$

$$P(\text{king or a spade}) = P(\text{king}) + P(\text{spade}) - P(\text{king and a spade})$$
$$= \frac{4}{42} + \frac{13}{52} - \frac{1}{52}$$
$$= \frac{16}{52}$$
$$= \frac{4}{13}$$

$$P(\text{not a king or a spade}) = 1 - P(\text{a king or a spade})$$
$$= 1 - \frac{4}{13} = \frac{9}{13}$$

Exercise 5.7

1. An unbiased six-sided die is thrown. Find the probability that the number obtained is:

    (i) Even $\qquad$ (ii) Prime $\qquad$ (iii) Even or prime

2. The probability that a woman will hit the target with a single shot at a rifle range is $\frac{3}{5}$. If she fires one shot, find the probability that she will miss the target.

3. A bag contains three blue discs, five white discs and four red discs. A disc is chosen at random. Find the probability that the disc chosen is:

    (i) Red $\qquad$ (ii) Blue or white $\qquad$ (iii) Red or white $\qquad$ (iv) Not red or white

4. A number is chosen at random from the whole numbers 1 to 12 inclusive. What is the probability that it is:

    (i) Even $\quad$ (ii) Divisible by 3 $\quad$ (iii) Even or divisible by 3 $\quad$ (iv) Not even or divisible by 3

5. A number is chosen at random from the whole numbers 1–30 inclusive. What is the probability that it is divisible by:

    (i) 3 $\qquad$ (ii) 5 $\qquad$ (iii) 3 or 5 $\qquad$ (iv) Not 3 or 5

6. A letter is selected at random from the word EXERCISES. Find the probability that the letter is:

    (i) I $\quad$ (ii) S $\quad$ (iii) A vowel $\quad$ (iv) A vowel or an S $\quad$ (v) Not a vowel or an S

7. In a class of 20 students, four of the nine girls and three of the 11 boys play on the school hockey team. A student from the class is chosen at random. What is the probability that the student chosen is:

   (i) On the hockey team   (ii) A boy

   (iii) A boy or on the hockey team   (iv) A girl or not on the hockey team

8. In the lotto, there are 45 numbers, numbered from 1 to 45. Find the probability that the first number drawn is:

   (i) An even number   (ii) A number greater than 24

   (iii) An odd number or a number greater than 24   (iv) A number divisible by 6

   (v) A number divisible by 4   (vi) A number divisible by 6 or 4

   (vii) Not a number divisible by 6 or 4

9. A card is selected at random from a pack of 52. Find the probability that the card is:

   (i) A spade or a club   (ii) A queen or a red card

   (iii) A heart or a red 10   (iv) Not a heart or a red 10

10. Two unbiased six-sided dice, one red and the other blue, are thrown together. Calculate the probability that:

    (i) The numbers are the same or the sum of the numbers is 10

    (ii) The sum of the numbers is 8 or the difference between the two numbers is 2

Using Venn diagrams

The Venn diagram shows two sets, B and Q, in the universal set U.

The number of elements in each region is also shown.

- 7 is the number of elements in B but not Q.
- 16 is the number of elements in Q but not B.
- 3 is the number of elements in both P and Q.
- 4 is the number of elements in neither B nor Q.

Notice the total number of elements is given by

$7 + 3 + 16 + 4 = 30$.

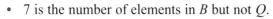

From the Venn diagram, the probability of B, written as $P(B)$, is equal to $\frac{7+3}{30} = \frac{10}{30} = \frac{1}{3}$.

Also, the probability of B and Q is written as $P(B \text{ and } Q) = P(B \cap Q) = \frac{3}{30} = \frac{1}{10}$.

Hence:

$$P(B \text{ only}) = \frac{7}{30}$$

$$P(Q \text{ only}) = \frac{16}{30} = \frac{8}{15}$$

$$P(B \text{ or } Q) = P(B \cup Q) = \frac{7 + 3 + 16}{30} = \frac{26}{30} = \frac{13}{15}$$

$$P(\text{neither } B \text{ nor } Q) = P(B \cup Q)' = \frac{4}{30} = \frac{2}{15}$$

Remember: $A' =$ 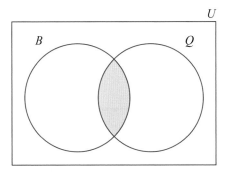 = everything outside A

Notice:

$$P(B \cup Q)' = 1 - P(B \cup Q)$$

$$= 1 - \frac{13}{15}$$

$$= \frac{2}{15}$$

Note: When two sets have no elements in common, then:

We say B and Q are **mutually exclusive** events. This means they cannot happen at the same time. In probability, this means that $P(B \text{ or } Q) = P(B) + P(Q)$.

EXAMPLE

A survey was carried out in a class with 30 Leaving Certificate students. The survey asked if they would:

   (i) Attend the school concert on Friday night (C)

  (ii) Support the school hockey team at the match on Saturday afternoon (H)

The Venn diagram shows the results.

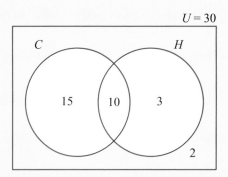

Find the probability a student selected at random from the class attends:

    (i) The concert only

   (ii) The hockey match only

  (iii) Neither of these two events

  (iv) Both of these events

Solution:

    (i) P(attends concert only) $= P(C$ only$) = \frac{15}{30} = \frac{1}{2}$

   (ii) P(attends hockey only) $= P(H$ only$) = \frac{3}{30} = \frac{1}{10}$

  (iii) P(attends neither event) $= P(C \cup H)' = \frac{2}{30} = \frac{1}{15}$

  (iv) P(attends both events) $= P(C \cap H) = \frac{10}{30} = \frac{1}{3}$

Exercise 5.8

1. There are 240 students in a primary school. The Venn diagram shows the numbers of students who own a mobile phone (M) and who own a computer (C).

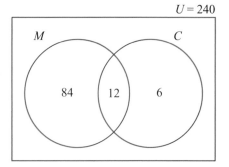

If a student is selected at random, find the probability that the student owned:

  (i) A mobile phone

  (ii) A computer

 (iii) Neither a mobile phone nor a computer

 (iv) A mobile phone but not a computer

  (v) Both a mobile phone and a computer

 (vi) We are told these 240 primary school students are a representative sample of their country. The country has a total of 900,000 primary school students. Find the expected number of primary school students with a mobile phone in the country.

2. In the given Venn diagram:

U = The teachers in a school

S = The teachers teaching Leaving Certificate classes

J = The teachers teaching Junior Certificate classes

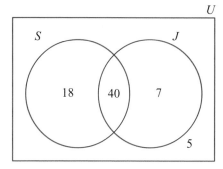

  (i) How many teachers are in the school?

If a teacher is selected at random, find the probability that the teacher:

  (ii) Teaches Leaving Certificate classes

 (iii) Teaches neither Leaving nor Junior Certificate classes

 (iv) Teaches Junior Certificate classes only

  (v) Teaches both Junior and Leaving Certificate classes

3. The Venn diagram shows the numbers of pensioners who as a daily pastime read (R), watch TV (T) and go for a walk (W).

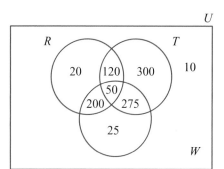

If a pensioner is selected at random, find the probability that the pensioner:

  (i) Goes for a walk

  (ii) Goes for a walk and watches TV

 (iii) Does none of these activities

 (iv) Reads only

  (v) Reads or watches TV

 (vi) Does at least two of the pastimes

4. Carry out your own class survey and show your results on a Venn diagram for:

   (i) Two events

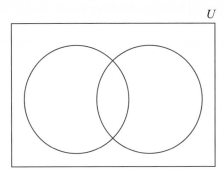

   (ii) Three events

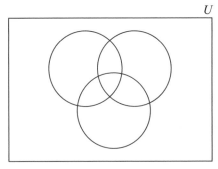

5. A restaurant owner carried out a survey to see if his customers liked wine or beer. He surveyed 135 customers. The Venn diagram shows his results.

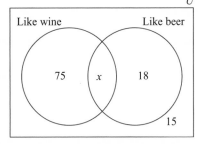

   (i) Find the value for x.

   (ii) What can you say about the customers in the region marked x?

   (iii) If one customer is chosen at random, what is the probability they like neither wine nor beer?

   (iv) One of the customers chosen at random liked wine. What is the probability that the customer also liked beer?

   (v) The next month, the owner expects to serve 570 customers. Estimate how many of those customers he will expect to like beer. Explain your answer.

   (vi) The waitress notices that customers who like wine only give much bigger tips than other customers. From the expected 570 customers, how many of them can the waitress expect a big tip from? Justify your answer.

6. Eighty passengers on a plane were surveyed as to how they spent their time on the flight. The activities were reading (R), listening to music (M) and watching the in-flight movie (I). The results are shown in the Venn diagram.

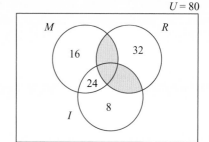

(i) What is the probability of selecting a passenger at random who enjoyed either music or reading?

(ii) Which of the following pairs of sets are mutually exclusive?

    (a) Selecting a passenger from M
        Selecting a passenger from R

    (b) Selecting a passenger from M
        Selecting a passenger from I

(iii) Justify each of your answers to **(ii)**.

Multiplication rule (AND)–Bernoulli trials

Successive events

> The probability that two events, A and then B, both happen and in that order is given by:
> $$P(A \text{ and } B) = P(A) \times P(B)$$
> where $P(B)$ has been worked out assuming that A has already occurred.

Order must be taken into account. Also, be very careful where the outcome at one stage affects the outcome at the next stage.

> When the question says **and**, then multiply.

The multiplication rule helps reduce the need to make out a sample space diagram.

EXAMPLE 1

An unbiased six-sided die is thrown and a fair coin is tossed. Find the probability of getting a 5 and a head.

Solution:

$$P(5) = \tfrac{1}{6}, \quad P(H) = \tfrac{1}{2}$$

$$P(5 \text{ and an } H) = P(5) \times P(H) \quad \text{('and' means multiply)}$$

$$= \tfrac{1}{6} \times \tfrac{1}{2}$$

$$= \tfrac{1}{12}$$

> ### EXAMPLE 2
>
> Two unbiased six-sided dice are thrown. What is the probability of getting two 4s?
>
> **Solution:**
>
> $$P(\text{4 on the first die}) = \tfrac{1}{6} \qquad P(\text{4 on the second die}) = \tfrac{1}{6}$$
>
> $$P(\text{two 4s}) = P(\text{4 on the first die}) \times P(\text{4 on the second die})$$
> $$= \tfrac{1}{6} \times \tfrac{1}{6} \quad \text{('and' means multiply)}$$
> $$= \tfrac{1}{36}$$

Note: A sample space diagram could have been used instead in Examples 1 and 2.

> ### EXAMPLE 3
>
> Aideen and Bernadette celebrate their birthdays in a particular week (Monday to Sunday inclusive). Assuming that the birthdays are equally likely to fall on any day of the week, what is the probability that:
> - **(i)** Both people were born on a Wednesday
> - **(ii)** One was born on a Monday and the other was born on a Friday
>
> **Solution:**
> **Method 1:** Represent the situation with a sample space diagram.
>
> There are $7 \times 7 = 49$ possible outcomes.
> - • represents both people born on Wednesday.
> - × represents one person born on Monday and the other person born on Friday.
>
> **(i)** $P(\text{both people born on Wednesday}) = \tfrac{1}{49}$
>
> **(ii)** $P(\text{one person born on Monday and the other born on Friday}) = \tfrac{2}{49}$

Method 2: Using the rules of probability.

P(any person was born on a particular day of the week) $= \frac{1}{7}$.

Let A_M stand for Aideen was born on Monday, B_F stand for Bernadette was born on Friday, etc.

(i) P(both people were born on a Wednesday)

$= P(A_W \text{ and } B_W)$

$= P(A_W) \times P(B_W)$ ('and' means multiply)

$= \frac{1}{7} \times \frac{1}{7}$

$= \frac{1}{49}$

(ii) P(one was born on Monday and the other was born on Friday)

$= P(A_M \text{ and } B_F \qquad \text{or} \qquad A_F \text{ and } B_M)$

$= P(A_M \text{ and } B_F) \qquad \text{or} \qquad P(A_F \text{ and } B_M)$

$= P(A_M) \times P(B_F) \quad + \qquad P(A_F) \times P(B_M)$ ('and' means multiply, 'or' means add)

$= \frac{1}{7} \times \frac{1}{7} \qquad\qquad + \qquad\qquad \frac{1}{7} \times \frac{1}{7}$

$= \frac{1}{49} + \frac{1}{49}$

$= \frac{2}{49}$

EXAMPLE 4

A bag contains four blue discs and two red discs. A disc is chosen at random from the bag, the colour noted then replaced in the bag. Another disc is then chosen from the bag. Find the probability that:

(i) Both discs are blue

(ii) The first disc is red and the second disc is blue

(iii) One disc is blue and the other red (in any order)

Solution:

A useful (and powerful) way to tackle this type of question is to use a tree diagram. This is sometimes referred to as a probability tree.

Let B represent that a blue disc is drawn and let R represent that a red disc is drawn.

In the diagram, we work from left to right.

On the first selection:

Probability a blue disc is drawn $= P(B) = \frac{4}{6} = \frac{2}{3}$

Probability a red disc is drawn $= P(R) = \frac{2}{6} = \frac{1}{3}$

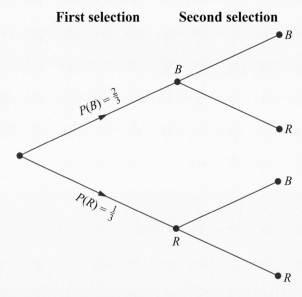

On the second selection, since the disc is replaced

$P(B) = \frac{4}{6} = \frac{2}{3}$ and $P(R) = \frac{2}{6} = \frac{1}{3}$ (i.e. unchanged).

Now we can complete our tree diagram.

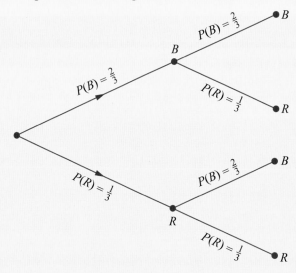

(i) Both discs are blue = $P(B)$ and $P(B)$

$$= \frac{2}{3} \quad \times \quad \frac{2}{3}$$

$$= \frac{4}{9}$$

Note: We multiply the probabilities along the branches to get the end result.

(ii) First disc red and second disc blue = $P(R)$ and $P(B)$

$$= \frac{1}{3} \quad \times \quad \frac{2}{3}$$

$$= \frac{2}{9}$$

(iii) One blue disc and other red disc (in any order)

$$= P(R) \quad \text{and} \quad P(B) \quad \text{or} \quad P(B) \quad \text{and} \quad P(R)$$

$$= \frac{1}{3} \quad \times \quad \frac{2}{3} \quad + \quad \frac{2}{3} \quad \times \quad \frac{1}{3}$$

$$= \frac{2}{9} \quad\quad\quad\quad + \quad\quad\quad \frac{2}{9}$$

$$= \frac{4}{9}$$

This involves two branches.

Note: The sum of the probabilities on the four branches sum to one, i.e. probabilities of

$$BB \quad + \quad BR \quad + \quad RB \quad + \quad RR$$

$$= \left(\tfrac{2}{3}\right)\left(\tfrac{2}{3}\right) + \left(\tfrac{2}{3}\right)\left(\tfrac{1}{3}\right) + \left(\tfrac{1}{3}\right)\left(\tfrac{2}{3}\right) + \left(\tfrac{1}{3}\right)\left(\tfrac{1}{3}\right)$$

$$= \frac{4}{9} \quad + \quad \frac{2}{9} \quad + \quad \frac{2}{9} \quad + \quad \frac{1}{9}$$

$$= \frac{9}{9}$$

$$= 1$$

EXAMPLE 5

Rushna is taking her driving test.
The test is in two parts: Theory and Practical.
She has to pass both parts of the test.

The probability that Rushna will pass the Theory is 0·9.
The probability that she will pass the Practical is 0·8.
If she fails her Theory she cannot take the Practical.

(a) Complete this tree diagram.

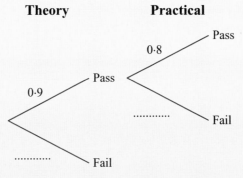

Theory   Practical

Pass

0·8

Pass

0·9

....

Fail

....

Fail

(b) Calculate the probability that Rushna fails the driving test.

Exercise 5.9

1. A fair coin is tossed and an unbiased die is thrown. Find the probability of the following.

    (i) A head and a 4   **(ii)** A tail and an odd number

    (iii) A tail and a number greater than 2   **(iv)** A head and a number divisible by 3

2. A fair coin is tossed and a fair five-sided spinner, with sides A, A, B, B, B, is spun.
    Find the probability of:

    (i) A head and an A

    (ii) A tail and a B

    (iii) A head and an A or a tail and a B

    (iv) A tail and an A or a head and an A

3. Andrew and Brendan celebrate their birthdays in a particular week (Monday to Sunday inclusive). Assuming that the birthdays are equally likely to fall on any day of the week, what is the probability of the following?

    (i) Andrew was born on Monday

    (ii) Brendan was born on Tuesday

    (iii) Both were born on Thursday

    (iv) One was born on Wednesday and the other was born on Sunday

    (v) Both were born on the same day

    (vi) Andrew and Brendan were born on different days

4. A fair coin is tossed twice. Copy and complete the tree diagram to show all the outcomes.

   (i) How many different outcomes are there?

   (ii) What is the probability of two tails?

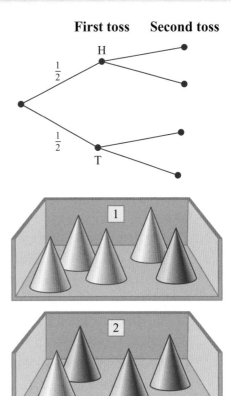

First toss   Second toss

5. Box 1 has four red cones and one blue cone.
   Box 2 has one red cone and three blue cones.
   A cone is chosen at random from box 1 and then a cone is chosen at random from box 2.
   Find the probability that:

   (i) Both are red

   (ii) Both are blue

   (iii) The first is red and the second is blue

   (iv) The first is blue and the second is red

   (v) One is red and the other is blue (in any order)

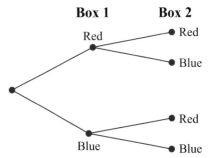

6. Jack has a die with four black sides and two white sides. He rolls the die twice.

   (i) Copy and complete the tree diagram.

   (ii) Find the probability that the die shows the same colour both times. (Each?)

   (iii) Find the probability that the die shows different colours both times. (Each?)

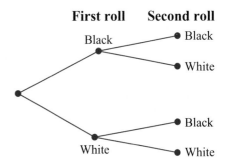

7. A coin is biased so that the probability of a tail is $\frac{1}{3}$. If the coin is tossed twice, find the probability of obtaining:

    (i) Tails on each toss

    (ii) No head on either toss

    (iii) The first tail on the second toss

8. A bowl contains 12 pieces of fruit. There are four oranges and the remainder are apples. A piece of fruit is taken at random from the bowl and eaten. A second piece of fruit is then taken at random from the bowl.

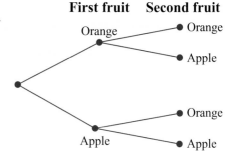

    (i) The tree diagram shows all the ways in which two pieces of fruit can be taken from the bowl. Copy the diagram and write the probabilities on it.

    (ii) Use your tree diagram to calculate the probability that:

       (a) One piece of fruit is an orange and the other is an apple

       (b) Both pieces are an apple

       (c) Both pieces are an orange

9. In a lottery, 28 numbered balls are used. Seven of the balls are red.

    (i) A ball is drawn at random and replaced. Then a second ball is drawn. Find the probability that:

       (a) The first is red

       (b) Both are red

       (c) The first is red and the second is not red

       (d) One is red and the other is not red

    (ii) If the first ball drawn is not replaced, find the probability that:

       (a) Both are red

       (b) One is red and the other not red, in any order

10. A ball enters a chute at S. The probabilities of entering some of the chutes are shown in the diagram.

    (i) What are the probabilities of the ball going down each of the chutes labelled *P*, *Q* and *R*?

    (ii) Calculate the probability of the ball landing in the following tray.

       (a) *A*   **(b)** *C*   **(c)** *B*

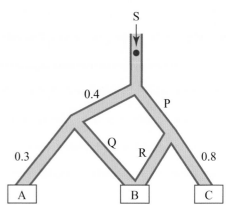

11. A fair coin is tossed three times. Copy and complete the tree diagram to show all the outcomes.

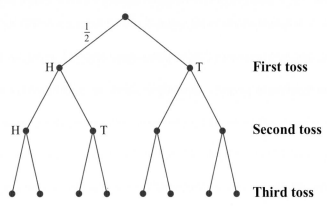

First toss

Second toss

Third toss

(i) How many different outcomes are there?

(ii) What is the probability of three tails?

(iii) What is the probability of no heads?

(iv) What is the probability of two heads and one tail?

(v) What is the probability of getting the first tail on the third toss?

Expected value

When considering the average outcome of an experiment, the mean value μ is often called the expected value and is written as $E(x)$.

To calculate the expected value, we multiply every possible outcome by the probability for that outcome occuring and then add these values together, as in the following example:

A fair spinner, with five equal sectors numbered as shown, is spun.

Find $E(x)$, the expected value, of one spin.

Solution: Using a probability distribution table:

Outcome x	Probability of outcome $p(x)$	$xp(x)$
9	$\frac{1}{5}$	$\frac{9}{5}$
11	$\frac{1}{5}$	$\frac{11}{5}$
12	$\frac{1}{5}$	$\frac{12}{5}$
16	$\frac{1}{5}$	$\frac{16}{5}$
17	$\frac{1}{5}$	$\frac{17}{5}$

Adding these (five) values for $xp(x)$ gives $E(x)$, the expected value of one spin.

In English we write: Expected value equals the sum of each outcome multiplied by the probability of each outcome.

In Mathematics we write: $E(x) = \sum xp(x)$

$$E(x) = \frac{9}{5} + \frac{11}{5} + \frac{12}{5} + \frac{16}{5} + \frac{17}{5} = \frac{65}{5} = 13$$

Note: $E(x)$ does not have to be an actual outcome.

Note: In this case, because the probability of each result is the same,

$$\text{the expected value} = E(x) = \text{mean} = \frac{9 + 17 + 11 + 16 + 12}{5}$$

$$= \frac{65}{5} = 13$$

Applications of expected value

The expected value can be used in areas such as decision-making, insurance premiums and in gambling to see if a game is fair. In gambling, a game is said to be fair if the stake (amount bet) and the expected value are equal. In a casino, the gambling games are arranged so that the casino always wins. In other words, in a casino the expected gain for a customer is always negative. However, an individual customer could walk in off the street, make one bet, win and then leave. However, over the long term the casino always wins. All forms of gambling where the expected gain is negative indicate a long-term profit for the casino.

To calculate the expected value, we need the **payout** and its **associated probability** for each outcome. Then we multiply each payout by its probability and add the results.

In short, expected value $= \Sigma$ (payout)(probability).

Note: The term 'expected value' can be misleading. It is not to be confused with 'the most probable value'. The expected value is generally not a typical value that the random variable can take. Expected value is similar to the long-run average of many independent repetitions of the same experiment.

EXAMPLE 1

(i) The cost of a text to enter a competition is €1. The competition has one prize, a new car valued at €35,000. The prize is awarded at random from the entries received. Given that 86,500 individual entries are received, calculate the expected value per entry, correct to the nearest cent.

From your calculations, comment on whether or not this competition is good value.

(ii) Given that the number of entries received was 19,600 and not the number mentioned in (i), calculate the expected value per entry, correct to the nearest cent.

Does this lower number of entries received improve the value of the competition? Justify your answer.

Solution:

(i) $\qquad P(\text{win car}) = \dfrac{1}{86{,}500}$

$\qquad P(\text{not win car}) = \dfrac{86{,}499}{86{,}500}$

The probability distribution table shows:

Amount won, x	€0	€35,000
Probability $p(x)$	$\frac{86,499}{86,500}$	$\frac{1}{86,500}$

$E(x) = \Sigma x\, p(x)$

$E(x) = (0)\left(\dfrac{86,499}{86,500}\right) + (35,000)\left(\dfrac{1}{86,500}\right)$

$E(x) = \quad 0 \quad + \quad 0{\cdot}404624277$

$E(x) = \quad 0{\cdot}40 \quad = \quad 40$ cent

The entry cost is €1, with an expected value of 40 cent.

Hence, the expected gain $= 0{\cdot}40 - 1 = -0{\cdot}60$ cent.

∴ The competition is not good value.

Many individuals participate in this type of (popular) competition because the amount 'lost' is very insignificant compared with the potential (but unlikely) large gain.

(ii) $\quad P(\text{win car}) = \dfrac{1}{19,600}$

$P(\text{not win car}) = \dfrac{19,599}{19,600}$

The probability distribution table:

Amount won €x	0	35,000
Probability $p(x)$	$\frac{19,599}{19,600}$	$\frac{1}{19,600}$

Expected value $= E(x) = \Sigma x\, p(x)$

$\qquad = (0)\left(\dfrac{19,599}{19,600}\right) + 35,000\left(\dfrac{1}{19,600}\right)$

$\qquad = \quad 0 \quad + \quad 1{\cdot}7857$

$\qquad = €1{\cdot}79$

This lower number of entries increases the expected value. Therefore, the lower number of entries improves the value of the competition.

Thus, the expected gain $= 1{\cdot}79 - 1 = +€0{\cdot}79$.

∴ Entering this competition is excellent value.

However, as in part **(i)**, the amount of money involved is very small and the 'gain' is insignificant.

EXAMPLE 2

In a certain country, each year one out of every 1,000 people die and two out of every 1,000 people are permanently disabled. An insurance company offers the following death or permanent disability policy that pays €100,000 when you die or €50,000 if you are permanently disabled. It charges €600 a year for this benefit. Is the company likely to make a profit selling this policy?

Solution:

To answer this question, imagine the company sells this policy to 1,000 individuals chosen at random from the population. The amount the company pays out on an individual policy, €100,000 (if you die), €50,000 (if you are permanently disabled) or €0 (if neither happens), is a random variable because its value is based on the outcome of a random event.

It helps to put the information in a probability distribution table:

Outcome	Death	Disability	Neither
Payout	100,000	50,000	0
Probability	$\frac{1}{1,000}$	$\frac{2}{1,000}$	$\frac{997}{1,000}$

Expected payout = $\sum$ (payout)(probability)

$$= 100,000\left(\frac{1}{1,000}\right) + 50,000\left(\frac{2}{1,000}\right) + 0\left(\frac{997}{1,000}\right) = €200$$

Thus, the total payout per policy is €200.

Since the company is charging €600 per policy, the company can expect to make €600 − €200 = €400 profit per policy per year (not bad).

Note: We can't predict what will happen during any given year, but we can work out what we expect to happen.

Exercise 5.10

1. A game with a spinner as shown is played.

   If the spinner lands on white, you lose €6.

   If the spinner lands on black, you win €16.

   (i) Calculate the expected value for this game.

   (ii) Is this game fair? Justify your answer.

2.

| 1 | 10 | 8 | 3 |

A card is chosen at random from the four cards shown above. Find $E(x)$, the expected value, of one choice.

3. A fair six-sided die is used in a game. The probabilities of getting the six different numbers on the die are shown in the probability distribution table below.

Number (x)	1	2	3	4	5	6
Probability $p(x)$	$\frac{1}{6}$	$\frac{1}{6}$	$\frac{1}{6}$	$\frac{1}{6}$	$\frac{1}{6}$	$\frac{1}{6}$

   (i) Find the expected value of the random variable x, where x is the number thrown.

   (ii) It costs €4 to play this game at a funfair. The player rolls a die once and wins back the number of euro shown on the die. Using your results from (i), complete the following sentence:

   If you play this game 25 times you will expect to win/lose a total of € _____.

   (iii) If the expected value of a game is zero, then we say the game is fair. What should the cost be to roll the die in order to make the game fair?

4. A fair 12-sided die has scores 1, 1, 1, 1, 1, 1, 3, 3, 3, 4, 6, 6. Complete the following probability distribution table and show that the expected outcome for one throw of the die equals $\frac{31}{12}$.

Score, x	1	3	4	6
Probability, $p(x)$	$\frac{6}{12} = \frac{1}{2}$	$\frac{3}{12} =$		

5. A charity got a licence to run a raffle. There is one grand prize of €20,000 and 20 additional prizes of €500. Tickets cost €10. When you read the small print, you discover that 10,000 tickets will be sold. Sheila bought one ticket and all the tickets were sold.

   (i) Calculate the probability that Sheila wins **(a)** the grand prize **(b)** a €500 prize **(c)** no prize.

   (ii) Represent the situation with a probability distribution.

   (iii) Calculate the expected value.

   (iv) Is this a good bet? Justify your answer.

6. The diagram shows two wheels.

    The first wheel is divided into four equal segments numbered 1, 2, 3 and 4.

    The second wheel is divided into three equal segments numbered 5, 6 and 7.

    A game consists of spinning the two wheels and noting the segments that stop at the arrows, then adding the two numbers together. For example, the outcome shown is 3 + 5 = 8.

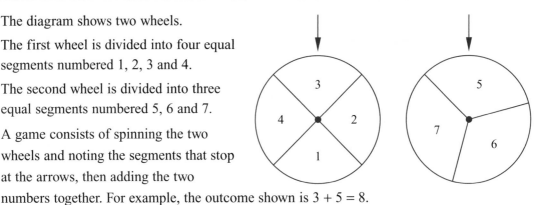

   (i) Complete the following table.

First wheel \ Second wheel	5	6	7
1			
2			
3	8		
4			11

   (ii) What is the probability of a total score of 11?

   (iii) What is the probability of a total score of 9?

   (iv) Hence, complete the following frequency distribution table.

Total score, x	6	7	8	9	10	11
Probability, p(x)	$\frac{1}{12}$	$\frac{2}{12}$				

   (v) Calculate the expected value for this game.

7. The cost to text an answer to a competition is 80 cent. The competition has one main prize, a round-the-world holiday for two people valued at €24,000 and five consolation prizes of holidays in Ireland, each valued at €1,000. 22,142 individual valid answers are received. Calculate the expected value per entry correct to the nearest cent. Comment on your answer in terms of value to those entering the competition.

8. On a school fundraising evening, it was proposed to organise a game of 'spin and win' to make some money. The proposal was to charge €5 to spin the wheel. The wheel has six equal sectors, as shown, and all sectors are equally likely to stop at the arrow. However, the school's Maths teacher, who loves statistics, said that this is a fair game and will win no money at all for the school.

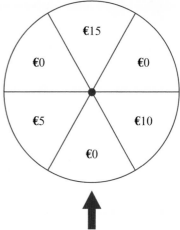

   (i) Is the Maths teacher correct? Justify your answer.
   (ii) How would you redesign the wheel so that the school would make an expected €1 for each spin?

9. The table below gives motor insurance information for a year for fully licensed 17- to 20-year-old drivers in Ireland. All drivers who had their own insurance policy are included.

	Number of drivers	Number of claims	Average cost per claim
Male	9,634	977	€6,108
Female	6,743	581	€6,051

Questions (i) to (v) below refer to drivers in the table above only.

   (i) What is the probability that a randomly selected male driver made a claim during the year? Give your answer correct to three decimal places.
   (ii) What is the probability that a randomly selected female driver made a claim during the year? Give your answer correct to three decimal places.
   (iii) What is the expected value of the cost of claims on a male driver's policy?
   (iv) What is the expected value of the cost of claims on a female driver's policy?
   (v) By comparing your answer for (iii) and (iv), do you agree or disagree with the statement 'Young male drivers should pay more for their motor insurance than young female drivers'? Justify your answer.

10. It costs €5 to play a game in which a coin is tossed twice. If the coin lands on heads both times, the player receives €15. Otherwise the player receives nothing.
   (i) Complete the following probability distribution table.

Event	Two heads (H, H)	Two tails (T, T)	Tail then head (T, H)	Head then tail (H, T)
P(event)			$\frac{1}{4}$	

   (ii) Find the expected value for this game. How would you make this a fair game?
   (iii) The game is played again but with new rules. It costs €5 to play the game. The coin is tossed three times. If the coin lands on heads three times the player receives €35, otherwise the player receives nothing. Is this a fair game? Justify your answer.

Terminology and notation

A function is a rule that changes one number (input) into another number (output). Functions are often represented by the letters f, g, h or k. We can think of a function, f, as a number machine which changes an input, x, into an output, $f(x)$.

Input

Output

$f(x)$, which denotes the output, is read as 'f of x'.

For example, let's represent the function 'double input and then add 5' by the letter f.

This can be written as:

$$f: x \rightarrow 2x + 5 \quad \text{or} \quad f(x) = 2x + 5 \quad \text{or} \quad y = 2x + 5$$
$$(\text{input, output}) = (x, f(x)) = (x, 2x + 5) = (x, y)$$

Note: A **function** is also called a **mapping** or simply a **map**.

One number is mapped onto another number.

In the above example, x is mapped onto $2x + 5$, usually written $f: x \rightarrow 2x + 5$.

Input number

If $f: x \rightarrow 2x + 5$, then $f(3)$ means 'input 3 into the function', i.e. it is the result of applying the function f to the number 3.

$$f(3) = 2(3) + 5 = 6 + 5 = 11 \qquad (\text{input} = 3, \text{output} = 11)$$
$$(\text{input, output}) = (3, f(3)) = (3, 11)$$

> A function does exactly the same to each input number and produces only one output number for each input number.

The set of numbers that are put into a function is called the **domain**.

The set of numbers that comes out of a function is called the **range**.

A function connects **every** input in the domain to an output in the range.

A function is another way of writing an algebraic formula that links input to output.

Types of functions	
Linear	$f\!:\!x \rightarrow ax$ or $f\!:\!x \rightarrow ax + b$
Quadratic	$f\!:\!x \rightarrow ax^2 + bx + c$
Cubic	$f\!:\!x \rightarrow ax^3 + bx^2 + cx\ d$
Exponential	$f\!:\!x \rightarrow ab^x$

EXAMPLE 1

The function g is defined as $g : x \rightarrow 3x - 2, \qquad x \in \mathbb{R}$.

(i) Find: (a) $g(6)$ (b) $g\!\left(\tfrac{4}{3}\right)$.

(ii) Find the number k such that $kg\!\left(\tfrac{4}{3}\right) = g(6)$.

(iii) Find the value of x for which $g(x) = 13$.

Solution:

$$g(x) = 3x - 2$$

(i) (a) $g(6) = 3(6) - 2$

$\qquad = 18 - 2$

$\qquad = 16$

(b) $g\!\left(\tfrac{4}{3}\right) = 3\!\left(\tfrac{4}{3}\right) - 2$

$\qquad = 4 - 2$

$\qquad = 2$

(ii) $kg\!\left(\tfrac{4}{3}\right) = g(6)$

$\qquad k(2) = 16$

$\qquad 2k = 16$

$\qquad k = 8$

(iii) $g(x) = 13$

$\qquad 3x - 2 = 13$

$\qquad 3x = 15$

$\qquad x = 5$

EXAMPLE 2

$f: x \rightarrow x^2 - x$ and $g(x) = x + 1$.

(i) Evaluate: **(a)** $f(-1)$ **(b)** $g\left(-\frac{1}{4}\right)$.

(ii) Find the two values of x for which $2f(x) = 3g(x)$.

Solution:

(i) **(a)** $f(x) = x^2 - x$

$f(-1) = (-1)^2 - (-1)$

$\qquad = 1 + 1$

$\qquad = 2$

(b) $g(x) = x + 1$

$g\left(-\frac{1}{4}\right) = -\frac{1}{4} + 1$

$\qquad = \frac{3}{4}$

(ii)

$$2f(x) = 3g(x)$$
$$2(x^2 - x) = 3(x + 1)$$
$$2x^2 - 2x = 3x + 3$$
$$2x^2 - 2x - 3x - 3 = 0$$
$$2x^2 - 5x - 3 = 0$$
$$(2x + 1)(x - 3) = 0$$

$2x + 1 = 0 \quad$ or $\quad x - 3 = 0$

$2x = -1 \quad$ or $\qquad x = 3$

$x = -\frac{1}{2} \quad$ or $\qquad x = 3$

EXAMPLE 3

$f: x \rightarrow x^3 - 3x^2 - 10x + 15$

(i) Evaluate: **(a)** $f(-1)$ **(b)** $f(5)$

(ii) Find the value of k for which $k f(1) = f(4)$.

Solution:

(i) **(a)** $f(x) = x^3 - 3x^2 - 10x + 15$

$f(-1) = (-1)^3 - 3(-1)^2 - 10(-1) + 15$

$f(-1) = -1 - 3 + 10 + 15$

$f(-1) = 21$

(b) $f(x) = x^3 - 3x^2 - 10x + 15$

$f(5) = (5)^3 - 3(5)^2 - 10(5) + 15$

$f(5) = 125 - 75 - 50 + 15$

$f(5) = 15$

(ii) $\quad k f(1) = f(4)$

Find $f(1)$:

$f(1) = (1)^3 - 3(1)^2 - 10(1) + 15$

$f(1) = 1 - 3 - 10 + 15$

$f(1) = 3$

Find $f(4)$:

$f(4) = (4)^3 - 3(4)^2 - 10(4) + 15$

$f(4) = 64 - 48 - 40 + 15$

$f(4) = -9$

$k f(1) = f(4)$

$k(3) = -9$

$k = -3$

EXAMPLE 4

$f : x \rightarrow 2(5)^x$

(i) Evaluate: (a) $f(3)$ (b) $f(-1)$ (c) $f(0)$.

(ii) Find the value of x for which $f(x) = 50$.

Solution:

(i) (a) $f(x) = 2(5)^x$
$f(3) = 2(5)^3$
$f(3) = 2(125)$
$f(3) = 250$

(b) $f(x) = 2(5)^x$
$f(-1) = 2(5)^{-1}$
$f(-1) = 2(0.2)$
$f(-1) = 0.4$

(c) $f(x) = 2(5)^x$
$f(0) = 2(5)^0$
$f(0) = 2(1)$
$f(0) = 2$

(ii) $f(x) = 50$
$2(5)^x = 50$ (divide both sides by 2)
$(5)^x = 25$
$5^x = 5^2$
$\therefore x = 2$

Exercise 6.1

1. The function f is defined as $f : x \rightarrow 3x + 4$, $x \in \mathbb{R}$. Find the following.
   (i) $f(2)$ (ii) $f(5)$ (iii) $f(-1)$ (iv) $f(0)$ (v) $f\left(\frac{2}{3}\right)$

2. The function g is defined as $g : x \rightarrow 5x - 2$, $x \in \mathbb{R}$. Find the following.
   (i) $g(3)$ (ii) $g(-2)$ (iii) $g(0)$ (iv) $g(-1)$ (v) $g\left(\frac{2}{5}\right)$
   (vi) Find the value of x for which $g(x) = 18$.

3. The function f is defined as $f : x \rightarrow x^2 + 3x$, $x \in \mathbb{R}$. Find the following.
   (i) $f(3)$ (ii) $f(1)$ (iii) $f(0)$ (iv) $f(-2)$ (v) $3f(-4)$
   (vi) Find the two values of x for which $f(x) = 10$.

4. The function f is defined as $f : x \rightarrow 4 - 3x$, $x \in \mathbb{R}$.
   (i) Find: (a) $f(-2)$ (b) $f\left(-\frac{1}{3}\right)$ (ii) Find the number k such that $f(-2) = kf\left(-\frac{1}{3}\right)$.

5. The function f is defined as $f : x \rightarrow 7 - 4x, \qquad x \in \mathbb{R}$.
   Find the number k such that $kf\left(-\frac{3}{2}\right) = f(-8)$.

6. The function f is defined as $f : x \rightarrow x(x + 2), \qquad x \in \mathbb{R}$. Find the following.
   (i) $f(1)$ (ii) $f(-1)$ (iii) $f(2) + f(-2)$ (iv) $-2f(-3)$.
   (v) Find the two values of x for which $f(x) = 15$.

7. The function f is defined as $f : x \rightarrow x^2 + 2x - 1, \qquad x \in \mathbb{R}$. Find the following.
   (i) $f(0)$ (ii) $f(-1)$ (iii) $f\left(\frac{1}{2}\right)$ (iv) $f\left(\frac{3}{5}\right)$ (v) Find the two values of k for which $f(k) = -1$.

8. The function f is defined by $f : x \rightarrow 2x^3 - 3x^2 - 5x + 15, \qquad x \in \mathbb{R}$. Find the following.
   (i) $f(0)$ (ii) $f(-1)$ (iii) $f(3)$ (iv) Find the value of k for which $kf(-2) = f\left(\frac{5}{2}\right)$.

9. The function f is defined by $f : x \rightarrow 5x^3 + x^2 - 12x + 4, \qquad x \in \mathbb{R}$. Find the following.
   (i) $f(-2)$ (ii) $f(3) - f(-1)$ (iii) $-5f(1)$ (iv) Find the value of k for which $kf(0) = f(-1)$.

10. The function f is defined as $f : x \rightarrow x^2 - 1, \qquad x \in \mathbb{R}$.
    (i) Find: (a) $f(4)$ (b) $f(-3)$ (c) $f(2)$.
    (ii) For what value of $k \in \mathbb{R}$ is $2k + 1 + f(4) = f(-3)$?
    (iii) Find the values of x for which $f(x) - f(2) = 0$.
    (iv) Verify that $f(x - 1) = f(1 - x)$.

11. $f : x \rightarrow x^2 + 1$ and $g : x \rightarrow 2x$ are two functions defined on $\mathbb{R}$.
    (i) Find $f(\sqrt{3})$ and $g(1)$.
    (ii) Find the value of k for which $f(\sqrt{3}) = kg(1)$.
    (iii) Find the value of x for which $f(x) = g(x)$.
    (iv) Verify that $f(x + 2) = g(x^2 + 2x + 1) - f(x) + f(\sqrt{3})$.

12. The function f is defined as $f : x \rightarrow 2(3)^x$, where $x \in \mathbb{R}$.
    (i) Find: (a) $f(1)$ (b) $f(3)$ (c) $f(0)$.
    (ii) Find the value of x for which $f(x) = 18$.

13. The function f is defined as $f : x \rightarrow 5(4)^x$, where $x \in \mathbb{R}$.
    (i) Find: (a) $f(1)$ (b) $f(4)$ (c) $f(0)$ (d) $f\left(\frac{1}{2}\right)$.
    (ii) Find the value of x for which $f(x) = 320$.

14. A train is moving along a track. At the instant it passes a marker it begins to accelerate. From the time the train passes the marker, its distance from the marker is given by $s = t^2 + 2t$, where s is in metres and t is in seconds.
    (i) How far has the train travelled in the first 12 seconds after it passes the marker?
    (ii) After how many seconds is the train a distance of 48 m from the marker?

15. A missile is fired straight up in the air. The height, h metres, of the missile above the firing position is given by $h = t(100 - 8t)$ where t is the time in seconds from the instant the missile was fired.

    (i) Find the height of the missile after 5 seconds.

    (ii) Find the height of the missile after 12 seconds.

    (iii) Find the two times when the height of the missile is 200 m.

16. The speed, v, of an object at time t is given by $v = 24 + 10t - t^2$, where t is in seconds and v is in metres per second.

    (i) Find the speed of the object when $t = 0$ sec.

    (ii) Find the speed of the object after 7 seconds.

    (iii) Find the two times when the speed of the object is 40 m/s.

17. A population of 100 rabbits increases according to the function $y = 100(2{\cdot}5)^t$, where y represents the number of rabbits and t is the time in years.

    (i) Find the number of rabbits after two years.

    (ii) Find the number of rabbits, to the nearest rabbit, after six years.

18. A car bought for €23,000 depreciates according to the function $y = 23{,}000(0{\cdot}8)^t$, where y represents the value of the car and t is the time in years.

    (i) Find the value of the car after three years.

    (ii) Find the value of the car, to the nearest euro, after eight years.

Functions with missing coefficients

In some questions coefficients of the functions are missing and we are asked to find them. In this type of question we are given equations in disguise, and by solving these equations we can calculate the missing coefficients.

Notation

$f(x) = y$

$f(2) = 3$ means when $x = 2$, $y = 3$, or the point $(2, 3)$ is on the graph of the function.

$f(-1) = 0$ means when $x = -1$, $y = 0$, or the point $(-1, 0)$ is on the graph of the function.

EXAMPLE 1

$f : x \rightarrow 3x + k$ and $g : x \rightarrow x^2 + hx - 8$ are two functions defined on $\mathbb{R}$.

(i) If $f(-2) = 1$, find the value of k.

(ii) If $g(-3) = -5$, find the value of h.

Solution:

(i) $f(x) = 3x + k$

Given: $f(-2) = 1$

$\therefore 3(-2) + k = 1$

$-6 + k = 1$

$k = 7$

(ii) $g(x) = x^2 + hx - 8$

Given: $g(-3) = -5$

$\therefore (-3)^2 + h(-3) - 8 = -5$

$9 - 3h - 8 = -5$

$-3h + 1 = -5$

$-3h = -6$

$3h = 6$

$h = 2$

EXAMPLE 2

$g : x \rightarrow ax^2 + bx - 3$ is a function defined on $\mathbb{R}$.

If $g(2) = 15$ and $g(-1) = -6$, write down two equations in a and b.

Hence, calculate the value of a and the value of b.

Solution:

$$g(x) = ax^2 + bx - 3$$

Given: $g(2) = 15$

$\therefore a(2)^2 + b(2) - 3 = 15$

$a(4) + b(2) - 3 = 15$

$4a + 2b - 3 = 15$

$4a + 2b = 18$

$2a + b = 9$ ①

Given: $g(-1) = -6$

$\therefore a(-1)^2 + b(-1) - 3 = -6$

$a(1) + b(-1) - 3 = -6$

$a - b - 3 = -6$

$a - b = -3$ ②

We now solve between equations ① and ②.

$2a + b = 9$ ①

$\underline{a - b = -3}$ ②

$3a = 6$ (add)

$a = 2$

Put $a = 2$ into ① or ②.

$2a + b = 9$ ①

$2(2) + b = 9$

$4 + b = 9$

$b = 5$

Thus, $a = 2$ and $b = 5$.

EXAMPLE 3

The graph of the quadratic function
$f : x \to x^2 + px + q$, $\quad x \in \mathbb{R}$, is shown.
Find the value of p and the value of q.

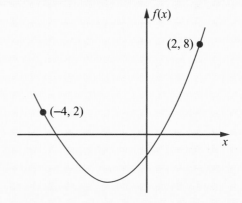

Solution:

$$f(x) = x^2 + px + q$$

The graph goes through the point $(-4, 2)$. | The graph goes through the point $(2, 8)$.

Given: $\qquad f(-4) = 2$ | **Given:** $\qquad f(2) = 8$

$\therefore \qquad (-4)^2 + p(-4) + q = 2$ | $\therefore \qquad (2)^2 + p(2) + q = 8$

$\qquad\qquad 16 - 4p + q = 2$ | $\qquad\qquad 4 + 2p + q = 8$

$\qquad\qquad -4p + q = -14$ | $\qquad\qquad 2p + q = 4 \quad$ ②

$\qquad\qquad 4p - q = 14 \qquad$ ① |

We now solve between equations ① and ②.

$\qquad\qquad 4p - q = 14 \quad$ ① $\qquad\qquad\qquad\qquad 2p + q = 4 \qquad$ ②

$\qquad\qquad \underline{2p + q = 4 \quad ②} \qquad\qquad\qquad\qquad \downarrow$

$\qquad\qquad\quad 6p = 18 \quad$ (add) $\qquad\qquad\qquad 2(3) + q = 4$

$\qquad\qquad\qquad p = 3 \qquad\qquad\qquad\qquad\qquad\quad 6 + q = 4$

Put $p = 3$ into ① or ②. $\qquad\qquad\qquad\qquad\qquad\qquad q = -2$

Thus, $p = 3$ and $q = -2$.

Alternatively, let $y = f(x)$, i.e. $y = x^2 + px + q$.

$(-4, 2)$ is on the graph of the curve. | $(2, 8)$ is on the graph of the curve.

$\therefore \qquad 2 = (-4)^2 + p(-4) + q$ | $\therefore \qquad 8 = (2)^2 + p(2) + 1$

(put in $x = -4$, $y = 2$) | (put in $x = 2$, $y = 8$)

$\qquad\qquad 2 = 16 - 4p + q$ | $\qquad\qquad 8 = 4 + 2p + q$

$\qquad -14 = -4p + q$ | $\qquad\qquad 4 = 2p + q \qquad$ ②

$\qquad\; 14 = 4p - q \qquad$ ① |

Then solve the simultaneous equations ① and ② as before to get $p = 3$ and $q = -2$.

Exercise 6.2

1. Let $f(x) = 5x + k$ where $k \in \mathbb{R}$. If $f(1) = 7$, find the value of k.

2. Let $g(x) = 3x + h$ where $h \in \mathbb{R}$. If $g(-1) = 1$, find the value of h.

3. Let $h(x) = ax + 7$ where $a \in \mathbb{R}$. If $h(-3) = -2$, find the value of a.

4. Let $k(x) = x^2 - 3x + b$ where $b \in \mathbb{R}$. If $k(-1) = -6$, find the value of b.

5. Let $f(x) = ax^2 + 3x$ where $a \in \mathbb{R}$. If $f(-1) = -1$, find the value of a.

6. Let $f(x) = (x + k)(x + 3)$ where $k \in \mathbb{R}$. If $f(-2) = -6$, find the value of k.

7. Let $g(x) = a^2x^2 - 7ax + 6$ where $a \in \mathbb{R}$. If $g(2) = -6$, find two possible values of a.

8. Let $f(x) = x^2 + ax + b$ where $a, b \in \mathbb{R}$.

   (i) Find the value of a, given that $f(2) = f(-4)$.

   (ii) If $f(-5) = 12$, find the value of b.

9. Let $f(x) = 5x^3 + x^2 + ax + 8$ where $a \in \mathbb{R}$. If $f(-1) = 16$, find the value of a.

10. Let $f(x) = x^3 + ax^2 - 4x + b$ where $a, b \in \mathbb{R}$.

   (i) If $f(0) = 7$, find the value of b.

   (ii) If $f(3) = -5$, find the value of a.

11. $f : x \to 2x + a$ and $g : x \to 3x + b$.

   If $f(2) = 7$ and $g(1) = -1$, find the value of a and the value of b.

12. $h : x \to 2x + a$ and $k : x \to b - 5x$ are two functions defined on $\mathbb{R}$.

   If $h(1) = -5$ and $k(-1) = 4$, find the value of a and the value of b.

13. $f : x \to 3x + a$ and $g : x \to ax + b$ are two functions defined on $\mathbb{R}$.

   $f(2) = 8$ and $g(2) = 1$.

   (i) Find the value of a and the value of b.

   (ii) Find $f(-1)$ and $g(4)$.

   (iii) Using your values of a and b from (i), find the two values of x for which
      $ax^2 - (a - b)x + 2ab = 0$.

14. $h : x \to 2x - a$ and $k : x \to ax + b$ are two functions defined on $\mathbb{R}$, where a and $b \in \mathbb{Z}$.

   $h(3) = 1$ and $k(5) = 8$.

   (i) Find the value of a and the value of b.

   (ii) Hence, list the values of x for which $h(x) \geq k(x)$, $x \in \mathbb{N}$.

15. $g : x \to ax^2 + bx + 1$ is a function defined on $\mathbb{R}$.

   (i) If $g(1) = 2$ and $g(-1) = 6$, write down two equations in a and b.

   (ii) Hence, calculate the value of a and the value of b.

16. $g : x \rightarrow px^2 + qx - 3$ is a function defined on $\mathbb{R}$.

  (i) If $g(1) = 4$ and $g(-1) = -6$, write down two equations in p and q.

  (ii) Hence, calculate the value of p and the value of q.

  (iii) Find the two values of x for which $px^2 + qx - 3 = 0$.

17. $g : x \rightarrow ax^2 + bx + 1$ is a function defined on $\mathbb{R}$.

  (i) If $g(1) = 0$ and $g(2) = 3$, write down two equations in a and b.

  (ii) Hence, calculate the value of a and the value of b.

  (iii) Using your values of a and b from **(ii)**, find the two values of x for which
    $ax^2 + bx = bx^2 + ax$.

18. $f : x \rightarrow ax^2 + bx + c$, where a, b and c are real numbers.

  (i) If $f(0) = -3$, find the value of c.

  (ii) If $f(-1) = 6$ and $f(2) = 3$, find the value of a and the value of b.

19. $h : x \rightarrow x^2 + x + q$ is a function defined on $\mathbb{R}$, where $q \in \mathbb{Z}$.

  (i) If $h(-3) = 0$, find the value of q.

  (ii) Hence, solve the equation $h(x + 5) = 0$.

20. $f(x) = x^3 - ax^2 + 5x + b,$ where $a, b \in \mathbb{R}$.

  (i) If $f(1) = 6$ and $f(3) = 18$, write two equations in a and b.

  (ii) Hence, calculate the value of a and the value of b.

21. $f(x) = ab^x$, where $a, b \in N$.

  (i) If $f(0) = 8$ and $f(1) = 32$, write two equations in a and b.

  (ii) Hence, calculate the value of a and the value of b.

22. $f(x) = ab^x$, where $a, b \in N$.

  (i) If $f(1) = 4$ and $f(2) = 12$, write two equations in a and b.

  (ii) Hence, calculate the value of a and the value of b.
    Give your answers in fraction form.

23. The graph of the linear function $f : x \rightarrow ax + b, x \in \mathbb{R}$
  is shown. Find the values of a and b.

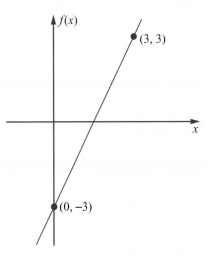

24. The graph of the quadratic function
    $f : x \rightarrow x^2 + bx + c, \quad x \in \mathbb{R}$, is shown.

    (i) Find the values of b and c.

    (ii) Hence, find the value of k.

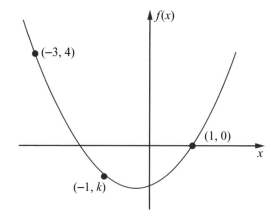

25. The graph of the quadratic function
    $g : x \rightarrow x^2 + px + q, \qquad x \in \mathbb{R}$, is shown.

    (i) Find the values of p and q.

    (ii) Hence, find the values of a, b and c.

    (iii) Solve the equation:

    $$\frac{c-1}{b} = \frac{1}{x} + \frac{1}{x+p}$$

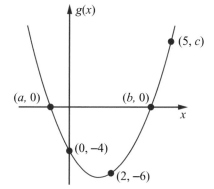

26. The graph of the quadratic function
    $g : x \rightarrow ax^2 + bx - 3, \qquad x \in \mathbb{R}$, is shown.

    (i) Find the values of a and b.

    (ii) Hence, calculate the value of h and k.

    (iii) Solve the equation:

    $$\frac{1}{x} + \frac{1}{x+k} + h = 0$$

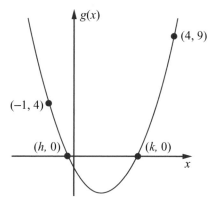

27. The graph of the quadratic function
    $h : x \rightarrow c + bx - x^2, \qquad x \in \mathbb{R}$, is shown.

    (i) Find the value of b and c.

    (ii) $k : x \rightarrow px + q$ is a function defined on $\mathbb{R}$.
    If $k(0) = -1$ and $k(1) = 1$, find the value
    of p and the value of q.

    (iii) Hence, find the two values of x for
    which $k(x) = h(x)$.

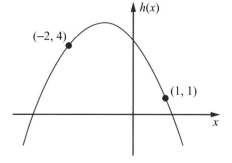

28. The graph of the cubic function
    $f : x \rightarrow ax^3 - 3x^2 + bx + 3$, where $a, b \in N$,
    is shown.

    Find the values of a and b.

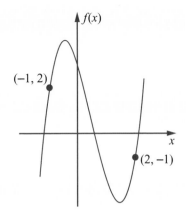

29. The graph of the cubic function
    $f : x \rightarrow x^3 + ax^2 + 4x + b$, where $a, b \in N$,
    is shown.

    (i) Find the values of a and b.

    (ii) Hence, find the value of k.

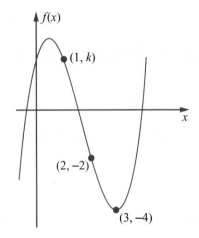

30. The graph of the exponential
    function $f : x \rightarrow ab^x$, where $a, b \in N$,
    is shown.

    Find the values of a and b.

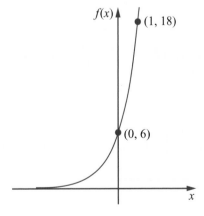

31. The graph of the exponential
function $f : x \rightarrow ab^x$, where $a, b \in N$,
is shown.

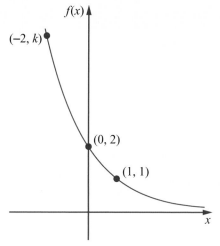

(i) Find the values of a and b.

(ii) Hence, find the value of k.

32. Let $f(x) = x^2 + bx + c, \quad x \in \mathbb{R}$. The solutions of $f(x) = 0$ are -5 and 2.

(i) Find the value of b and the value of c.

(ii) If $f(-3) = k$, find the value of k.

(iii) Solve the equation $f(x) - k = 0$.

33. Let $g(x) = x^2 + bx + c, \quad x \in \mathbb{R}$. The solutions of $g(x) = 0$ are symmetrical about the
line $x = -1$.

(i) If $x = 1$ is one solution of $g(x) = 0$, find the other solution.

(ii) Find the value of b and the value of c.

Limits of a function

The phrase 'x approaches zero', written $x \rightarrow 0$, means that x can be made as close to 0 as
we please without actually reaching 0.

Similarly, the phrase 'x approaches 4', written $x \rightarrow 4$, means that x can be made as close to
4 as we please without actually reaching 4.

Definition of a limit

$$\lim_{x \to a} f(x) = L$$

Means that $f(x)$ approaches the number L as x approaches a.

Note: lim is the abbreviation for limit.

On our course, finding $\lim_{x \to a} f(x)$ will give the same result as $f(a)$.

EXAMPLE

Evaluate: **(i)** $\lim\limits_{x\to5}(6-2x)$ **(ii)** $\lim\limits_{x\to2}(2x^3-x^2+3x-7)$ **(iii)** $\lim\limits_{x\to3}(7(2)^x)$

Solution:

(i) $\lim\limits_{x\to5}(6-2x)$

$= 6-2(5)$

$= 6-10$

$= -4$

(ii) $\lim\limits_{x\to2}(2x^3-x^2+3x-7)$

$= 2(2)^3-(2)^2+3(2)-7$

$= 16-4+6-7$

$= 11$

(iii) $\lim\limits_{x\to3}(7(2)^x)$

$= 7(2)^3$

$= 7(8)$

$= 56$

Exercise 6.3

In questions 1–15, evaluate the limit.

1. $\lim\limits_{x\to2}(x+3)$

2. $\lim\limits_{x\to3}(5x-2)$

3. $\lim\limits_{x\to1}(7x+4)$

4. $\lim\limits_{x\to6}(13-2x)$

5. $\lim\limits_{x\to4}(x^2+5x-2)$

6. $\lim\limits_{x\to3}(3x^2+2x-8)$

7. $\lim\limits_{x\to1}(x^2-6x-11)$

8. $\lim\limits_{x\to3}(12+2x-4x^2)$

9. $\lim\limits_{x\to0}(x^3+2x^2+x-9)$

10. $\lim\limits_{x\to4}(4x^3-3x^2+x+1)$

11. $\lim\limits_{x\to5}(2x^3-9x+5)$

12. $\lim\limits_{x\to6}(x^3+5x^2-3x)$

13. $\lim\limits_{x\to3}(3(4)^x)$

14. $\lim\limits_{x\to2}(2(5)^x)$

15. $\lim\limits_{x\to4}\left(9\left(\dfrac{1}{3}\right)^x\right)$

Composite functions

When one function is followed by another function, the result is a **composite** function.

Input $\longrightarrow$ $\boxed{f(x)}$ $\longrightarrow$ $\boxed{g(x)}$ $\longrightarrow$ Output

Applying function g after applying function f is written in three different ways:

1. $g\circ f(x)$ **2.** $gf(x)$ **3.** $g[f(x)]$

All are pronounced 'g after f' and means do f followed by g.

Consider the two functions $f(x) = x + 3$ and $g(x) = 5 - 2x$, where the domain of f is $\{1, 2, 3, 4\}$ and the domain of g is the range of f.

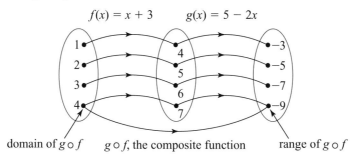

$$g \circ f = \{(1, -3), (2, -5), (3, -7), (4, -9)\}$$

We can work out a single **rule** for the composite function.

$$f(x) = x + 3 \qquad g(x) = 5 - 2x$$

$$x \qquad\qquad (x + 3) \qquad\qquad \begin{aligned} 5 &- 2(x + 3) \\ = \; 5 &- 2x - 6 \\ = -1 &- 2x \end{aligned}$$

In this case, $gf(x) = -1 - 2x$.

Check: $gf(3) = -1 - 2(3) = -1 - 6 = -7$ (same as before)

EXAMPLE

$f(x) = 2x + 1$ and $g(x) = 7 - x$.

(i) Find: (a) $fg(3)$ (b) $gf(-1)$

(ii) Find an expression in x for $fg(x)$ and write your answer in the form $ax + b$.

Solution:

(i) (a)
$$\begin{aligned} fg(3) &= f(7 - 3) \\ &= f(4) \\ &= 2(4) + 1 \\ &= 8 + 1 \\ &= 9 \end{aligned}$$

(b)
$$\begin{aligned} gf(-1) &= g[2(-1) + 1] \\ &= g(-2 + 1) \\ &= g(-1) \\ &= 7 - (-1) \\ &= 7 + 1 \\ &= 8 \end{aligned}$$

(ii)
$$\begin{aligned} fg(x) &= f(7 - x) \\ &= 2(7 - x) + 1 \\ &= 14 - 2x + 1 \\ &= 15 - 2x \end{aligned}$$

Check: $fg(3) = 15 - 2(3) = 15 - 6 = 9$ (same as before)

So, $fg(x) = 15 - 2x$.

Exercise 6.4

1. Given $f(x) = 4x - 1$, $g(x) = 2 + 3x$ and $h(x) = 1 - x$, calculate the following.

   (i) $f(2)$ (ii) $g(-1)$ (iii) $h(-3)$

   (iv) $gf(1)$ (v) $fg(-2)$ (vi) $fh(-4)$

   (vii) $h \circ f(1)$ (viii) $g \circ f(\frac{1}{2})$ (ix) $h \circ h(-1)$

2. Given $f(x) = 3x + 2$, $g(x) = 7 - 2x$ and $h(x) = x - 5$, find and simplify expressions for each of these composite functions.

   (i) $f \circ g(x)$ (ii) $h \circ f(x)$ (iii) $g \circ h(x)$

   (iv) $h \circ h(x)$ (v) $f \circ h(x)$ (vi) $f \circ f(x)$

3. Given $f(x) = x^2 + 2$ and $g(x) = x + 7$ are two functions, evaluate the following.

   (i) $f \circ g(1)$ (ii) $g \circ f(2)$ (iii) $g \circ f(-3)$

   (iv) $g \circ g(4)$ (v) $f \circ g(-2)$ (vi) $f \circ f(-1)$

   (vii) Find an expression for $f \circ g(x)$.

4. $f(x) \rightarrow x + 1$ and $g(x) \rightarrow 2^x$.

   (i) Show that $g(2) = f(3)$.

   (ii) Find: (a) $g \circ f(x)$ (b) $f \circ g(x)$.

   (iii) Show that (a) $g \circ f(3)$ and (b) $f \circ g(3)$ are perfect squares.

5. $f(x) = 2x - 5$ and $g(x) = x^2 - 1$. Solve the following equations.

   (i) $f \circ f(x) = 1$ (ii) $f \circ g(x) = 11$ (iii) $g \circ f(x) = 24$

6. Given that $f(x) = 2x + 5$, $g(x) = 4x + a$ and $f g(x) = g f(x)$, find the value of a.

7. The diagram shows the graph of $y = f(x)$.
   Use the graph to write the following.

   (i) $f(2)$ (ii) $f \circ f(2)$

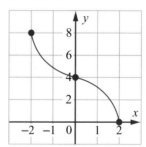

8. A gas meter indicates the amount of gas in cubic metres used by a consumer. The number of therms of heat from x cubic metres of gas is given by the function f where $f(x) = 36x$, where $x \geq 0$.

A particular gas company's charge in € for t therms is given by the function g where $g(t) = 20 + 0.03t$.

   (i) How many therms of heat are produced from 120 cubic metres of gas?

  (ii) What is the cost of using 4,968 therms?

 (iii) Find the cost of using the following amounts of gas from this gas company.

   (a) 100 cubic metres   **(b)** 150 cubic metres   **(c)** 440 cubic metres

 (iv) Find the rule, in its simplest form, for the function gf where $gf(x)$ is the cost of using x cubic metres of gas and verify one answer from part **(iii)**.

   (v) Use your rule to find the cost of 550 cubic metres of gas.

Notation

The notation $y = f(x)$ means 'the value of the output y depends on the value of the input x, according to some rule called f'. Hence, y and $f(x)$ are interchangeable and the y-axis can also be called the $f(x)$-axis.

Note: It is very important not to draw a graph outside the given values of x.

Graphing linear functions

The first four letters in the word **linear** spell **line**. Therefore, the graph of a linear function will be a straight line. A linear function is usually given in the form $f : x \rightarrow ax + b$, where $a \neq 0$ and a, b are constants. For example, $f : x \rightarrow 2x + 5$. As the graph is a straight line, two points are all that is needed to graph it. In the question, you will always be given a set of inputs, x, called the **domain**.

To graph a linear function, do the following.

1. Choose two suitable values of x, in the given domain.
   (Two suitable values are the smallest and largest values of x.)
2. Substitute these in the function to find the two corresponding values of y.
3. Plot the points and draw the line through them.

Note: $-3 \leq x \leq 2$ means 'x is between -3 and 2, including -3 and 2'.

EXAMPLE

Graph the function $f : x \rightarrow 2x + 1$ in the domain $-3 \leq x \leq 2$, $\quad x \in \mathbb{R}$.

Solution:

Let $y = f(x) \Rightarrow y = 2x + 1$.

x	$2x + 1$	y
-3	$-6 + 1$	-5
2	$4 + 5$	5

Plot the points $(-3, -5)$ and $(2, 5)$ and join them with a straight line.

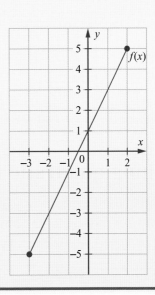

Exercise 7.1

In questions 1–15, graph the function in the given domain.

1.	$f : x \rightarrow 2x + 3$	in the domain	$-3 \leq x \leq 2,$	$x \in \mathbb{R}$
2.	$g : x \rightarrow 3x + 2$	in the domain	$-2 \leq x \leq 3,$	$x \in \mathbb{R}$
3.	$f : x \rightarrow 4x + 3$	in the domain	$-3 \leq x \leq 3,$	$x \in \mathbb{R}$
4.	$g : x \rightarrow 2x - 5$	in the domain	$-1 \leq x \leq 5,$	$x \in \mathbb{R}$
5.	$h : x \rightarrow x - 2$	in the domain	$-2 \leq x \leq 5,$	$x \in \mathbb{R}$
6.	$g : x \rightarrow 5x - 2$	in the domain	$-1 \leq x \leq 2,$	$x \in \mathbb{R}$
7.	$k : x \rightarrow x$	in the domain	$-3 \leq x \leq 3,$	$x \in \mathbb{R}$
8.	$f : x \rightarrow 2x$	in the domain	$-2 \leq x \leq 2,$	$x \in \mathbb{R}$
9.	$g : x \rightarrow -x$	in the domain	$-3 \leq x \leq 3,$	$x \in \mathbb{R}$
10.	$h : x \rightarrow 2 - x$	in the domain	$-4 \leq x \leq 4,$	$x \in \mathbb{R}$
11.	$f : x \rightarrow 4 - 3x$	in the domain	$-2 \leq x \leq 4,$	$x \in \mathbb{R}$
12.	$g : x \rightarrow -1 - x$	in the domain	$-4 \leq x \leq 3,$	$x \in \mathbb{R}$
13.	$h : x \rightarrow \frac{1}{2} x$	in the domain	$-2 \leq x \leq 4,$	$x \in \mathbb{R}$
14.	$f : x \rightarrow \frac{1}{3} x + 1$	in the domain	$-3 \leq x \leq 3,$	$x \in \mathbb{R}$
15.	$g : x \rightarrow \frac{1}{2} - \frac{1}{4} x$	in the domain	$-2 \leq x \leq 4,$	$x \in \mathbb{R}$

16. Using the same axes and scales, graph the functions
$f : x \rightarrow x - 6, \ g : x \rightarrow -2x$ in the domain $-1 \leq x \leq 5,$ $x \in \mathbb{R}.$
   (i) From your graph, write down the coordinates of the point of intersection of f and g.
   (ii) Verify your answer to part (i) by solving the simultaneous equations $x - y = 6$ and $2x + y = 0.$

17. Using the same axes and scales, graph the functions
$f : x \rightarrow 2x - 1, \ g : x \rightarrow 2 - x$ in the domain $-2 \leq x \leq 3,$ $x \in \mathbb{R}.$
   (i) From your graph, write down the coordinates of the point of intersection of f and g.
   (ii) Verify your answer to part (i) by solving the simultaneous equations
   $2x - y = 1$ and $x + y = 2.$

Graphing quadratic functions

A **quadratic** function is usually given in the form $f : x \rightarrow ax^2 + bx + c, \ a \neq 0,$ and a, b, c are constants. For example, $f : x \rightarrow 2x^2 - x + 3.$ Because of its shape, quite a few points are needed to plot the graph of a quadratic function. In the question, you will always be given a set of inputs, $x,$

called the **domain**. With these inputs, a table is used to find the corresponding set of outputs, y or $f(x)$, called the **range**. When the table is completed, plot the points and join them with a **smooth curve**.

Notes on making the table:

1. Work out each column separately, i.e. all the x^2 values first, then all the x values and finally the constant. (Watch for patterns in the numbers.)
2. Work out each corresponding value of y.
3. The **only** column that changes sign is the x term (middle) column.
   If the given values of x contain 0, then the x term column will make one sign change, either from + to − or from − to +, where $x = 0$.
4. The other two columns **never** change sign. They remain either all + or all −.
   These columns keep the sign given in the question.

Note: Decide where to draw the x-axis and y-axis by looking at the table to see what the largest and smallest values of x and y are. In general, the units on the x-axis are larger than the units on the y-axis. Try to make sure that the graph extends almost the whole width and length of the page.

EXAMPLE

Graph the function $g : x \rightarrow 5 + 3x - 2x^2$ in the domain $-2 \le x \le 3, \qquad x \in \mathbb{R}$.

Solution:

Let $y = g(x) \Rightarrow y = 5 + 3x - 2x^2$.

x	$-2x^2 + 3x + 5$	y
-2	$-8 - 6 + 5$	-9
-1	$-2 - 3 + 5$	0
0	$-0 + 0 + 5$	5
1	$-2 + 3 + 5$	6
2	$-8 + 6 + 5$	3
3	$-18 + 9 + 5$	-4

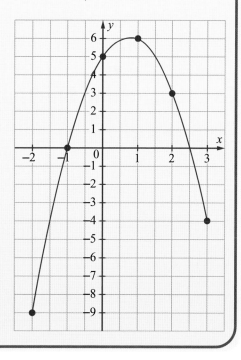

Exercise 7.2

In questions 1–6, graph the function in the given domain.

1. $g : x \rightarrow x^2 - 2x - 8$ in the domain $-3 \leq x \leq 5$, $x \in \mathbb{R}$.

2. $f : x \rightarrow x^2 + 2x - 3$ in the domain $-4 \leq x \leq 2$, $x \in \mathbb{R}$.

3. $f : x \rightarrow 2x - x^2$ in the domain $-2 \leq x \leq 4$, $x \in \mathbb{R}$.

4. $g : x \rightarrow 2x^2 + 3x - 2$ in the domain $-3 \leq x \leq 2$, $x \in \mathbb{R}$.

5. $f : x \rightarrow 2x^2 - x - 4$ in the domain $-2 \leq x \leq 3$, $x \in \mathbb{R}$.

6. $g : x \rightarrow 3 + 5x - 2x^2$ in the domain $-1 \leq x \leq 4$, $x \in \mathbb{R}$.

7. On the same axes and scales, graph the functions
   $f : x \rightarrow 5 + 2x - x^2$, $g : x \rightarrow 2 - x$ in the domain $-2 \leq x \leq 4$, $x \in \mathbb{R}$.

8. On the same axes and scales, graph the functions
   $f : x \rightarrow 2x^2 - 3x - 8$, $g : x \rightarrow 3x - 2$ in the domain $-2 \leq x \leq 4$, $x \in \mathbb{R}$.

9. On the same axes and scales, graph the functions
   $f : x \rightarrow x^2 - 2x - 4$, $g : x \rightarrow 2x + 1$ in the domain $-3 \leq x \leq 5$, $x \in \mathbb{R}$.

   (i) From your graph, write down the coordinates of the points of intersection of f and g.

   (ii) Verify the x values in part **(i)** by solving the equation $g(x) = f(x)$.

10. On the same axes and scales, graph the functions
   $f : x \rightarrow 5 - x - 2x^2$, $g : x \rightarrow 1 - 3x$ in the domain $-2 \leq x \leq 3$, $x \in \mathbb{R}$.

   (i) From your graph, write down the coordinates of the points of intersection of f and g.

   (ii) Verify the x values in part **(i)** by solving the equation $g(x) = f(x)$.

Graphing cubic functions

A **cubic** function is usually given in the form $f : x \rightarrow ax^3 + bx^2 + cx + d$, $a \neq 0$ and a, b, c and d are constants. For example, $f : x \rightarrow x^3 - 2x^2 - 6x + 5$. As with graphing quadratic functions, quite a few points are needed to plot the graph of a cubic function. In the question, you will always be given a set of inputs, x, called the **domain**. With these inputs, a table is used to find the corresponding set of outputs, y or $f(x)$, called the **range**. When the table is completed, plot the points and join them with a **smooth curve**.

Notes on making the table:

1. Work out each column separately, i.e. all the x^3 terms first, then all the x^2 terms, then all the x terms and finally the constant term. (Watch for patterns in the numbers.)
2. Work out each corresponding value of y.

3. Only **two** columns may change sign, the x^3 and x term columns. If the given values of x contain 0, then the x^3 and x term columns will make **one** sign change, either from + to − or − to +, where $x = 0$. So the only two signs to work out are the ones at the beginning of the x^3 and x term columns, which are changed at $x = 0$. The simplest way to find the first sign in these two columns is to multiply the sign of the first given value of x by the sign of the coefficient of x^3 and x.

4. The other two columns **never** change sign. They remain all + or all −. These columns keep the sign given in the question.

Note: Decide where to draw the x-axis and y-axis by looking at the table to see what the largest and smallest values of x and y are. In general, the units on the x-axis are larger than the units on the y-axis.

Try to make sure that the graph extends almost the whole width and length of the page.

EXAMPLE

Graph the function $f : x \to x^3 + 3x^2 - x - 3$ in the domain $-4 \le x \le 2$, $\quad x \in \mathbb{R}$.

Solution:

Let $y = f(x) \Rightarrow y = x^3 + 3x^2 - x - 3$.

x	$x^3 + 3x^2 - x - 3$	y
−4	$-64 + 48 + 4 - 3$	−15
−3	$-27 + 27 + 3 - 3$	0
−2	$-8 + 12 + 2 - 3$	3
−1	$-1 + 3 + 1 - 3$	0
0	$0 + 0 + 0 - 3$	−3
1	$1 + 3 - 1 - 3$	0
2	$8 + 12 - 2 - 3$	15

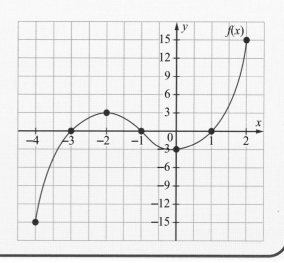

Exercise 7.3

In questions 1–10, graph the function in the given domain.

1. $f : x \to x^3 + x^2 - 2x - 1$ in the domain $-3 \le x \le 2$, $x \in \mathbb{R}$.

2. $g : x \to x^3 - 4x^2 + x + 6$ in the domain $-2 \le x \le 4$, $x \in \mathbb{R}$.

3. $f : x \to 2x^3 - 3x^2 - 6x + 2$ in the domain $-2 \le x \le 3$, $x \in \mathbb{R}$.

4. $g : x \rightarrow 2x^3 - 2x^2 - 3x + 10$ in the domain $-2 \le x \le 2,$ $x \in \mathbb{R}.$

5. $f : x \rightarrow 6 + 6x - x^2 - x^3$ in the domain $-3 \le x \le 3,$ $x \in \mathbb{R}.$

6. $g : x \rightarrow 6 + 5x - 2x^2 - x^3$ in the domain $-4 \le x \le 3,$ $x \in \mathbb{R}.$

7. $f : x \rightarrow 4 + 8x + x^2 - 2x^3$ in the domain $-2 \le x \le 3,$ $x \in \mathbb{R}.$

8. $g : x \rightarrow 2x - x^2 - x^3$ in the domain $-3 \le x \le 2,$ $x \in \mathbb{R}.$

9. $f : x \rightarrow x^3 - 3x^2 - 2$ in the domain $-2 \le x \le 4,$ $x \in \mathbb{R}.$

10. $g : x \rightarrow 3 + 5x - x^3$ in the domain $-3 \le x \le 3,$ $x \in \mathbb{R}.$

11. On the same axes and scales, graph the functions
$f : x \rightarrow x^3 - 2x^2 - 4x + 1$ and $g : x \rightarrow 3x + 1$ in the domain $-2 \le x \le 4,$ $x \in \mathbb{R}.$

12. On the same axes and scales, graph the functions
$f : x \rightarrow x^3 - 3x^2 + x - 3$ and $g : x \rightarrow 3 - 2x - x^2$ in the domain $-4 \le x \le 2,$ $x \in \mathbb{R}.$
From your graph, write down the coordinates of the points of intersection of f and g.

13. On the same axes and scales, graph the functions
$f : x \rightarrow x^3 - 2x^2 - 6x + 2$, $g : x \rightarrow 2x^2 - 7x - 4$, $h : x \rightarrow 2 - 3x$ in the domain
$-2 \le x \le 4,$ $x \in \mathbb{R}.$
From your graph, write down the coordinates of the points of intersection of f, g and h.

Graphing exponential functions

An **exponential** function is in the form $f : x \rightarrow ab^x$ where $a \in \mathbb{N}$ and $b, x \in \mathbb{R}$. For example, $f : x \rightarrow 2(3)^x$. Because of its shape, quite a few points are needed to plot the graph of an exponential function. In the question, you will always be given a set of inputs, x, called the **domain**. With these inputs, a table is used to find the corresponding set of outputs, y of $f(x)$, called the **range**. When the table is completed, plot the points and join them with a **smooth curve**.

An exponential function is a curve which starts horizontal and then rises into a vertical position.

The value of a in the given function is equal to the point where the curve crosses the y-axis.

Thus, $a = y$-intercept.

The value for b is known as the 'base'. The bigger b is, the steeper the curve will rise.

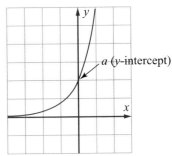

Note: If $b > 1$, the curve is increasing.
If $0 < b < 1$, the curve is decreasing.

Method for graphing functions of the form $y = ab^x$

1. Use a table to find suitable coordinates on the curve.
2. Join these points with a smooth curve.

EXAMPLE

Graph the function $f : x \rightarrow 4(2)^x$ in the domain $-5 \le x \le 1$, $\quad x \in \mathbb{R}$.

Solution:

Let $y = f(x) = 4(2)^x$.

x	$4(2)^x$	y
-5	$4(2)^{-5}$	0.125
-4	$4(2)^{-4}$	0.25
-3	$4(2)^{-3}$	0.5
-2	$4(2)^{-2}$	1
-1	$4(2)^{-1}$	2
0	$4(2)^{0}$	4
1	$4(2)^{1}$	8

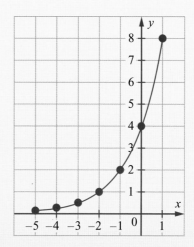

Note: $4(2)^x$ could also be written as $4(2^x)$ or 4×2^x.

Exercise 7.4

In questions 1–6, graph the function in the given domain.

1. $f : x \rightarrow 4^x$ in the domain $-2 \le x \le 2$, $\quad x \in \mathbb{R}$.

2. $g : x \rightarrow 3(2)^x$ in the domain $-4 \le x \le 2$, $\quad x \in \mathbb{R}$.

3. $g : x \rightarrow 2(3)^x$ in the domain $-3 \le x \le 1$, $\quad x \in \mathbb{R}$.

4. $f : x \rightarrow 2\left(\frac{1}{2}\right)^x$ in the domain $-2 \le x \le 3$, $\quad x \in \mathbb{R}$.

5. $g : x \rightarrow 6\left(\frac{1}{3}\right)^x$ in the domain $-1 \le x \le 3$, $\quad x \in \mathbb{R}$.

6. $f : x \rightarrow 2\left(\frac{1}{5}\right)^x$ in the domain $-1 \le x \le 3$, $\quad x \in \mathbb{R}$.

7. (i) On the same axis and scale, graph the functions

$f : x \to \left(\tfrac{1}{2}\right)^x$ and $g : x \to 3^x$ in the domain $-3 \leq x \leq 2$.

(ii) From your graph, estimate the points of intersection of f and g.

8. (i) On the same axis and scale, graph the functions

$f : x \to 3\left(\tfrac{1}{2}\right)^x$ and $g : x \to 4 - 2x$ in the domain $-1 \leq x \leq 3$.

(ii) From your graph, estimate the points of intersection of f and g.

9. (i) On the same axis and scale, graph the functions

$f : x \to 5^x$ and $g : x \to 2 + x - x^2$ in the domain $-2 \leq x \leq 1$.

(ii) From your graph, estimate the points of intersection of f and g.

Using graphs

Once we have drawn the graph, we are usually asked to use it to answer some questions. Below are examples of the general types of problem where graphs are used.

Notes: 1. $y = f(x)$, so $f(x)$ can be replaced by y.

2. In general, if given x find y, and vice versa.

Examples of the main types of problem once the graph is drawn

EXAMPLE 1

Find the values of x for which $f(x) = 0$.

This question is asking:
'Where does the curve meet the x-axis?'

Solution:
Write down the values of x where the graph meets the x-axis.
From the graph: $x = -1$ or $x = 1$ or $x = 3$.

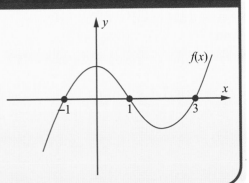

EXAMPLE 2

Find the values of x for which $f(x) = 6$.

This question is asking:

'When $y = 6$, what are the values of x?'

Solution:

Draw the line $y = 6$. Where this line meets the curve, draw broken perpendicular lines onto the x-axis.

Write down the values of x where these broken lines meet the x-axis.

From the graph:

When $y = 6$, $x = -1\cdot1$ or $x = 1\cdot3$ or $x = 2\cdot9$.

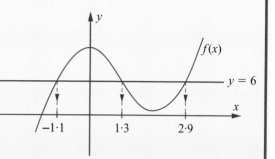

EXAMPLE 3

Find the value of $f(-1\cdot6)$.

This question is asking:

'When $x = -1\cdot6$, what is the value of y?'

Solution:

From $x = -1\cdot6$ on the x-axis, draw a broken perpendicular line to meet the curve. From this draw a broken horizontal line to meet the y-axis. Write down the value of y where this line meets the y-axis.

From the graph:

$f(-1\cdot6) = -7$

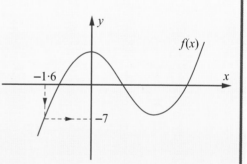

EXAMPLE 4

Local maximum and minimum points or the local maximum and minimum values

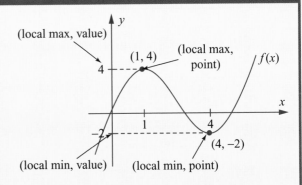

Often we are asked to find the local maximum and minimum points or the local maximum and minimum values. Consider the graph on the right. The local maximum and minimum points are where the graph turns, $(1, 4)$ and $(4, -2)$, respectively. The local maximum and minimum values are found by drawing a line from the turning points to the y-axis and reading the values where these lines meet the y-axis. The maximum and minimum values are 4 and -2, respectively.

EXAMPLE 5

Increasing and decreasing

Graphs are read from left to right.

Increasing: $f(x)$ is increasing where the graph is **rising** as we go from left to right.

Decreasing: $f(x)$ is decreasing where the graph is **falling** as we go from left to right.

Find the values of x for which:

(i) $f(x)$ is increasing

(ii) $f(x)$ is decreasing

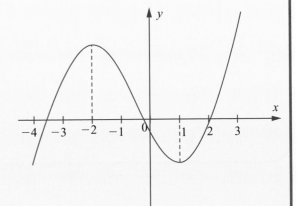

Solution:

(i) $f(x)$ increasing, graph rising from left to right.
   The values of x are:
   $-4 \leq x < -2$ and $1 < x \leq 3$

(ii) $f(x)$ decreasing, graph falling from left to right.
   The values of x are: $-2 < x < 1$

Note: At $x = -2$ and $x = 1$, the graph is neither increasing nor decreasing.

EXAMPLE 6

Two functions graphed on the same axes and scales
The diagram shows the graph of two functions: $f(x)$, a curve, and $g(x)$, a line.

Find the values of x for which:

(i) $f(x) = g(x)$ (ii) $f(x) \leq g(x)$ (iii) $f(x) \geq g(x)$

Solution:

(i) $f(x) = g(x)$
    (curve = line)
    The values of x are 0·4, 1·4
    and 3·1.

(ii) $f(x) \leq g(x)$
    (curve equal to and below
    the line)
    The values of x are
    $-1 \leq x \leq 0\cdot4$ and $1\cdot4 \leq x \leq 3\cdot1$.

(iii) $f(x) \geq g(x)$
    (curve equal to and above the line)
    The values of x are
    $0\cdot4 \leq x \leq 1\cdot4$ and $3\cdot1 \leq x \leq 4$.

Note: If the question uses $f(x) < g(x)$ or $f(x) > g(x)$, then the values of x where the graphs meet (0·4, 1·4 and 3·1) are **not** included in the solution.

EXAMPLE 7

Graph the function $f : x \rightarrow 2 - 9x + 6x^2 - x^3$ in the domain $-1 \leq x \leq 5$, $x \in \mathbb{R}$.
Use your graph to estimate:

(i) The values of x for which $f(x) = 0$

(ii) $f(-0\cdot5)$

(iii) The values of x for which $f(x)$ is increasing

(iv) The values of x for which $f(x) = 2$

(v) The coordinates of the local maximum and local minimum points

Solution:

Let $y = f(x) \Rightarrow y = 2 - 9x + 6x^2 - x^3$.

x	$-x^3 + 6x^2 + 9x + 2$	y
-1	$+1 + 6 + 9 + 2$	18
0	$+0 + 0 + 0 + 2$	2
1	$-1 + 6 - 9 + 2$	-2
2	$-8 + 24 - 18 + 2$	0
3	$-27 + 54 - 27 + 2$	2
4	$-64 + 96 - 36 + 2$	-2
5	$-125 + 150 - 45 + 2$	-18

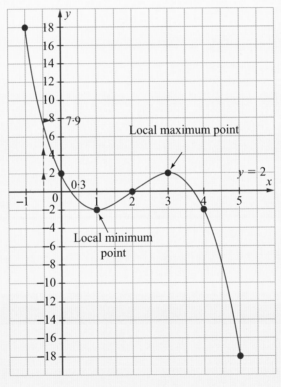

(i) **Estimate the values of x for which $f(x) = 0$.**

This question is asking, 'Where does the curve meet the x-axis?'

The curve meets the x-axis at 0·3, 2 and 3·7.

Therefore, the values of x for which $f(x) = 0$ are 0·3, 2 and 3·7.

Note: 'Find the values of x for which $2 - 9x + 6x^2 - x^3 = 0$' is another way of asking the same question.

(ii) **Estimate the value of $f(-0.5)$.**

This question is asking, 'When $x = -0.5$, what is the value of y?'

From $x = -0.5$ on the x-axis, draw a broken perpendicular line to meet the curve.

From this, draw a broken horizontal line to meet the y-axis.

This line meets the y-axis at 7·9.

Therefore, $f(-0.5) = 7.9$.

(iii) **Estimate the values of x for which $f(x)$ is increasing.**

This question is asking, 'Where is the curve increasing as we go from left to right?'

From the graph, the curve is increasing between 2 and 3.

Therefore, the values of x for which $f(x)$ is increasing are $1 < x < 3$.

Note: $x = 1$ is not included because at $x = 1$ there is a turning point and $f(x)$ is not increasing.

$x = 3$ is not included because at $x = 3$ there is a turning point and $f(x)$ is not increasing.

(iv) **Estimate the values of x for which $f(x) = 2$.**

This question is asking, 'When $y = 2$, what are the values of x?'

Draw the line $y = 2$.

Where this line meets the curve, draw broken perpendicular lines to meet the x-axis.

These lines meet the x-axis at 0 and 3.

Therefore, the values of x for which $f(x) = 2$ are 0 and 3.

Note: 'Estimate the values of x for which $2 - 9x + 6x^2 - x^3 = 0$' is another way of asking the same question.

(v) From the graph we can see:

The local maximum point is at $(3, 2)$.

The local minimum point is at $(1, -2)$.

Exercise 7.5

1. Below is a graph of the function $f : x \rightarrow x^3 - 3x^2 + 4$ in the domain $-2 \leq x \leq 4$, $\quad x \in \mathbb{R}$.

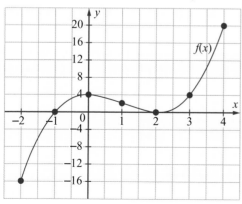

Use your graph to do the following.
   (i) Find the values of x for which $f(x) = 0$.
  (ii) Find the coordinates of the local maximum and minimum points of f.
 (iii) Find the local maximum and minimum values.
 (iv) Estimate the value of $f(3 \cdot 5)$.
  (v) Find the values of x for which $f(x)$ is decreasing.
 (vi) Estimate the values of x for which $f(x) = 2$.

2. Below is a graph of the function $f : x \rightarrow 2(\frac{3}{4})^x$ in the domain $-5 \le x \le 8, \quad x \in \mathbb{R}$.

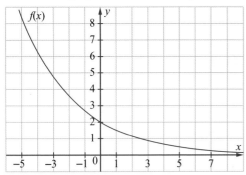

Use your graph to do the following.
   (i) Estimate the value of x for which $f(x) = 1$.
  (ii) Estimate the value of x for which $f(x) = 4$.
 (iii) Estimate the value of $f(-3)$.
 (iv) Estimate the value of $f(2)$.

3. Graph the function $f : x \rightarrow x^3 + 4x^2 + x - 6$ in the domain $-4 \le x \le 2, \quad x \in \mathbb{R}$.
   Use your graph to do the following.
   (i) Find the values of x for which $f(x) = 0$.
  (ii) Estimate the value of $f(1 \cdot 4)$.
 (iii) Estimate the local maximum and minimum values.
 (iv) Estimate the values of x for which $f(x) = -2$.

4. Let $f(x) = 2x^3 - 3x^2 - 12x + 4$ for $x \in \mathbb{R}$.
   (i) Complete the table.

x	$-2 \cdot 5$	-2	-1	0	1	2	3	$3 \cdot 5$
$f(x)$	-16							11

   (ii) Draw the graph of $f(x)$ in the domain $-2 \cdot 5 \le x \le 3 \cdot 5, \qquad x \in \mathbb{R}$.
  (iii) Write down the coordinates of the local maximum and the local minimum points.
  (iv) Use your graph to find the values of x for which $f(x)$ is decreasing.
   (v) Estimate the values of x for which $f(x) = 0$.

5. Graph the function $g : x \rightarrow x^3 - 4x^2 + 5$ in the domain $-2 \leq x \leq 4$, $x \in \mathbb{R}$.
   (i) Write down the coordinates of the local maximum point.
   (ii) Estimate the values of x for which $f(x) = 0$.
   (iii) Use your graph to solve the equation $x^3 - 4x^2 + 2 = 0$.

6. On the same axes and scales, graph the functions
   $f : x \rightarrow x^3 - 3x^2 - 4x + 12$, $g : x \rightarrow 9 - 3x$ in the domain $-2 \leq x \leq 4$, $x \in \mathbb{R}$.
   Use your graphs to find the values of x for which:
   (i) $f(x) = 0$ (ii) $f(x) = 12$ (iii) $f(x) = g(x)$ (iv) $f(x) \geq g(x)$ (v) $f(x) \leq g(x)$

7. Graph the function $f : x \rightarrow x^3 - 3x + 2$ in the domain $-3 \leq x \leq 3$, $x \in \mathbb{R}$.
   Use your graph to find the following.
   (i) The local maximum and minimum values.
   (ii) The coordinates of the local maximum and minimum points.
   (iii) The range of values of x for which $f(x)$ is decreasing.

8. Let $f(x) = x^3 + 2x^2 - 7x - 2$ for $x \in \mathbb{R}$.
   (i) Complete the following table.

x	-4	-3	-2	-1	0	1	2	3
$f(x)$		10				-6		

   (ii) Draw the graph of f.
   (iii) Estimate the values of x for which $f(x) = 0$.
   (iv) Use the graph to find the least value of $f(x)$ in $0 \leq x \leq 3$.

9. On the same axes and scales, graph the functions
   $f : x \rightarrow x^3 - 2x^2 - 6x + 4$ and $g : x \rightarrow 2x - 5$ in the domain $-2 \leq x \leq 4$, $x \in \mathbb{R}$.
   Use your graphs to find the following.
   (i) The two values of x for which $f(x) = g(x)$.
   (ii) The range of values of x for which $f(x) \leq g(x)$.
   (iii) The range of values of x for which $f(x) \geq g(x)$.

10. Let $f(x) = x^3 + x^2 + x - 2$ for $x \in \mathbb{R}$.
    (i) Complete the table.

x	-2	-1	0	1	2
$f(x)$	-8				

    (ii) Draw the graph of $f(x)$ in the domain $-2 \leq x \leq 2$.
    (iii) Use the same axes and scales, and in the same domain, graph the function
    $g : x \rightarrow x^2 + x - 6$ for $x \in \mathbb{R}$.
    (iv) Use your graph to estimate the point where $f = g$.

11. Currently, 8,000 bacteria are present in a culture. When an antibiotic is added to the culture, the number of bacteria is reduced by half every hour. This decay process is represented by the function: $f : x \rightarrow 8{,}000\left(\frac{1}{2}\right)^{x}$, where x is the number of hours that have passed.

(i) Complete the following table.

x = no. of hours	0	1	2	3	4	5
$f(x) = 8{,}000\left(\frac{1}{2}\right)^{x}$ = no. of bacteria	8,000			1,000		

(ii) Draw the graph of f.

(iii) How many bacteria remain after eight hours?

(iv) After how many hours will fewer than 130 bacteria be present?

12. Each year a tennis club has a tournament. Play starts with 128 participants. During each round, half of the players are eliminated. This can be represented by the function $f : x \rightarrow 128\left(\frac{1}{2}\right)^{x}$, where x is the number of rounds which have been played.

(i) Draw a graph of this decay function for the first four rounds (i.e. for $0 \le x \le 4$).

(ii) How many players remain in the tournament after five rounds?

(iii) After how many rounds will there be a winner?

13. Bacteria can multiply at an alarming rate when each bacteria splits into two new cells, thus doubling. If we start with only one bacteria which can double every hour, its growth is represented by the function $f : x \rightarrow 2^{x}$.

(i) Use the function to find how many bacteria there would be after exactly 24 hours.

(ii) Draw a graph of this growth function for the first six hours (i.e. for $0 \le x \le 6$).

14. In 1986 there was an accident at a nuclear power plant at Chernobyl in the Ukraine. The result of this accident was that radioactive substances were released into the atmosphere.

As a result of this contamination, the hay in Austria was contaminated by a radioactive chemical called iodine-131.

Iodine-131 has a half-life of eight days (this is the time it takes for half of the radioactivity to decay). If the radioactivity level starts at 100%, the decay can be represented by the function $f : x \to 100 \left(\frac{1}{2}\right)^x$, where x represents the number of half-lives which have passed.

(i) What percentage of the radioactivity remains after 16 days?

(ii) Draw a graph of this decay function for the first seven half-lives (i.e. for $0 \le x \le 7$).

(iii) It is safe to feed the hay to cows when 10% of the iodine-131 remains. Use your graph to estimate, to the nearest day, how long the farmers needed to wait to use this hay.

Trapezoidal rule and graphs

The trapezoidal rule can be used to estimate the area between the graph of a function and the x-axis.

Consider the graph of the function $f(x)$ in the domain $0 \le x \le 6$. The trapezoidal rule can be used to calculate the area between the curve and the x-axis (shaded region). However, the negative y values must be taken as positive.

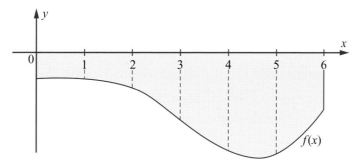

To find the area:

1. Divide the figure into a number of strips of equal width.
   Note: the number of strips can be even or odd.

2. Number and measure each height, h.

3. Use the following formula:

$$\text{Area} = \frac{\text{w}}{2} \left[h_1 + h_7 + 2 \left(h_2 + h_3 + h_4 + h_5 + h_6 \right) \right]$$

$$\text{Area} = \frac{\text{width}}{2} \left[\text{first height} + \text{last height} + 2 \left(\text{sum of all remaining heights} \right) \right]$$

Exercise 7.6

1. The diagram shows the curve $f : x \rightarrow x^2 + 3$ in the domain $0 \leq x \leq 4$, $\quad x \in \mathbb{R}$.

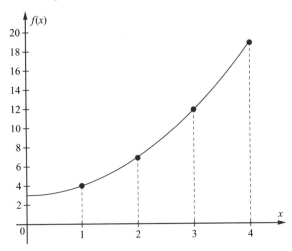

(i) Complete the following table.

x	0	1	2	3	4
$f(x)$					

(ii) Hence, use the trapezoidal rule to estimate the area between the curve and the x-axis.

2. Graph the function $f : x \rightarrow 13 + 4x - x^2$ in the domain $0 \leq x \leq 6$, $\quad x \in \mathbb{R}$.
   Use the trapezoidal rule to estimate the area between the curve and the x-axis.

3. Graph the function $f : x \rightarrow 8 + 2x - x^2$ in the domain $-2 \leq x \leq 3$, $\quad x \in \mathbb{R}$.
   Use the trapezoidal rule to estimate the area between the curve and the x-axis.

4. Graph the function $f : x \rightarrow x^3 - 6x^2 + 9x + 6$ in the domain $0 \leq x \leq 4$, $\quad x \in \mathbb{R}$.
   Use the trapezoidal rule to estimate the area between the curve and the x-axis.

5. Graph the function $f : x \rightarrow x^3 + 3x^2 - x + 12$ in the domain $-4 \leq x \leq 1$, $\quad x \in \mathbb{R}$.
   Use the trapezoidal rule to estimate the area between the curve and the x-axis.

6. Graph the function $f : x \rightarrow -6 + 6x - x^2 - x^3$ in the domain $-3 \leq x \leq 3$, $\quad x \in \mathbb{R}$.
   Use the trapezoidal rule to estimate the area between the curve and the x-axis.

Differentiation, or differential calculus, is the branch of mathematics measuring rates of change.

Slope of a line

On the right is part of the graph of the line $y = 3x$.

There is a relationship between x and y. For every increase in x, there is three times this increase in y.

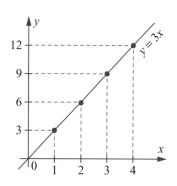

> Rate of change of y = 3 times rate of change of x.

From coordinate geometry, the slope of the line $y = 3x$ is 3.

> Slope = 3

> Rate of change = slope

The key word here is **slope**. The slope of a line will give **the rate of change** of the variable on the vertical axis with respect to the variable on the horizontal axis. Therefore, to find the rate of change we need only to find the slope.

Note: The y-axis is usually the vertical axis and the x-axis is the horizontal axis. Therefore, the slope of a line will give the rate of change of y with respect to (the change in) x.

Slope of a curve

Consider the curve below and the tangents that are constructed on it.

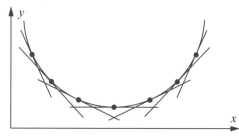

The slope of the curve at a point is equal to the slope of the tangent at that point. As we move along the curve, the slope of each tangent changes. In other words, the rate of change of y with respect to x changes. We need to find a method of finding the slope of the tangent at each point on the curve. The method of finding the slope of a tangent to a curve at any point on the curve is called **differentiation**.

Suppose we want to find the slope of the curve $y = x^2 + 1$ at the point $P(1, 2)$.

In the series of diagrams below, it is as if we are looking through a microscope at chords *PS*, *PR* and *PQ* drawn between points close together on the curve. As the chords become smaller, the points *S*, *R*, *Q* move closer to *P* and the slope of the chord approaches the slope of the tangent at *P*.

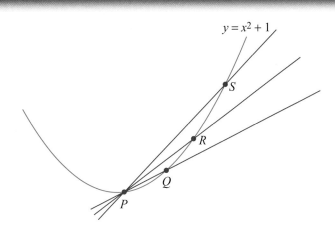

Below we find the slopes of chords *PS*, *PR* and *PQ*, where $P = (1, 2)$, $Q = (1.01, 2.0201)$, $R = (1.05, 2.1025)$ and $S = (1.1, 2.21)$ are all points on the curve $y = x^2 + 1$.

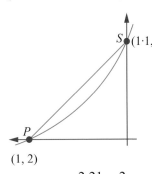
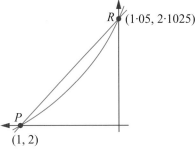
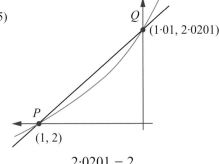

$$\text{Slope } PS = \frac{2.21 - 2}{1.1 - 1}$$
$$= \frac{0.21}{0.1}$$
$$= 2.1$$

$$\text{Slope } PR = \frac{2.1025 - 2}{1.05 - 1}$$
$$= \frac{0.1025}{0.05}$$
$$= 2.05$$

$$\text{Slope } PQ = \frac{2.0201 - 2}{1.01 - 1}$$
$$= \frac{0.0201}{0.01}$$
$$= 2.01$$

This suggests (but does not prove) that the slope of the curve $y = x^2 + 1$ at the point $(1, 2)$ is 2.

We could say 'as the line becomes a tangent to the curve at the point *P*, its slope becomes 2'.

This idea of points getting closer together is referred to as a limit in mathematics.

The process of finding this limiting value is called differentiation. For neatness, this limit is written as $\frac{dy}{dx}$ (pronounced 'dee *y*, dee *x*') or $f'(x)$ (pronounced '*f* dash of *x*' or '*f* prime of *x*').

$\frac{dy}{dx}$ or $f'(x)$ is called the differential coefficient or first derivative of *y* with respect to *x*.

The advantage of the notation $\frac{dy}{dx}$ is that it tells us which quantities are being compared.

$\frac{dy}{dx}$ is the derivative of *y* with respect to *x*.

$\frac{ds}{dt}$ is the derivative of *s* with respect to *t*.

$\frac{dA}{dr}$ is the derivative of *A* with respect to *r*.

Differentiation by rule

The general rule

if: $y = x^n$ then $\dfrac{dy}{dx} = nx^{n-1}$

$y = ax^n$ then $\dfrac{dy}{dx} = nax^{n-1}$

In words:

Multiply by the power and reduce the power by 1.

EXAMPLE 1

Differentiate with respect to x.

(i) $y = 5x^2$ **(ii)** $y = 9x$ **(iii)** $y = 4x^3$ **(iv)** $y = -4x$ **(v)** $y = -7x^2$ **(vi)** $y = 7$

Solution:

(i) $y = 5x^2$ $\dfrac{dy}{dx} = 2 \times 5x^{2-1} = 10x^1 = 10x$

(ii) $y = 9x = 9x^1$ $\dfrac{dy}{dx} = 1 \times 9x^{1-1} = 9x^0 = 9 \; (x^0 = 1)$

(iii) $y = 4x^3$ $\dfrac{dy}{dx} = 3 \times 4x^{3-1} = 12x^2$

(iv) $y = -4x = -4x^1$ $\dfrac{dy}{dx} = 1 \times -4x^{1-1} = -4x^0 = -4$

(v) $y = -7x^2$ $\dfrac{dy}{dx} = 2 \times -7x^{2-1} = -14x^1 = -14x$

(vi) $y = 7 = 7x^0$ $\dfrac{dy}{dx} = 0 \times 7x^{0-1} = 0$

Part **(vi)** leads to the rule

The derivative of a constant is zero.

Note: The line $y = 7$ is a horizontal line. Its slope is 0. Therefore, its derivative (also its slope) equals zero.
In other words, the derivative of a constant always equals zero.

After practice, $\dfrac{dy}{dx}$ can be written down from inspection.

Sum or difference

If the expression to be differentiated contains more than one term, just differentiate, separately, each term in the expression.

EXAMPLE 2

(i) If $y = 3x^2 - 5x + 4$, find $\dfrac{dy}{dx}$.

(ii) If $f(x) = 4x^3 + x^2 - x - 6$, find $f'(x)$.

Solution:

(i) $y = 3x^2 - 5x + 4$

$\dfrac{dy}{dx} = 6x - 5$

(ii) $f(x) = 4x^3 + x^2 - x - 6$

$f'(x) = 12x^2 + 2x - 1$

Exercise 8.1

Find $\dfrac{dy}{dx}$ in questions 1–16.

1. $y = x^3$
2. $y = x^2$
3. $y = 8x$
4. $y = \dfrac{1}{4}x^2$

5. $y = 2$
6. $y = \dfrac{x^3}{3}$
7. $y = -5x$
8. $y = \dfrac{5x}{2}$

9. $y = -5$
10. $y = x^2 - 3x$
11. $y = x^3 - 4$
12. $y = \dfrac{x^2}{10} + 3x$

13. $y = x^2 - \dfrac{3}{2}x^3$
14. $y = x^3 + 4x^2 + x$
15. $y = 14 - 3x$
16. $y = \dfrac{3}{2}x + 1$

Find $f'(x)$ in questions 17–25.

17. $f(x) = x^2 + 4$
18. $f(x) = x - x^3$
19. $f(x) = 4 + 3x$

20. $f(x) = \dfrac{1}{20}x^2 - x$
21. $f(x) = 14 + \dfrac{3}{2}x - \dfrac{1}{8}x^3$
22. $f(x) = x^2 - x - 6$

23. $f(x) = 2x^3 - 2x^2 + 4x$
24. $f(x) = 1 - 2x - 5x^3$
25. $f(x) = \dfrac{1}{3}x^2 - \dfrac{1}{2}x^3$

Evaluating derivatives

Often we may be asked to find the value of the derivative for a particular value of the function.

EXAMPLE

(i) If $y = 2x^3 - 4x + 3$, find the value of $\dfrac{dy}{dx}$ when $x = 1$.

(ii) If $s = 4t^2 + 10t - 7$, find the value of $\dfrac{ds}{dt}$ when $t = -2$.

Solution:

(i) $\qquad y = 2x^3 - 4x + 3$

$\qquad \dfrac{dy}{dx} = 6x^2 - 4$

$\qquad \left.\dfrac{dy}{dx}\right|_{x=1} = 6(1)^2 - 4$

$\qquad\qquad = 6 - 4 = 2$

(ii) $\qquad s = 4t^2 + 10t - 7$

$\qquad \dfrac{ds}{dt} = 8t + 10$

$\qquad \left.\dfrac{ds}{dt}\right|_{t=-2} = 8(-2) + 10$

$\qquad\qquad = -16 + 10 = -6$

Exercise 8.2

1. If $y = 3x^2 + 4x + 2$, find the value of $\dfrac{dy}{dx}$ when $x = 1$.

2. If $y = 2x^3 + 4x^2 + 3x - 5$, find the value of $\dfrac{dy}{dx}$ when $x = 2$.

3. If $y = 4x^3 - 3x^2 + 5x - 3$, find the value of $\dfrac{dy}{dx}$ when $x = -1$.

4. If $s = 3t - 2t^2$, find $\dfrac{ds}{dt}$ when $t = 2$.

5. If $s = t^3 - 2t^2 - t + 1$, find $\dfrac{ds}{dt}$ when $t = -1$.

6. If $A = 3r^2 - 5r$, find $\dfrac{dA}{dr}$ when $r = 3$.

7. If $V = 3h - h^2 - 3h^3$, find $\dfrac{dV}{dh}$ when $h = 2$.

8. If $h = 20t - 5t^2$, find $\dfrac{dh}{dt}$ when $t = 4$.

9. If $A = \pi r^2$, find $\dfrac{dA}{dr}$ when $r = 5$, leaving your answer in terms of π.

10. If $V = \frac{4}{3}\pi r^3$, find $\dfrac{dV}{dr}$ when $r = 3$, leaving your answer in terms of π.

11. The table below shows some values of two functions, f and g, and of their derivatives f' and g'.

x	1	2	3	4
$f(x)$	5	4	−1	3
$g(x)$	1	−2	2	−5
$f'(x)$	5	6	0	7
$g'(x)$	−6	−4	−3	4

From the table above, answer the following.

(i) $f(x) + g(x)$ when $x = 2$

(ii) $f(x) - g(x)$ when $x = 3$

(iii) $f'(x) + g'(x)$ when $x = 1$

(iv) $f'(x) - g'(x)$ when $x = 4$

(v) $\dfrac{d}{dx}(f(x) + g(x))$ when $x = 3$

Second derivatives

The derivative of $\dfrac{dy}{dx}$, that is, $\dfrac{d}{dx}\left(\dfrac{dy}{dx}\right)$, is denoted by $\dfrac{d^2y}{dx^2}$ and is called the **second derivative of y with respect to x**.

$\dfrac{d^2y}{dx^2}$ is pronounced 'dee two y, dee x squared'.

The derivative of $f'(x)$ is denoted by $f''(x)$ and is called the **second derivative of $f(x)$ with respect to x**.

EXAMPLE 1

(i) If $y = 7x^2 - 5x + 3$, find $\dfrac{d^2y}{dx^2}$.

(ii) If $f(x) = 2x^3 - x^2 - 8$, find $f''(x)$.

Solution:

(i) $y = 7x^2 - 5x + 3$

$\dfrac{dy}{dx} = 14x - 5$

$\dfrac{d^2y}{dx^2} = 14$

(ii) $f(x) = 2x^3 - x^2 - 8$

$f'(x) = 6x^2 - 2x$

$f''(x) = 12x - 2$

Evaluating second derivatives

EXAMPLE 2

(i) If $f(x) = x^3 + x^2 + x + 1$, find $f''(x)$ and $f''(2)$.

(ii) If $h = 10 + 3t - t^2$, evaluate $\dfrac{d^2h}{dt^2}$ when $t = 3$.

Solution:

(i) $f(x) = x^3 + x^2 + x + 1$

$f'(x) = 3x^2 + 2x + 1$

$f''(x) = 6x + 2$

$f''(2) = 6(2) + 2$

$f''(2) = 12 + 2$

$f''(2) = 14$

(ii) $\qquad h = 10 + 3t - t^2$

$\qquad \dfrac{dh}{dt} = 3 - 2t$

$\qquad \dfrac{d^2h}{dt^2} = -2$

$\qquad \left.\dfrac{d^2h}{dt^2}\right|_{t=2} = -2$

Note: In (ii), $\dfrac{d^2h}{dt^2} = -2$, a constant.

EXAMPLE 3

(i) If $y = 2x^2 - 3x + 2$, show that $y + \dfrac{dy}{dx} + \dfrac{d^2y}{dx^2} = 2x^2 + x + 3$.

(ii) If $y = 4x^3$, show that $y\left(\dfrac{d^2y}{dx^2}\right) - \dfrac{2}{3}\left(\dfrac{dy}{dx}\right)^2 = 0$.

Solution:

(i) $\quad y = 2x^2 - 3x + 2$

$\quad \dfrac{dy}{dx} = 4x - 3$

$\quad \dfrac{d^2y}{dx^2} = 4$

$\qquad y + \dfrac{dy}{dx} + \dfrac{d^2y}{dx^2}$

$\qquad = 2x^2 - 3x + 2 + 4x - 3 + 4$

$\qquad = 2x^2 + x + 3$ as required

(ii)　$y = 4x^3$

$\dfrac{dy}{dx} = 12x^2$

$\dfrac{d^2y}{dx^2} = 24x$

$y\dfrac{d^2y}{dx^2} - \dfrac{2}{3}\left(\dfrac{dy}{dx}\right)^2$

$= (4x^3)(24x) - \dfrac{2}{3}(12x^2)^2$

$= 96x^4 - \dfrac{2}{3}(144x^4)$

$= 96x^4 - 96x^4$

$= 0$ as required

Note: $\left(\dfrac{dy}{dx}\right)^2 \neq \dfrac{d^2y}{dx^2}$

Exercise 8.3

In questions 1–8, find $\dfrac{d^2y}{dx^2}$.

1. $y = 4x^3 + 6x^2$ 　　　2. $y = x^2 - x^3$

3. $y = 2x^2 - 3$ 　　　4. $y = 7 - 3x$

5. $y = 4x - 2x^3$ 　　　6. $y = 4 - 3x - x^2$

7. $y = ax^2 + bx + c$ where $a, b, c \in \mathbb{R}$

8. $y = px^3 + qx^2 + rx + s$ where $p, q, r, s \in \mathbb{R}$

9. If $f(x) = 3x^2 - 4x - 7$, evaluate: (i) $f'(-1)$ 　　(ii) $f''(-1)$

10. If $f(x) = 3 - 2x + x^3$, evaluate: (i) $f'(-5)$ 　　(ii) $f''(-5)$

11. If $s = 3t - 2t^2$, find the value of the following. (i) $\dfrac{ds}{dt}$ 　(ii) $\dfrac{d^2s}{dt^2}$ when $t = 2$

12. If $V = 3h - h^2 - 3h^3$, find $\dfrac{d^2V}{dh^2}$ when $h = 1$.

13. (i) If $y = x^3 - x + 2$, show that: $y + \dfrac{dy}{dx} + \dfrac{d^2y}{dx^2} = x^3 + 3x^2 + 5x + 1$.

　　(ii) If $y = 3x^2 + 2x$, show that: $y\dfrac{d^2y}{dx^2} - 3x\dfrac{dy}{dx} - 6x = 0$.

14. (i) If $y = 4x^3 - 6x^2$, show that: $x^2\dfrac{d^2y}{dx^2} - 2x\dfrac{dy}{dx} - 12x^2 = 0$.

　　(ii) If $y = x^2 - 3x + 2$, show that: $\left(\dfrac{dy}{dx}\right)^2 - 2y\dfrac{d^2y}{dx^2} = 1$.

15. $f(x) = x^3 + 1$. If $f''(a) = 18$, find the value of a, $a \in \mathbb{R}$.

Finding the slope and equation of a tangent to a curve at a point on the curve

$\dfrac{dy}{dx}$ = the slope of a tangent to a curve at any point on the curve.

To find the slope and equation of a tangent to a curve at a given point (x_1, y_1), on the curve, do the following.

1. Find $\dfrac{dy}{dx}$.

2. Evaluate $\dfrac{dy}{dx}\bigg|_{x=x_1}$ (this gives the slope of the tangent, m).

3. Use m (from step 2) and the given point (x_1, y_1) in the equation $(y - y_1) = m(x - x_1)$.

Note: Sometimes only the value of x is given. When this happens, substitute the value of x into the original function to find y for step 3.

EXAMPLE

Find the equation of the tangent to the curve $y = 3 + 2x - x^2$ at the point $(2, 3)$.

Solution:

$$y = 3 + 2x - x^2$$

Step 1: $\dfrac{dy}{dx} = 2 - 2x$

Step 2: At the point $(2, 3)$, $x = 2$.

$$m = \frac{dy}{dx}\bigg|_{x=2} = 2 - 2(2) = 2 - 4 = -2$$

Step 3: $m = -2,$ $\quad x_1 = 2,$ $\quad y_1 = 3$

$$(y - y_1) = m(x - x_1)$$
$$(y - 3) = -2(x - 2)$$
$$y - 3 = -2x + 4$$
$$2x + y - 3 - 4 = 0$$
$$2x + y - 7 = 0$$

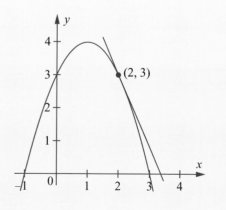

Exercise 8.4

1. Find the slope of the tangent to the curve $x^2 - 3x + 2$ at the point $(1, 0)$.

2. Find the slope of the tangent to the curve $y = 3 - 3x - x^2$ at the point $(2, -7)$.

3. Find the slope of the tangent to the curve $y = x^2 - 2x - 3$ at the point $(1, -4)$.

4. Find the equation of the tangent to the curve $y = x^2 - x - 2$ at the point $(2, 0)$.

5. Find the equation of the tangent to the curve $y = x^3 - 2x^2 - 4x + 1$ at the point $(-1, 2)$.

6. Show that the points $(2, 0)$ and $(3, 0)$ are on the curve $y = x^2 - 5x + 6$.
   Find the equations of the tangents to the curve at these points and investigate if these two tangents are at right angles to each other.

7. Show that the tangent to the curve $y = 3x^2 - 4x + 11$ at the point $(1, 10)$ is parallel to the line $2x - y + 5 = 0$.

Given $\dfrac{dy}{dx}$ to find the coordinates of the corresponding points on a curve

Sometimes the value of $\dfrac{dy}{dx}$ (slope of the curve at any point on it) is given and we need to find the coordinates of the point, or points, corresponding to this slope.

When this happens, do the following.

1. Find $\dfrac{dy}{dx}$.

2. Let $\dfrac{dy}{dx}$ equal the given value of the slope and solve this equation for x.

3. Substitute the x values obtained in step 2 into the original function to get the corresponding values of y.

EXAMPLE 1

Find the coordinates of the points on the curve $y = x^3 - 3x^2 - 8x + 5$ at which the tangents to the curve make angles of $45°$ with the positive sense of the x-axis.

Solution:

$$y = x^3 - 3x^2 - 8x + 5$$

Step 1: $\dfrac{dy}{dx} = 3x^2 - 6x - 8$

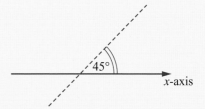

Step 2: Angle of $45° \Rightarrow$ slope $= 1$ (as $\tan 45° = 1$)

$$\text{Let } \dfrac{dy}{dx} = 1. \qquad \text{(given slope in disguise)}$$

$$3x^2 - 6x - 8 = 1$$
$$3x^2 - 6x - 9 = 0$$
$$x^2 - 2x - 3 = 0$$
$$(x - 3)(x + 1) = 0$$
$$x - 3 = 0 \quad \text{or} \quad x + 1 = 0$$
$$x = 3 \quad \text{or} \quad x = -1$$

Step 3: Find the y values.

$y = x^3 - 3x^2 - 8x + 5$	$y = x^3 - 3x^2 - 8x + 5$
$x = 3$	$x = -1$
$y = (3)^3 - 3(3)^2 - 8(3) + 5$	$y = (-1)^3 - 3(-1)^2 - 8(-1) + 5$
$= 27 - 27 - 24 + 5$	$= -1 - 3 + 8 + 5$
$= -19$	$= 9$
point $(3, -19)$	point $(-1, 9)$

Thus, the required points are $(3, -19)$ and $(-1, 9)$.

Note: $\tan 135° = -1$.

EXAMPLE 2

Find the coordinates of the point on the curve $y = x^2 - x$ where the tangent to the curve is parallel to the line $y = 3x - 5$.

Step 1: Curve: $y = x^2 - x$ Line: $y = 3x - 5$

$$\dfrac{dy}{dx} = 2x - 1 \qquad\qquad\qquad \dfrac{dy}{dx} = 3$$

Step 2: Slope of curve = slope of line (given)

$$2x - 1 = 3$$
$$2x = 4$$
$$x = 2$$

Thus, the required point is (2, 2).

Step 3: $y = x^2 - x$

$$x = 2$$
$$y = (2)^2 - 2$$
$$= 4 - 2 = 2$$

Note: Parallel lines have equal slopes.

Exercise 8.5

1. Find the coordinates of the point on the curve $y = 2x^2 - 3x + 2$ at which the tangent to the curve has a slope of 1.

2. Find the coordinates of the point on the curve $y = 3x^2 + 2x + 5$ at which the tangent to the curve has a slope of -10.

3. Find the coordinates of the points on the curve $y = x^3 - 3x^2$ at which the tangents to the curve have a slope of 9.

4. Find the coordinates of the points on the curve $y = 2x^3 - 3x^2 - 13x + 2$ at which the tangents to the curve make angles of $135°$ with the positive sense of the x-axis.

5. Find the coordinates of the point on the curve $y = 2x^2 - 2x + 5$ at which the tangents to the curve are parallel to the line $y = 2x - 3$.

6. Find the coordinates of the points on the curve $y = 2x^3 - 3x^2 - 12x$ at which the tangents to the curve are parallel to the line $y = 24x + 3$.

7. The equation of a curve may be written in the form $y = a(x + p)(x + q)$. The curve intersects the x-axis at A(-2, 0) and B(4, 0). The curve of $y = f(x)$ is shown in the diagram below.

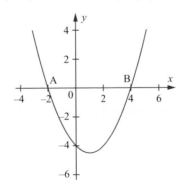

(i) Write down the value of p and q, where $p < q$.

(ii) Given that the point $(6, 8)$ is on the curve, find the value of a.

(iii) Write the equation of the curve in the form $y = ax^2 + bx + c$.

(iv) Find $\dfrac{dy}{dx}$.

(v) A tangent is drawn to the curve at a point H. The gradient of this tangent is 7. Find the coordinates of H.

8. $f(x) = \dfrac{x^3}{3} - x^2 - 8x + c$ where $c \in \mathbb{Z}$.

   (i) If $f(6) = 0$, show that $c = 12$.

   (ii) (a) Write down $f'(x)$.   (b) Calculate $f'(-3)$.

   (iii) (a) Calculate $f(-3)$.   (b) Find the equation of the tangent to $y = f(x)$ at $x = -3$.

   (iv) Use your answer to (ii) (a) to find the x-coordinates of two points where $f'(x) = 16$.

9. (i) What is the slope of the x-axis?

   (ii) Show that the tangent of the curve $f(x) = x^2 - 2x + 5$, at the point where $x = 1$, is parallel to the x-axis.

   (iii) For what value of x is the tangent to the graph of $y = x^2 - 6x + 5$ parallel to the x-axis?

10. Find the value of a if the slope of the tangent to the curve $y = x^2 + ax$ is 2 at the point where $x = 3$.

11. (i) The curve $y = ax^2 + bx + 6$ contains $(2, 4)$. Write down an equation in a and b.

    (ii) Find $\dfrac{dy}{dx}$. Hence, write another equation in a and b when the slope of the tangent at $(2, 4)$ is 3.

    (iii) By solving the equations found in (i) and (ii), find the value of a and the value of b.

12. The slope of the tangent to the curve $y = px^2 + 1$ at the point $(1, q)$ is 6. Find the value of p and the value of q.

13. Let $f(x) = x^3 + ax^2 + 2$ for all $x \in \mathbb{R}$ and for $a \in \mathbb{R}$.

    (i) Find $f'(x)$.

    (ii) The slope of the tangent to the curve $y = f(x)$ at $x = -1$ is 9. Find the value of a.

Maximum and minimum points

$\dfrac{dy}{dx}$ can also be used to find the local maximum or local minimum points on a curve.

On the right is part of the graph of a cubic function. At the turning points, A and B, the tangents to the curve are horizontal (parallel to the x-axis). In other words, at these points the slope of the tangent is zero. These turning points are also called the **local maximum point**, point A, and the **local minimum point**, point B.

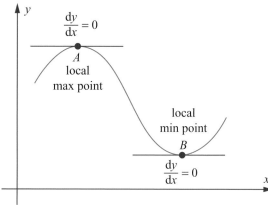

At a maximum or minimum point, $\dfrac{dy}{dx} = 0.$

To find the maximum or minimum points on a curve, do the following.

1. Find $\dfrac{dy}{dx}$.

2. Let $\dfrac{dy}{dx} = 0$ and solve this equation for x.

3. Substitute the x values obtained in step 2 into the original function to get the corresponding values of y.

Step 4.

Method 1: By comparing the y values we can determine which point is the local maximum or minimum point. The point with the greater y value is the local maximum point and the point with the lower y value is the local minimum point.

Method 2: Find $\dfrac{d^2y}{dx^2}$.

Substitute the x values obtained in step 2 into $\dfrac{d^2y}{dx^2}$.

If $\dfrac{d^2y}{dx^2} > 0$, then it is the minimum point.

If $\dfrac{d^2y}{dx^2} < 0$, then it is the maximum point.

Note: The graph of a quadratic function $f(x) = ax^2 + bx + c$ has only one turning point.
  1. If $a > 0$, the turning point will be a minimum.
  2. If $a < 0$, the turning point will be a maximum.

Using calculus, find the coordinates of the local maximum point and the local minimum point of the curve $y = x^3 - 6x^2 + 9x + 4$.

Graph of $y = x^3 - 6x^2 + 9x + 4$

Solution:

Step 1: $y = x^3 - 6x^2 + 9x + 4$

$$\frac{dy}{dx} = 3x^2 - 12x + 9$$

Step 2: Let $\frac{dy}{dx} = 0$.

$$3x^2 - 12x + 9 = 0$$
$$x^2 - 4x + 3 = 0$$
$$(x - 3)(x - 1) = 0$$
$$x - 3 = 0 \quad \text{or} \quad x - 1 = 0$$
$$x = 3 \quad \text{or} \quad x = 1$$

Step 3: Find the y values.

$y = x^3 - 6x^2 + 9x + 4$	$y = x^3 - 6x^2 + 9x + 4$
$x = 3$	$x = 1$
$y = (3)^3 - 6(3)^2 + 9(3) + 4$	$y = (1)^3 - 6(1)^2 + 9(1) + 4$
$= 27 - 54 + 27 + 4$	$= 1 - 6 + 9 + 4$
$= 4$	$= 8$
point $(3, 4)$	point $(1, 8)$

Step 4:

Method 1: Thus, the local maximum point is $(1, 8)$ and the local minimum point is $(3, 4)$.

Method 2: $\frac{dy}{dx} = 3x^2 - 12x + 9$

$$\frac{d^2y}{dx^2} = 6x - 12$$

$$\left.\frac{d^2y}{dx^2}\right|_{x=3} = 6(3) - 12 = 18 - 12 = 6 > 0 \therefore \text{Local minimum at } x = 3.$$

and $$\left.\frac{d^2y}{dx^2}\right|_{x=1} = 6(1) - 12 = 6 - 12 = -6 < 0 \therefore \text{Local maximum at } x = 1.$$

Thus, the local maximum point is $(1, 8)$ and the local minimum point is $(3, 4)$.

Exercise 8.6

In questions 1–3, find, using calculus, the coordinates of the local minimum point of the curve.

1. $y = x^2 - 4x + 3$ 2. $y = x^2 + 6x + 1$ 3. $y = 2x^2 - 8x + 3$

In questions 4–6, find, using calculus, the coordinates of the local maximum point of the curve.

4. $y = 7 - 6x - x^2$ 5. $y = 5 - 4x - x^2$ 6. $y = 1 - 12x - 3x^2$

In questions 7–9, find, using calculus, the coordinates of the local maximum and the local minimum points of the curve.

7. $y = x^3 - 3x^2 - 9x + 4$ 8. $y = 8 + 9x - 3x^2 - x^3$ 9. $y = 2x^3 - 9x^2 + 12x + 1$

10. Find the turning points of the function $y = 27x - x^3$ and determine their nature.

11. Find the turning points of the function $y = x^3 - 6x^2$ and determine their nature.

12. The diagram represents the graph of $y = x(6 - x)$.

    (i) Find the equation of l, the axis of symmetry of the graph.

    (ii) Find the maximum value of y.

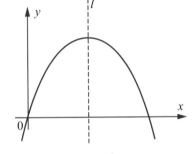

13. Part of the graph of $y = f(x) = x^2 - 2x$ is shown. The x-coordinate of the local minimum point is R. Calculate the value of R.

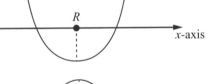

14. Part of the graph of $y = f(x) = -x^2 + 5x - 20$ is shown. The x-coordinate of the local maximum point is S. Calculate the value of S.

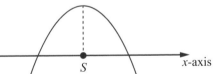

15. Part of the graph of $y = f(x) = 2x^3 + 15x^2 + 24x - 6$ is shown.

The x-coordinate of the local minimum and maximum points are Q and P, respectively.

Calculate the value of Q and the value of P.

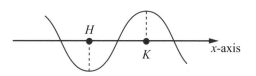

16. Part of the graph of $y = f(x) = 36x - 3x^2 - 2x^3$ is shown.

The x-coordinates of the local minimum and local maximum points are H and K, respectively.

Calculate the value of H and the value of K.

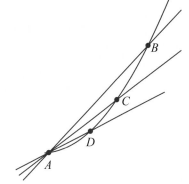

17. Points $A = (3, 5)$, $B = (3·2, 6·24)$, $C = (3·1, 5·61)$ and $D = (3·04, 5·2416)$ are points on the curve $y = x^2 - 4$.

  (i) Find the slopes of **(a)** AB **(b)** AC **(c)** AD.

  (ii) Find $\dfrac{dy}{dx}$ at $x = 3$.

  (iii) Explain the link between **(i)** and **(ii)**.

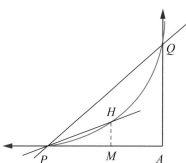

18. The diagram on the right is an enlarged portion of the curve $y = x^2$ near the point $P(4, 16)$. A point Q, with coordinates $(4·01, 16·0801)$, near to P is shown.

  (i) Show that P and Q are points on the curve $y = x^2$.

  (ii) Find the slope of the chord $[PQ]$.

H is a point on the curve whose x-coordinate is $4·005$.

  (iii) Find the y-coordinate of H.

  (iv) Find the slope of the chord $[PH]$.

  (v) Find $\dfrac{dy}{dx}$ at P.

  (vi) Comment on your results from **(ii)**, **(iv)** and **(v)**.

19. Given $f(x) = x^2 + bx + c$ has a local minimum at $x = -2$ and contains the point (3, 25), find the value of b and the value of c.

20. Let $f(x) = x^3 + ax^2 + 2$ for all $x \in \mathbb{R}$ and for $a \in \mathbb{R}$.
    $f(x)$ has a turning point (a local maximum or a local minimum) at $x = 2$.
    (i) Find the value of a and the coordinates of the turning point at $x = 2$.
    (ii) Find the coordinates of the other turning point of $f(x)$.
    (iii) Sketch the graph of $f(x)$.

21. (i) Verify that $x = -1$ is a root of the equation
    $x^3 - 9x^2 + 15x + 25 = 0$.

    (ii) The diagram shows a graph of part of the function $f : x \rightarrow x^3 - 9x^2 + 15x + 25$.
    There are turning points at C and D.
    The curve intersects the x-axis at A and D and the y-axis at B.
    Find the coordinates of A, B, C and D.

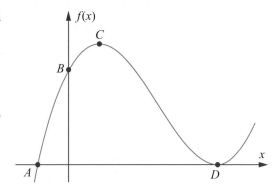

22. The diagram shows part of the function $f(x) = x^2 - 8x - 9$ in the domain $-2 \le x \le 10$, $x \in \mathbb{R}$.
    (i) Write down an approximation for the coordinates of the local minimum of $f(x)$.
    (ii) Find $f'(x)$.
    (iii) Copy the diagram and sketch the graph of $f'(x)$ in the domain $-2 \le x \le 10$, $x \in \mathbb{R}$, clearly indicating where $f'(x)$ cuts the x-axis.
    (iv) Comment on the link between (i) and (iii).

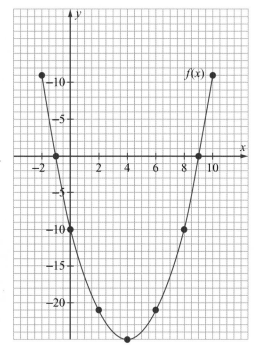

23. The diagram shows part of the function
$f(x) = 2x^3 - 3x^2 - 12x + 6$ in the domain $-2 \le x \le 3$, $x \in \mathbb{R}$.

   (i) Write down approximate coordinates of the local maximum and local minimum points of $f(x)$.

   (ii) Find $f'(x)$.

   (iii) Copy the diagram and sketch the graph of $f'(x)$ in the domain $-2 \le x \le 3$, $x \in \mathbb{R}$, clearly indicating where $f'(x)$ cuts the x-axis

   (iv) Comment on the link between **(i)** and **(iii)**.

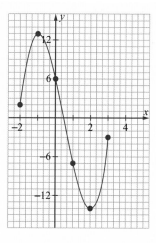

24. The diagram shows a section of the graphs
$y = f(x) = x^2 - 7x + 10$ and $f'(x)$ and $f''(x)$.

   Which graph, a, b, or c, corresponds to the following?

   (i) $f(x)$

   (ii) $f'(x)$

   (iii) $f''(x)$

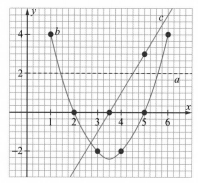

25. The diagram shows a section of the graphs
$y = f(x) = x^3 + 3x^2 - 9x + 6$ and $f'(x)$ and $f''(x)$.

   Which graph, a, b, or c, corresponds to the following?

   (i) $f(x)$

   (ii) $f'(x)$

   (iii) $f''(x)$

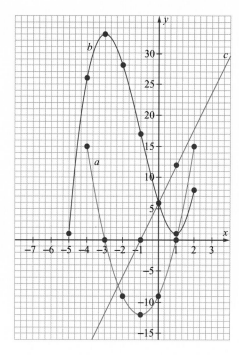

263

Increasing and decreasing

$\dfrac{dy}{dx}$, being the slope of a tangent to a curve at any point on the curve, can be used to determine if, and where, a curve is increasing or decreasing.

Note: Graphs are read from left to right.

Where a curve is increasing, the tangent to the curve will have a positive slope.
Therefore, where a curve is increasing, $\dfrac{dy}{dx}$ will be positive.

Where a curve is decreasing, the tangent to the curve will have a negative slope.
Therefore, where a curve is decreasing, $\dfrac{dy}{dx}$ will be negative.

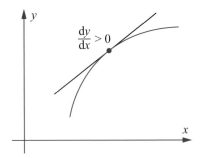

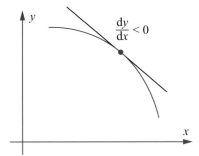

Note: (Any real number)^2 will always be a positive number unless the number is zero.

EXAMPLE 1

If $y = x^3 + x - 4$, show that $\dfrac{dy}{dx} > 0$ for all values of x.

Solution

$y = x^3 + x - 4$ $\qquad\qquad$ $\therefore \dfrac{dy}{dx} = 3x^2 + 1$

Since $3x^2$ must always be greater than or equal to zero,
$3x^2 + 1$ must always be greater than zero.

$\therefore \dfrac{dy}{dx} = 3x^2 + 1 > 0$ for all values of x.

EXAMPLE 2

The diagram shows three tangents
p, q and and r to a section of a graph.

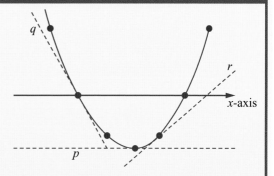

(i) Which tangent has a negative slope?
Explain your answer.

(ii) Describe the slopes of each of the other
two tangents.

Solution

(i) A tangent with a negative slope means the graph is decreasing.
∴ q is the tangent with a negative slope.

(ii) The tangent p is parallel to the x-axis. The tangent p makes no angle with the x-axis
and has slope zero.

r has a positive slope, which is associated with an increasing graph.

Exercise 8.7

1. Let $f(x) = x^2 - 2x - 8$. Find the values of x for which $f(x)$ is (i) decreasing (ii) increasing.

2. Let $f(x) = 12 - 6x - x^2$. Find the values of x for which $f(x)$ is (i) increasing (ii) decreasing.

3. Let $f(x) = x^3 + 4x - 2$. Show that $\dfrac{dy}{dx} > 0$ for all $x \in \mathbb{R}$.

4. Let $f(x) = 5 - 2x - x^3$. Show that $\dfrac{dy}{dx} < 0$ for all $x \in \mathbb{R}$.

5. Show that the curve $y = x^2 - 3x + 5$ is increasing at the point $(2, 3)$.

6. Show that the curve $y = 10 - x - 2x^2$ is decreasing at the point $(3, -11)$.

7. An artificial ski slope is
described by the function
$h = 165 - 120s + 60s^2 - 10s^3$,
where s is the horizontal distance
and h is the height of the slope.
Show that the slope is all downhill.

8. The diagram shows four tangents a, b, c and d to a
   section of a graph.
   (i) Which tangent has a negative slope?
      Justify your answer.
   (ii) Which tangent has a slope of zero?
   (iii) Which tangent has the steepest slope?

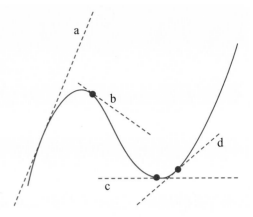

9. The letters A to E are placed at particular points on the
   curve $y = f(x)$, as in the diagram.
   (i) Which of the points is a local maximum?
   (ii) Which of the points is a local minimum?
   (iii) What is the slope of the curve $y = f(x)$
      at the point marked D?
   (iv) In passing from point B, through point C to

   point D, is $\dfrac{dy}{dx} > 0$ or is $\dfrac{dy}{dx} < 0$? Justify your answer.

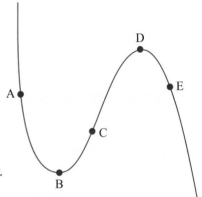

Rates of change

The derivative $\dfrac{dy}{dx}$ is called the rate of change of y with respect to x.

It shows how changes in y are related to changes in x.

If $\dfrac{dy}{dx} = 4$, then y is increasing four times as fast as x increases.

If $\dfrac{dy}{dx} = -5$, then y is decreasing five times as fast as x increases.

The derivative $\dfrac{dh}{dt}$ is called the rate of change of h with respect of t.

The derivative $\dfrac{dR}{dV}$ is called the rate of change of R with respect to V.

If s denotes the displacement (position) of a particle from a fixed point p at time t, then:

> **1.** Velocity $= v = \dfrac{ds}{dt}$,
> the rate of change of position with respect to time.
>
> **2.** Acceleration $= a = \dfrac{dv}{dt} = \dfrac{d^2s}{dt^2}$,
> the rate of change of velocity with respect to time.

To find $\dfrac{d^2s}{dt^2}$, simply find $\dfrac{ds}{dt}$ and differentiate this.

In other words, differentiate twice.

Note: 'Speed' is often used instead of 'velocity'. However, speed can never be negative, whereas velocity can be negative.

If $\dfrac{ds}{dt} > 0$, the particle is moving away from p (distance from p is increasing).

If $\dfrac{ds}{dt} < 0$, the particle is moving towards p (distance from p is decreasing).

EXAMPLE 1

A particle moves along a straight line such that, after t seconds, the distance, s metres, is given by $s = t^3 - 9t^2 + 15t - 3$. Find the following.

   (i) The velocity and acceleration of the particle in terms of t.
  (ii) The values of t when its velocity is zero.
 (iii) The acceleration after $3\frac{1}{2}$ seconds.
 (iv) The time at which the acceleration is 6 m/s^2 and the velocity at this time.

Solution:

(i) $\qquad s = t^3 - 9t^2 + 15t - 3$

$\qquad v = \dfrac{ds}{dt} = 3t^2 - 18t + 15 \qquad$ (velocity at any time t)

$\qquad a = \dfrac{d^2s}{dt^2} = 6t - 18 \qquad$ (acceleration at any time t)

(ii) Values of t when velocity is zero

$$\text{Velocity} = 0$$

$$\therefore \qquad \frac{ds}{dt} = 0$$

$$\therefore \quad 3t^2 - 18t + 15 = 0$$

$$t^2 - 6t + 5 = 0$$

$$(t - 1)(t - 5) = 0$$

$$t - 1 = 0 \quad \text{or} \quad t - 5 = 0$$

$$t = 1 \quad \text{or} \qquad t = 5$$

Thus, the particle is stopped after
1 second and again after 5 seconds.

(iv) Time at which acceleration is 6 m/s²

$$\text{Acceleration} = 6 \text{ m/s}^2$$

$$\therefore \qquad \frac{d^2s}{dt^2} = 6$$

$$\therefore \quad 6t - 18 = 6$$

$$6t = 24$$

$$t = 4$$

After 4 seconds, the acceleration is 6 m/s².

(iii) Acceleration after $3\frac{1}{2}$ seconds

$$\text{Acceleration} = \frac{d^2s}{dt^2} = 6t - 18$$

When $t = 3\frac{1}{2}$,

$$\text{acceleration} = 6\left(3\frac{1}{2}\right) - 18$$

$$\left(\text{put in } t = 3\frac{1}{2}\right)$$

$$= 21 - 18$$

$$= 3$$

$$\therefore \quad \text{Acceleration after } 3\frac{1}{2} \text{ seconds} = 3 \text{ m/s}^2.$$

Velocity after 4 seconds

$$\text{Velocity} = 3t^2 - 18t + 15$$

When $t = 4$,

$$\text{velocity} = 3(4)^2 - 18(4) + 15$$

$$(\text{put in } t = 4)$$

$$= 48 - 72 + 15$$

$$= -9 \text{ m/s}$$

After 4 seconds, the velocity is −9 m/s.
The negative value means it is going in the
opposite direction to which it started after
4 seconds.

EXAMPLE 2

A ball is thrown vertically up in the air. The height, h metres, reached above the ground t
seconds after it was thrown is given by $h = 8t - t^2$.

Find the following.

(i) The height of the ball after 3 seconds

(ii) The speed of the ball after 1 second

(iii) The height of the ball when its speed is 4 m/s

(iv) After how many seconds does the ball begin to fall back downwards?

Solution:

(i) Height at $t = 3$

$$h = 8t - t^2$$

When $t = 3$,

$$h = 8(3) - (3)^2$$

(put in $t = 3$)

$$h = 24 - 9$$

$$h = 15$$

∴ Height after 3 seconds = 15 m.

(ii) Speed after 1 second

$$h = 8t - t^2$$

$$\frac{dh}{dt} = 8 - 2t$$

(this is the speed in terms of t)

∴ Speed after 1 second

$$= 8 - 2(1) = 8 - 2 = 6$$

(put in $t = 1$)

∴ Speed after 1 second = 6 m/s.

(iii) Height of the ball when the speed is 4 m/s

Given: speed = 4

∴ $\dfrac{dh}{dt} = 4$

∴ $8 - 2t = 4$

$$-2t = -4$$

$$2t = 4$$

$$t = 2$$

$$h = 8t - t^2$$

When $t = 2$,

$$h = 8(2) - (2)^2$$

(put in $t = 2$)

$$h = 16 - 4 = 12 \text{ m}$$

∴ When the speed is 4 m/s, the height of the ball = 12 m.

(iv) After how many seconds does the ball begin to fall downwards?

The ball begins to fall downwards when it has reached its maximum height. It reaches its maximum height when its speed = 0.

Speed = 0

∴ $\dfrac{dh}{dt} = 0$

∴ $8 - 2t = 0$

$$-2t = -8$$

$$2t = 8$$

$$t = 4$$

∴ Ball begins to fall downwards after 4 seconds.

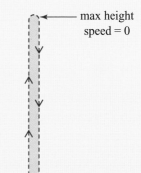

max height
speed = 0

EXAMPLE 3

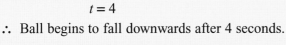

The revenue of a company €R in month t is modelled by the formula

$$R(t) = 800t^3 - 4{,}000t^2 + 200t + 480{,}000$$

January is set as $t = 1$, February is set as $t = 2$ and so on. Use the formula to predict
(i) the revenue in October **(ii)** the rate at which revenue is growing in October.

Solution:

(i) October output given by substituting $t = 10$.

$$R(t) = 800t^3 - 4{,}000t^2 + 200t + 480{,}000$$
$$R(10) = 800(10)^3 - 4{,}000(10)^2 + 200(10) + 480{,}000$$
$$= 800{,}000 - 400{,}000 + 2{,}000 + 480{,}000$$
$$= 882{,}000$$

∴ The revenue in October is €882,000.

(ii) The rate of change of R is given by $\dfrac{dR}{dt}$.

$$R(t) = 800t^3 - 4{,}000t^2 + 200t + 480{,}000$$

$$\frac{dR}{dt} = 2{,}400t^2 - 8{,}000t + 200$$

$$\left.\frac{dR}{dt}\right|_{t=10} = 2{,}400(10)^2 - 8{,}000(10) + 200$$

$$= 240{,}000 - 80{,}000 + 200 = 160{,}200$$

∴ The rate of change in October is €160,200 per month.

Exercise 8.8

1. The distance in kilometres (S) of a cyclist from his home after t hours is given by

$$S = t^3 - 3t^2 + 3t + 4.$$

  (i) How far is the cyclist from his home at the start?

  (ii) Find $\dfrac{dS}{dt}$.

  (iii) Hence or otherwise, find the speed of the cyclist at $t = 3$.

  (iv) Find the value of t when the cyclist is momentarily stopped and how far is the cyclist from his home at this point?

2. The temperature of a piece of charcoal, T degrees, after t hours in the ashes of a fire is given by the formula $T = 270 + 80t - 20t^2$ for $0 \le t \le 6$.

  (i) Find $\dfrac{dT}{dt}$.

  (ii) Calculate the time at which the charcoal starts to cool down.

  (iii) Calculate the maximum temperature of the charcoal during the six hours.

  (iv) Calculate the rate, in degrees per hour, at which the charcoal is cooling after five hours.

3. The population, P, of a new town is modelled by the formula $P = t^3 - t^2 + 25t + 10,000$, where t is measured in years. t is set at 0 in the year 2000. Use the formula to predict:
   (i) The population in the year 2020
   (ii) The rate of population growth in 2020

4. The population, P in hundreds, of an endangered species was monitored over t years. P is modelled by the equation

$$P = t^2 - 6t + 18 \text{ for } 1 \le t \le 6.$$

   (i) Find $\dfrac{dP}{dt}$.

   (ii) Find the smallest population of the species.
   (iii) Calculate the rate at which the population is growing after four years.

5. The number of hairs, H, on the body of a mammal over a lifetime of 60 years is modelled by the equation $H = 80t^2 - \dfrac{4t^3}{3}$ for $0 \le t \le 60$, where t is the time, measured in years.

   (i) Calculate the rate of hair gain after 20 years.
   (ii) Calculate the rate of hair loss after 50 years.
   (iii) Calculate the age at which the mammal has the most hair.

6. The graph shows the depth of water, y cm, at a point P during a nine-hour period. The time is given in hours from midnight to 09:00.

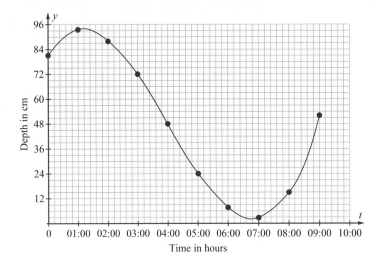

Time in hours

(i) Use the graph to write down an estimate of the value of t when:

   (a) The depth of water is minimum

   (b) The depth of water is maximum

   (c) The depth of the water is increasing most rapidly

(ii) The depth of water can be modelled by the function $y = t^3 - 12t^2 + 24t + K$, where t is time in hours after mid night.

   (a) Write down the value of K.

   (b) By using $\dfrac{dy}{dt}$, find the rate of change of depth at 03:00.

7. A jet is moving along an airport runway. At the instant it passes a marker, it begins to accelerate to take-off. From the time the jet passes the marker, its distance from the marker is given by $s = 2t^2 + 3t$, where s is in metres and t is in seconds.

  (i) Find the speed of the jet at the instant it passes the marker ($t = 0$).

  (ii) The jet has to reach a speed of 83 metres per second to take off. After how many seconds will the jet reach this speed?

 (iii) How far is the jet from the marker at that time?

 (iv) Find the acceleration of the jet.

8. A distress flare is tested by firing it vertically upwards from the top of a tower. The height, h metres, of the flare above the ground is given by $h = 20 + 90t - 5t^2$, where t is the time in seconds from the instant the flare is fired. The flare is designed to explode 7 seconds after firing.

(i) Find the height above the ground at which the flare explodes.

(ii) Find the speed of the flare at the instant it explodes.

(iii) If the flare failed to explode, find the greatest height above the ground it would reach before falling back down.

9. A car begins to slow down at P in order to stop at a red traffic light at Q.

The distance of the car from P, after t seconds, is given by $s = 12t - \dfrac{3}{2}t^2$, where s is in metres.

(i) Find the speed of the car as it passes P.

(ii) Find the time taken to stop.

(iii) The car stops exactly at Q. Find the distance from P to Q.

10. An automatic valve controls the flow of gas, R cm^3/s, in an experiment. The flow of gas varies with the time, t seconds, as given by the equation $R = 8t - t^2$.
Find the following.

(i) $\dfrac{dR}{dt}$, the rate of change of R with respect to t

(ii) The value of $\dfrac{dR}{dt}$ after 6 seconds

(iii) The time when the rate of flow is a maximum

(iv) After how many seconds is the rate of flow equal to:

(a) -4 cm^3/s (b) 2 cm^3/s

11. The volume of water, V, in cm^3, that remains in a leaking tank after t seconds is given by
$V = 45{,}000 - 300t + 0{\cdot}5t^2$.

(i) After how many seconds will the tank be empty?

(ii) Find the rate of change of the volume with respect to t when $t = 50$ seconds.

12. A ball bearing rolls along the ground. It starts to move at $t = 0$ seconds. The distance that it has travelled at t seconds is given by $s = t^3 - 6t^2 + 9t$. Find the following.

(i) $\dfrac{ds}{dt}$ and $\dfrac{d^2s}{dt^2}$, its speed and acceleration, in terms of t.

(ii) The speed of the ball bearing when $t = 4$ seconds

(iii) The acceleration of the ball bearing when $t = 3$ seconds

(iv) The times at which the speed is zero

(v) The time at which the acceleration is zero

(vi) The time at which the acceleration is 6 m/s^2

(vii) The time at which the speed is 24 m/s

13. A research student stands at the window of the building where he works and fires a projectile into the air in such a way that its height above the ground, h metres, at time t seconds after firing is given by the formula $h = 8 + 22t - 5t^2$.

t	0	1	2	3	4	5
h						

(i) Copy and complete the table above. Draw the graph of h against t, putting t on the x-axis with a scale of 2 cm to 1 second and h on the y-axis with a scale of 1 cm to 4 m.

(ii) (a) Find $\dfrac{dh}{dt}$. (b) Explain why the maximum height is reached at $t = 2.2$ and find this maximum height.

(iii) From your graph, estimate correct to one decimal place the time at which the projectile hits the ground.

(iv) Explain the physical significance of the number 8 in the formula $h = 8 + 22t - 5t^2$.

14. An aircraft is travelling at a steady speed horizontally and is at a height of 2,000 m above the ground.

A parachutist jumps from the plane and descends **for 8 seconds** without opening his parachute. The function that represents his height above the ground is

$$f(t) = 2{,}000 - 4t - 16t^2,$$

where t is the time in seconds and $t \le 8$.

After 8 seconds he opens his parachute and descends to the ground. The function which represents his height above the ground for this part of the descent is

$$g(t) = 1200 - 4t^2,$$

where t is the time in seconds and $t > 8$.

(i) Copy and complete a table of values for both parts of the descent using intervals of 2 seconds for time.
Finish the table at time $t = 18$.

$t =$	0	2	4	6	8		8	10	12	14	16	18
2,000 $- 4t$ $- 16t^2$						**1,200** $- 4t^2$						
$f(t)$						$g(t)$						

(ii) On the same coordinate axes, draw the graph of $f(t)$ and $g(t)$. Use an appropriate scale for t as the horizontal axis and for $f(t)$, $g(t)$ as the vertical axis.

(iii) Use your graph to estimate how many seconds it takes for the parachutist to reach the ground.

(iv) Find $f'(6)$.

(v) Find $g'(11)$.

(vi) Is the rate of change of $f(t)$ at 6 seconds greater than $g(t)$ at 11 seconds? Explain the physical significance of the difference between the two values.

CHAPTER 9

PATTERNS, SEQUENCES AND SERIES

Patterns 1

Much of mathematics is about patterns. Some are simple and numeric:

$$2, 4, 6, 8, 10, \ldots \qquad \frac{1}{2}, \frac{2}{3}, \frac{3}{4}, \frac{4}{5}, \ldots \qquad 10, 21, 32, 43, 54, \ldots$$

You should be able to write down the next three numbers in the list; you may even be able to predict the 10th number in the list *without* having to write out all the terms.

Other numeric patterns are more complicated:

$$1, 2, 4, 8, 16, \ldots \qquad 1, 0, 2, 0, 0, 3, 0, 0, 0, 4, \ldots \qquad 1, 2, 6, 24, 120, 720, \ldots$$

Even if you see a pattern and can write out the next number, it is much more difficult to predict what the 20th number or the 100th number in the list would be. If those numbers represented the population of the planet or the number of cancerous cells in a patient, then it would be very important to be able to predict future values.

Not all patterns are numeric. For example:

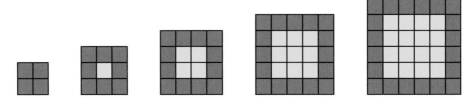

Is it possible to predict the number of squares in the 10th diagram? What about the number of yellow squares in the 10th diagram? What about the purple squares?

Many young children like to watch how tall they are growing and use some simple measuring techniques to record their growth. Is it possible to predict a child's height as each year passes?

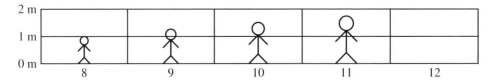

As an eight-year-old, Freddie was 1 m tall. By nine he was 1·25 m tall and by 10 he had reached 1·5 m. Could you use this information to calculate his height when he is 12 years old? What about when Freddie is 21? Do you see a problem?

Sequences

A **sequence** is a set of numbers, separated by commas, in which each number after the first is formed by some definite rule.

Each number in a sequence is a **term** of that sequence. The first number is the **first term** and is denoted by T_1. Similarly, the second term is denoted by T_2 and so on.

3, 7, 11, 15, . . .

Each number after the first is obtained by adding 4 to the previous number. In this example, 3 is called the **first term**, 7 is the **second term** and so on.

1, 3, 9, 27, . . .

Each number after the first is obtained by multiplying the previous number by 3. In this example, 1 is called the **first term**, 3 is the **second term** and so on.

The general term, T_n

Very often a sequence is given by a **rule** which defines the **general term**. We use T_n to denote the general term of the sequence. T_n may be used to obtain any term of a sequence. T_1 will represent the first term, T_2 the second term and so on.

Notes: **1.** The general term, T_n, is often called the nth term.

      2. n used with this meaning must always be a positive whole number. It can never be fractional or negative.

      3. A sequence is often called a progression.

Consider the sequence whose general term is $T_n = 3n + 2$.

We can find the value of any term of the sequence by putting in the appropriate value for n on both sides:

$$T_n = 3n + 2$$

$$T_1 = 3(1) + 2 = 3 + 2 = 5 \qquad \text{(first term, put in 1 for } n)$$

$$T_2 = 3(2) + 2 = 6 + 2 = 8 \qquad \text{(second term, put in 2 for } n)$$

$$T_5 = 3(5) + 2 = 15 + 2 = 17 \qquad \text{(fifth term, put in 5 for } n)$$

In each case, n is replaced with the same number on both sides.

The notation $T_n = 3n + 2$ is very similar to function notation when n is the input and T_n is the output, i.e. (input, output) $= (n, T_n)$.

EXAMPLE

The nth term of a sequence is given by $T_n = n^2 + 3$.

(i) Write down the first three terms of the sequence.

(ii) Show that: (a) $\dfrac{T_5}{T_2} = T_1$ (b) $2T_4 = T_6 - 1$

Solution:

(i) $T_n = n^2 + 3$

$T_1 = 1^2 + 3 = 1 + 3 = 4$ (put in 1 for n)

$T_2 = 2^2 + 3 = 4 + 3 = 7$ (put in 2 for n)

$T_3 = 3^2 + 3 = 9 + 3 = 12$ (put in 3 for n)

Thus, the first three terms are 4, 7, 12.

(ii) (a) From (i), $T_1 = 4$ and $T_2 = 7$.

$T_5 = 5^2 + 3 = 25 + 3 = 28$

$\dfrac{T_5}{T_2} = \dfrac{28}{7} = 4$

$T_1 = 4$

$\therefore \dfrac{T_5}{T_2} = T_1$

(b) $T_4 = 4^2 + 3 = 16 + 3 = 19$

$T_6 = 6^2 + 3 = 36 + 3 = 39$

$2T_4 = 2(19) = 38$

$T_6 - 1 = 39 - 1 = 38$

$\therefore 2T_4 = T_6 - 1$

Exercise 9.1

In questions 1–8, write down the next four terms.

1. 1, 5, 9, 13, . . .
2. 40, 35, 30, 25, . . .
3. −11, −9, −7, −5, . . .
4. 13, 10, 7, 4, . . .
5. 2·5, 2·9, 3·3, 3·7, . . .
6. 2·8, 2·2, 1·6, 1, . . .
7. 1, 2, 4, 8, . . .
8. 2, 6, 18, 54, . . .

In questions 9–20, write down the first four terms of the sequence defined by the given nth term.

9. $T_n = 2n + 3$
10. $T_n = 3n + 1$
11. $T_n = 4n - 1$
12. $T_n = 5n - 3$
13. $T_n = 1 - 2n$
14. $T_n = 3 - 4n$
15. $T_n = n^2 + 5$
16. $T_n = n^2 + 2n$
17. $T_n = \dfrac{n + 1}{n}$
18. $T_n = \dfrac{2n}{n + 1}$
19. $T_n = 2^n$
20. $T_n = 3^n$

21. The *n*th term of a sequence is given by $T_n = 5n + 2$.

    (i) Write down the first three terms of the sequence.
    (ii) Show that: (a) $2T_5 = T_4 + T_6$ (b) $6(T_7 - 1) = T_2(T_3 + 1)$

22. The *n*th term of a sequence is given by $T_n = n^2 + 2$.

    (i) Write down the first three terms of the sequence.

    (ii) Show that: (a) $\dfrac{T_4}{T_2} = T_1$ (b) $\dfrac{T_6 - 2}{T_4} = \dfrac{T_2}{T_1}$

23. The *n*th term of a sequence is given by $T_n = \dfrac{n + 2}{n + 1}$.

    (i) Write down T_1, T_2 and T_3, the first, second and third terms.
    (ii) Show that $T_1 + T_2 > 2T_3$.

Patterns 2

A pattern of repeating coloured blocks is easy enough to continue, but the challenge is to be able to predict what happens much further along.

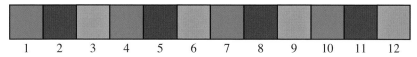

Looking at the orange blocks, there is an interesting pattern:

The 1st orange block is at position 3.	$3 = 3 \times 1$
The 2nd orange block is at position 6.	$6 = 3 \times 2$
The 3rd orange block is at position 9.	$9 = 3 \times 3$
The 4th orange block is at position 12.	$12 = 3 \times 4$

The 8th orange block should be at position $3 \times 8 = 24$.

We can predict that there will be another orange block at position $3 \times 9 = 27$. We can jump much further along and predict an orange block at position 99 (because $3 \times 33 = 99$).

So what about the 100th block? If the 99th is orange, then the 100th must be green and the 101st must be blue. To understand the sequence of this pattern, we need to find one sequence of colours which is easy to predict. From that we can deduce the positions of the other colours.

⬤ EXAMPLE

A repeating pattern consists of blocks coloured yellow, purple, green, yellow, . . . and so on.

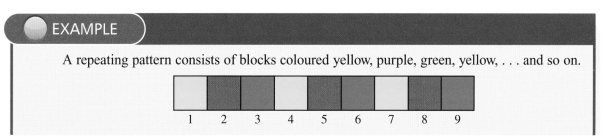

____ **(i)** Complete the table.

Block position	Colour
1	Yellow
2	
	Green
⋮	⋮

(ii) List the positions of the first three yellow blocks. Is there a pattern?

(iii) List the positions of the first three purple blocks. Is there a pattern?

(iv) List the positions of the first three green blocks. Is there a pattern?

(v) What is the colour of the 48th block?

(vi) What is the colour of the 50th block?

(vii) What is the colour of the 100th block?

Solution:

(i) The completed table:

Block position	Colour
1	Yellow
2	Purple
3	Green
4	Yellow
5	Purple
6	Green
7	Yellow
8	Purple
9	Green

(ii) Yellow blocks: 1, 4, 7, . . .

Yes. Starting with 1 and adding 3 each time, the other positions can be found.

(iii) Purple blocks: 2, 5, 8, . . .

Yes. Starting with 2 and adding 3 each time, the other positions can be found.

(iv) Green blocks: 3, 6, 9, . . .

Yes. Starting with 3 and adding 3 each time, the other positions can be found.

Alternatively, the positions are multiples of 3, so the 1st green is at position $3 \times 1 = 3$, the 2nd green is at position $3 \times 2 = 6$, the 3rd green is at position $3 \times 3 = 9$ and so on.

(v) As 48 is a multiple of 3 (48 can be divided exactly by 3), it must be a green block.

(vi) Since the 48th block is green, the 50th must be purple.

(vii) Using a calculator, 100 is not a multiple of 3 (it divides in just over 33 times).
$3 \times 33 = 99$ which *is* a multiple of 3, so the 99th block must be green.

The 100th block is therefore yellow.

Exercise 9.2

1. A repeating pattern consists of blocks coloured green, yellow, green, yellow, . . . and so on.

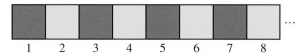

1   2   3   4   5   6   7   8

(i) Complete the table.

Block position	Colour
1	Green
2	Yellow
⋮	⋮

(ii) List the positions of the first three green blocks. Is there a pattern?

(iii) List the positions of the first three yellow blocks. Is there a pattern?

(iv) What is the colour of the 20th block?

(v) What is the colour of the 33rd block?

(vi) What is the colour of the 1,001st block?

2. A repeating pattern consists of blocks coloured red, white, blue, red, . . . and so on.

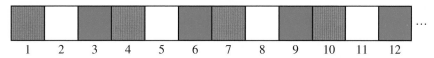

1   2   3   4   5   6   7   8   9   10   11   12

(i) List the positions of the first three red blocks. Is there a pattern?

(ii) List the positions of the first three white blocks. Is there a pattern?

(iii) List the positions of the first three blue blocks. Is there a pattern?

(iv) What is the colour of the 48th block?

(v) What is the colour of the 50th block?

(vi) What is the colour of the 100th block?

3. Players in a football competition are lined up in the following repeating sequence.

   (i) List the positions of the first four players in a blue shirt.

  (ii) List the positions of the first four players in an orange shirt.

 (iii) List the positions of the first four players in a yellow shirt.

  (iv) What is the colour of the shirt of the 15th player?

   (v) What is the colour of the shirt of the 20th player?

  (vi) Where in the line-up is the 8th player with an orange shirt?

 (vii) Where in the line-up is the 10th player with a blue shirt?

4. As part of the opening ceremony of a hockey competition, the hockey players parade in the following repeating sequence.

   (i) List the positions of the first three players in each colour.

  (ii) What is the colour of the shirt of the 12th player?

 (iii) What is the colour of the shirt of the 22nd player?

  (iv) What is the colour of the shirt of the 23rd player?

   (v) Where in the line-up is the 8th player with a green shirt?

  (vi) Where in the line-up is the 10th player with a yellow shirt?

Differences 1

Some sequences can be understood better by investigating the differences between the terms. For example, the sequence 2, 5, 8, . . . has the same difference between consecutive terms. We can say that the difference between the terms is constant.

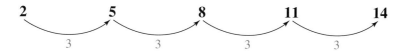

The differences are equal to 3 (which is a constant).

More complex sequences require us to check **the difference between the differences**. For example, the sequence 3, 6, 11, 18, 27, . . .

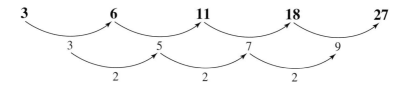

The first differences (3, 5, 7, . . .) are not constant, but the second differences are equal to 2 (which is a constant).

Exercise 9.3

In questions 1–6, find the first four terms and show that the difference between the terms is constant.

1. $T_n = 2n + 1$ 2. $T_n = 3n + 2$ 3. $T_n = 4n - 3$

4. $T_n = 5n + 2$ 5. $T_n = 3 - 2n$ 6. $T_n = 8 - 3n$

In questions 7–9, find the first four terms and show that the difference between the differences is constant.

7. $T_n = n^2 + 1$ 8. $T_n = n^2 - 2$ 9. $T_n = n^2 + n$

In questions 10–12, find the first four terms and show that the differences are such that this method of investigation will not produce a useful result.

10. $T_n = 2^n$ 11. $T_n = 3^n$ 12. $T_n = 3 + 2^n$

Viewing the sequence as a graph

The patterns we look for are based on the relationship between two sets of values – the positions in a sequence and the values or terms in the sequence.

For example, the sequence 1, 3, 5, 7, 9, . . . can be represented in this table:

Position	1	2	3	4	5
Terms	1	3	5	7	9

We can interpret the pairs (position, term) as points and plot (1, 1), (2, 3), (3, 5), (4, 7) and (5, 9).

The graph shows a line.

Note: The first four letters of the word **linear** spell line. A graph is linear if all the points can be joined by one straight line.

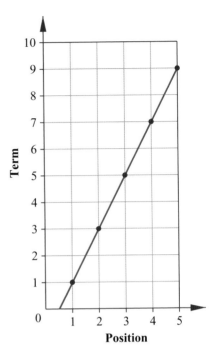

Exercise 9.4

In questions 1–8, find the first five terms and show your results on a graph. State whether the graph is linear or not. Put the position along the horizontal axis.

1. $T_n = 2n$
2. $T_n = 3n - 1$
3. $T_n = 4n + 1$
4. $T_n = n^2$
5. $T_n = n^2 - n$
6. $T_n = n(n + 2)$
7. $T_n = 2^n$
8. $T_n = n^3 - n^2$

9. (i) Find the first four terms in the sequence defined by $T_n = 2n + 3$.
    (ii) By forming pairs of the form (position, term), plot the sequence on a graph.
    (iii) Using $x = 1, 2, 3$ and 4, find four points on the line $y = 2x + 3$. What do you notice?

10. (i) Find the first four terms in the sequence defined by $T_n = 3n - 2$.
    (ii) By forming pairs of the form (position, term), plot the sequence on a graph.
    (iii) Using $x = 1, 2, 3$ and 4, find four points on the line $y = 3x - 2$. What do you notice?
    (iv) What is the slope of the line in your graph?
    (v) What is the connection between the slope and the numbers in the original sequence?

11. Two sequences are defined as follows:

    Sequence A: $T_n = 2n + 7$ \qquad Sequence B: $T_n = 7n + 2$

    (i) In which sequence will the terms increase more rapidly? Explain your answer.
    (ii) Verify your result by finding T_1 and T_5 of each sequence and compare your results.
    (iii) Use your results from part (ii) to sketch a graph showing the two sequences as lines.

12. John receives a gift of a money box with €4 in it for his birthday. John decides he will save a further €2 a day each day after his birthday.

    (i) Draw a table showing the amount of money John saved for the first five days (his birthday being the first day).

    (ii) How much money will John have in his money box on the 10th day?

    (iii) How much money will John have in his money box on the 25th day?

    (iv) By looking at the pattern in this question, can you explain why the amount of money John has on day 10 is not twice the amount he has on day 5?

    (v) How much money does John have in his money box on day 100?

    (vi) How much money has John actually put in his money box after 10 days? Explain how you arrived at this amount.

    (vii) John wants to buy a new computer game. The game costs €39.99. What is the minimum number of days John will have to save so that he has enough money to buy the computer game?

13. Owen has a money box. He starts with €1 and adds €3 each day.

    (i) Draw a table showing the amount of money Owen has for the first 10 days.

    (ii) Draw a graph to show the amount of money Owen has saved each day. Put *Number of days* along the horizontal axis and *Amount of money* on the vertical axis.

    (iii) Why will the scale for the *Number of days* be different to the scale for the *Amount of money*?

14. Amy and Bill are discussing phone network offers. Amy says that she gets no free texts at the beginning of the month but that she receives five free texts each night. Bill says that on his network he begins each month with 30 free texts and receives three additional free texts each night.

    (i) Draw a table showing the start number of texts and the number of texts available for the first six days.

Day	Amy's texts	Bill's texts
Start (1)	0	30
Day 2	5	33
⋮		
Day 6		

    (ii) Who has the most free texts after six days?

    (iii) Using graph paper, draw a graph showing the number of texts for both Amy and Bill for the first 20 days. You should allow the vertical axis to reach 150 texts.

     (iv) Are the two graphs linear or something else?

     (v) At what point does Amy seem to have a better offer than Bill?

     (vi) Will Amy and Bill ever have the same number of texts on a particular day? If so, which day? If not, why not?

15. Lenny begins the month with 20 free texts and receives two additional free texts each night. Jane does not have any free texts at the beginning of the month but receives three free texts each night.

     (i) Draw a table showing the number of free texts for both Lenny and Jane for the first 10 days.

     (ii) Represent both sets of results on a graph.

     (iii) Will Lenny and Jane ever have the same number of free texts on a certain day? If so, which day? If not, why not?

     (iv) Who in your opinion has the better deal for free texts each month? Give a reason for your answer.

16. A yellow flower measured 5 cm high at the beginning of the week and grew 2 cm each week afterwards.

A red flower measured 8 cm high at the beginning of the same week but grew only 1·5 cm each week afterwards.

     (i) Calculate the heights of each plant for the first five weeks and plot your results on a graph.

     (ii) Which plant will be taller?

     (iii) Will the plants ever be the exact same height?

     (iv) Give some reasons why the growth suggested by the graph may be unreliable.

Arithmetic sequence 1

Consider the sequence of numbers 2, 5, 8, 11, . . .

Each term after the first can be found by adding 3 to the previous term.

This is an example of an arithmetic sequence.

> A sequence in which each term after the first is found by adding a constant number is called an **arithmetic sequence**.

The first term of an arithmetic sequence is denoted by *a*. In other words, $T_1 = a$.

The constant number, which is added to each term, is called the **common difference** and is denoted by *d*.

Consider the arithmetic sequence 3, 5, 7, 9, 11, . . .

$$a = 3 \text{ and } d = 2$$

Each term after the first is found by adding 2 to the previous term.

Consider the arithmetic sequence 7, 2, −3, −8, . . .

$$a = 7 \text{ and } d = -5$$

Each term after the first is found by subtracting 5 from the previous term.

In an arithmetic sequence, the difference between any two consecutive terms is always the same.

$$\boxed{\text{Any term} - \text{previous term} = T_n - T_{n-1} = \text{constant} = d}$$

General term of an arithmetic sequence

In an arithmetic sequence, a is the first term and d is the common difference.

Thus, in an arithmetic sequence:

$$T_1 = a$$
$$T_2 = a + d$$
$$T_3 = a + 2d$$
$$T_4 = a + 3d, \quad \text{etc.}$$

Notice the coefficient of d is always one less than the term number.

Examples:
$$T_{10} = a + 9d$$
$$T_{15} = a + 14d$$
$$T_{50} = a + 49d$$

To go from one term, just add on another d.

$$\boxed{T_n = a + (n-1)d}$$

Note: Once we find a and d, we can answer any question about an arithmetic sequence.

EXAMPLE 1

The first three terms of an arithmetic sequence are 5, 8, 11, . . .

(i) Find the first term, a, and the common difference, d.

(ii) Find, in terms of n, an expression for T_n, the nth term, and hence or otherwise, find T_{17}.

(iii) Which term of the sequence is 122?

Solution:

(i) Find a and d. The first three terms are 5, 8, 11, . . .

$$a = T_1 = 5 \qquad\qquad d = T_2 - T_1 = 8 - 5 = 3$$

Note: Be careful: $d \neq T_1 - T_2$.

(ii) Find an expression for T_n.

$$\begin{aligned}
T_n &= a + (n - 1)d \\
&= 5 + (n - 1)3 \\
&= 5 + 3n - 3 \\
&= 3n + 2
\end{aligned}$$

Find T_{17}.

Method 1:

$$T_n = a + (n - 1)d$$
$$T_{17} = 5 + (17 - 1)(3)$$

(put in $n = 17$, $a = 5$ and $d = 3$)

$$T_{17} = 5 + 16(3)$$
$$T_{17} = 53$$

Method 2:

$$T_n = 3n + 2 \quad \text{(from part (ii))}$$
$$T_{17} = 3(17) + 2$$

(put in $n = 17$)

$$T_{17} = 53$$

(iii) Which term of the sequence is 122?

Method 1:

Equation given in disguise

$$T_n = 122$$
$$a + (n - 1)d = 122$$

(we know a and d, find n)

$$5 + (n - 1)(3) = 122$$
$$5 + 3n - 3 = 122$$
$$3n + 2 = 122$$
$$3n = 120$$
$$n = 40$$

Thus, the 40th term is 122.

Method 2:

Equation given in disguise

$$T_n = 122$$

($T_n = 3n + 2$, find n)

$$3n + 2 = 122$$
$$3n = 120$$
$$n = 40$$

EXAMPLE 2

The first three terms in an arithmetic sequence are $k + 2, 2k + 3, 5k - 2$, where k is a real number. Find the value of k and write down the first three terms.

Solution:
We use the fact that in an arithmetic sequence, the difference between any two consecutive terms is always the same. We are given the first three terms.

$$\therefore \quad T_3 \; - \; T_2 \; = \; T_2 \; - \; T_1 \qquad \text{(common difference)}$$
$$(5k - 2) - (2k + 3) = (2k + 3) - (k + 2) \qquad \text{(put in given values)}$$
$$5k - 2 - 2k - 3 = 2k + 3 - k - 2$$
$$3k - 5 = k + 1$$
$$2k = 6$$
$$k = 3$$

$T_1 = k + 2 = 3 + 2 = 5$
$T_2 = 2k + 3 = 2(3) + 3 = 9$
$T_3 = 5k - 2 = 5(3) - 2 = 13$

Thus, the first three terms are
5, 9, 13.

Exercise 9.5

In questions 1–9, find a and d for the arithmetic sequences and find, in terms of n, an expression for T_n, the nth term.

1. 1, 3, 5, . . .
2. 2, 5, 8, . . .
3. 3, 7, 11, . . .
4. 6, 11, 16, . . .
5. 9, 7, 5, . . .
6. 4, 1, –2, . . .
7. 8, 3, –2, . . .
8. 4, –2, –8, . . .
9. –5, –3, –1, . . .

10. The first three terms of an arithmetic sequence are 1, 4, 7.

   (i) Find the first term, a, and the common difference, d.

   (ii) Find, in terms of n, an expression for T_n, the nth term, and hence or otherwise, find T_{50}.

   (iii) Which term of the sequence is 88?

11. The first three terms of an arithmetic sequence are 4, 9, 14.

   (i) Find the first term, a, and the common difference, d.

   (ii) Find, in terms of n, an expression for T_n, the nth term, and hence or otherwise, find T_{45}.

   (iii) Which term of the sequence is equal to 249?

12. The first three terms of an arithmetic sequence are 40, 36, 32.

   (i) Find the first term, a, and the common difference, d.

   (ii) Find, in terms of n, an expression for T_n, the nth term, and hence or otherwise, find T_{15}.

   (iii) Which term of the sequence is 0?

13. The cost of visiting an exhibition is as follows.

Number of children	Price (€)
1	5
2	7
3	9
4	11

Number of adults	Price (€)
1	7
2	12
3	17
4	22

(i) Find a formula to calculate the cost of n children visiting the exhibition.

(ii) Verify that your formula works for three children.

(iii) Find a formula to calculate the cost of n adults visiting the exhibition.

(iv) Verify that your formula works for four adults.

(v) A group of six adults and 10 children are planning to visit the exhibition. How much will it cost?

14. A taxi charges €5 for a journey of 1 km, €8 for 2 km, €11 for 3 km and so on.

(i) Write out a table showing the cost of journeys up to 6 km.

(ii) Treating the costs as an arithmetic sequence, find the first term, a, and the common difference, d.

(iii) The taxi fare is a fixed charge plus a rate per kilometre. What is **(a)** the fixed charge and **(b)** the rate per kilometre?

(iv) How long a journey can be made with €100?

15. The instructions for cooking a chicken are 15 minutes per kg plus 20 minutes.

(i) How long is needed to cook a 1 kg chicken?

(ii) Write out a table showing the time needed to cook chickens weighing 1 kg, 2 kg, . . . , 6 kg.

(iii) Treating the times as an arithmetic sequence, find the first term, a, and the common difference, d.

(iv) Find a formula which calculates the time, in minutes, to cook a chicken weighing n kg.

(v) Use your formula to find out how long will it take to cook a 9 kg chicken.

(vi) What is the heaviest chicken that can be cooked within 4 hours?

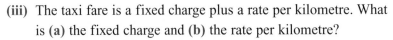

16. 5, 8, 11, . . . is an arithmetic sequence. Which term of the sequence is 179?

17. 3, 8, 13, 18, . . . is an arithmetic sequence. Which term of the sequence is 198?

18. Meriel's vocabulary was checked every two months beginning when she was 10 months old. At that time, she had a vocabulary of eight words. At 12 months she had a vocabulary of 11 words. By 14 months it was 14 words and by 16 months it was 17 words.

  (i) Taking the months as a sequence, how old was she when the 10th check was made?

  (ii) Find a formula, in terms of n, which will calculate Meriel's age when the nth check is made.

  (iii) Find a formula, in terms of n, which will calculate the vocabulary size when the nth check is made.

  (iv) Having a vocabulary of 5,000 words is not unusual. How old will Meriel be when she knows 5,000 words?

19. The first three terms in an arithmetic sequence are $2k - 1$, $2k + 1$, $3k$, where k is a real number. Find the value of k and write down the first three terms.

20. The first three terms in an arithmetic sequence are $k - 1$, $2k - 1$, $4k - 5$, where k is a real number. Find the value of k and write down the first three terms.

21. The first three terms in an arithmetic sequence are $k + 6$, $2k + 1$, $k + 18$, where k is a real number. Find the value of k and write down the first four terms.

22. The first three terms in an arithmetic sequence are $k - 2$, $2k + 1$, $k + 14$, where k is a real number.

  (i) Find the value of k and write down the first four terms.

  (ii) Find, in terms of n, an expression for T_n and hence or otherwise, find T_{21}.

  (iii) Which term of the sequence is 243?

Patterns 3

If we are asked to investigate pictures containing a mixture of colours or shapes, the first step is easy – number the diagrams! From this we can establish a connection between the diagram number and amount of colours or shapes in each one. This should lead us to a numeric pattern or sequence.

EXAMPLE

The diagram shows three shapes constructed using matchsticks.

  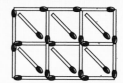

(i) If the pattern is continued, how many matchsticks will be needed for the 4th shape?

(ii) The amount of matchsticks used in the shapes form which type of sequence?

(iii) Find a formula, in terms of n, for the nth shape.

(iv) How many matchsticks will be needed for the 100th shape?

Solution:

Number the diagrams:

                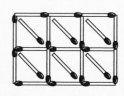

1   **2**   **3**   **4**

Count the matchsticks in each diagram and put these in a table:

Shape	1	2	3	4
Number of matchsticks	9	16	23	?

(i) The difference between the number of matchsticks used is $16 - 9 = 7$ and $23 - 16 = 7$. As the differences are the same, we can easily predict the next number in the sequence. Therefore, the 4th shape will need $23 + 7 = 30$ matchsticks.

Alternatively, you could draw the new shape and simply count the matchsticks.

(ii) The numbers 9, 16, 23, . . . form an arithmetic sequence, as the terms have a common difference ($d = 7$).

(iii) $a = T_1 = 9,$ $d = 7.$

$$T_n = a + (n - 1)d$$
$$= 9 + (n - 1)(7)$$
$$= 9 + 7n - 7$$
$$= 7n + 2$$

(iv)
$$T_n = 7n + 2$$
$$T_{100} = 7(100) + 2$$
$$= 702$$

Thus, 702 matchsticks will be needed for the 100th shape.

Exercise 9.6

1. These three diagrams were made using matches.

 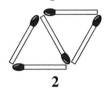 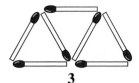

     1   **2**   **3**

  (i) If the pattern is continued, how many matches will be needed for the 4th, 5th and 6th diagrams?

  (ii) The amount of matches used in the diagrams form which type of sequence?

  (iii) Find a formula, in terms of n, for the nth diagram.

  (iv) How many matches will be needed for the 50th diagram?

  (v) Explain why there is no diagram with this pattern needing 200 matches.

2. The patterns shown are made from hexagonal tiles.

Pattern 1   Pattern 2   Pattern 3

  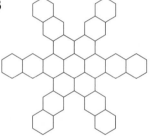

  (i) Construct a table showing the number of tiles for the first five patterns.

  (ii) Find a formula, in terms of n, for the number of tiles in the nth pattern.

  (iii) Which pattern is made from 253 tiles?

3. A series of shapes are made using matches.

  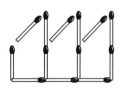

  (i) How many matches will be needed for the 4th and 5th shapes?

  (ii) Find a formula, in terms of n, for the nth shape.

  (iii) Which shape will need 49 matches?

4. Orange and black discs are arranged in rectangular patterns as shown.

   (i) How many discs will be in the 10th rectangle?

   (ii) How many black discs will be in the 10th rectangle?

   (iii) Describe two methods of finding the number of orange discs in the 10th rectangle.

   (iv) Explain why there is no rectangle with this pattern needing 99 discs.

   (v) Explain why there is no rectangle with this pattern needing 50 discs.

5. Rectangles containing red and white squares form a sequence as shown.

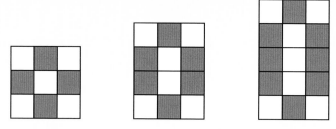

   (i) Copy and complete the table.

Rectangle	1	2	3	4	5	6
Number of white squares						
Number of red squares						
Total number of squares						

   (ii) Write down the number of white squares in the 10th rectangle.

   (iii) Write down the formula, in terms of n, for the number of white squares in the nth rectangle.

   (iv) Find a formula, in terms of n, for the number of red squares in the nth rectangle.

   (v) Use this formula to find the number of red squares in the 10th rectangle.

   (vi) Deduce the total number of squares in the 10th rectangle.

   (vii) Find a formula, in terms of n, for the total number of squares by using your answers from **(iii)** and **(iv)**.

   (viii) Verify your formula from **(vii)** by letting $n = 2$ and checking your table from **(i)**.

6. The set of diagrams have been made from straws.

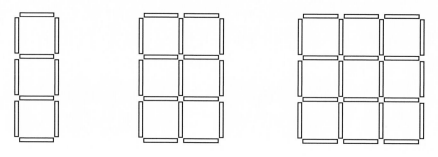

(i) How many straws will be needed for the 5th diagram?

(ii) Find a formula, in terms of n, for the nth diagram.

(iii) How many straws will be needed for the 20th diagram?

(iv) If $a : b$ is the ratio of the width to the height of the 1st diagram, find the value of a and the value of b.

(v) Which diagram has a ratio of its width to its height in the form $b : a$?

7. A long rectangular block is made using magnetic cubes. The sides are 1 cm. The diagram shows a block of four such cubes.

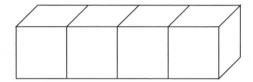

(i) How long is this block?

(ii) What is the surface area of this block?

(iii) If another block is attached to the end, what is the surface area?

(iv) What is the surface area of a block using 10 cubes?

(v) What is the surface area of a block using n cubes?

8. Patterns of dots are created as shown in this diagram.

(i) Draw the next two patterns.

(ii) Copy this table and complete it.

Diagram	1	2	3	4	5
Number of dots	5				

(iii) Find a formula, in terms of n, for the nth pattern.

(iv) Is it possible to predict from the table in **(i)** whether there is an even or an odd number of dots in the 50th diagram? Explain your answer.

(v) Is there an even or an odd number of dots in the 99th diagram?

(vi) Verify your predictions in **(iv)** and **(v)** by using the formula from **(ii)**.

9. A shop stacks two of its products as shown. The Economy brand is shown as a yellow square while the Deluxe brand is purple.

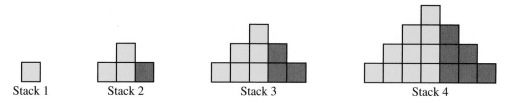

Stack 1   Stack 2   Stack 3   Stack 4

   (i) Write out, as a sequence, the number of Economy products in the first four stacks.

  (ii) Investigate whether the number of Economy products forms an arithmetic sequence.

 (iii) Write out, as a sequence, the number of Deluxe products in the first four stacks.

 (iv) Investigate whether the number of Deluxe products forms an arithmetic sequence.

10. A garden landscaper constructed small ponds of varying sizes. The diagram shows the three consecutive examples of a pond and the slabs that surround it.

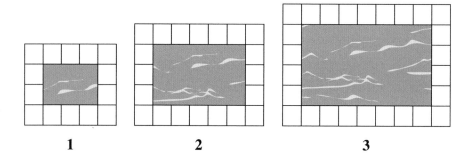

          1   2   3

   (i) Write out, as a sequence, the number of slabs needed for these three ponds.

  (ii) Investigate whether the sequence forms an arithmetic sequence. Explain your conclusion.

 (iii) Find a formula, in terms of n, for the number of slabs needed to surround the nth pond.

 (iv) Which pond would require 98 slabs to surround it?

  (v) Write out, as a sequence, the width (shown vertically) as a number of slabs needed for these three ponds.

 (vi) Find a formula, in terms of n, for the width of the nth pond.

(vii) What is the width and length of a pond which requires 98 slabs to surround it?

(viii) Draw the small pond that would precede the three shown and count the number of slabs needed. Verify that it fits in with the sequence you found earlier.

Arithmetic sequence 2

In some questions we are given two terms of an arithmetic sequence. In this case, we use the method of simultaneous equations to find a and d.

EXAMPLE

In an arithmetic sequence, the fifth term, T_5, is 19 and the eighth term, T_8, is 31. Find the first term, a, and the common difference, d.

Solution:

We are given two equations in disguise and we use these to find a and d.

$$T_n = a + (n - 1)d$$

Given: $\qquad T_5 = 19$ $\qquad\qquad$ Given: $\qquad T_8 = 31$

$\qquad \therefore a + 4d = 19 \quad$ ① $\qquad\qquad \therefore a + 7d = 31 \quad$ ②

Now solve the simultaneous equations ① and ② to find the value of a and the value of d.

Put $d = 4$ into ① or ②.

$$
\begin{array}{ll}
a + 7d = 31 & ② \\
-a - 4d = -19 & ① \times -1 \\
\hline
3d = 12 & \\
d = 4 &
\end{array}
$$

$$
\begin{array}{ll}
a + 4d = 19 & ① \\
a + 4(4) = 19 & \\
a + 16 = 19 & \\
a = 3 &
\end{array}
$$

Having found d, the next step is to find a.

Thus, $a = 3$ and $d = 4$.

Exercise 9.7

1. In an arithmetic sequence, the third term, T_3, is 7 and the fifth term, T_5, is 11.
    Find the first term, a, and the common difference, d.

2. In an arithmetic sequence, the fifth term, T_5, is 13 and the eighth term, T_8, is 22.
    Find the first term, a, and the common difference, d.

3. In an arithmetic sequence, the fourth term, T_4, is 19 and the seventh term, T_7, is 31.
    Find the first term, a, and the common difference, d.

4. In an arithmetic sequence, the fifth term, T_5, is 23 and the ninth term, T_9, is 43.
   Find the first term, a, and the common difference, d.

5. In an arithmetic sequence, the sixth term, T_6, is 35 and the eighth term, T_8, is 47.
   Find the first term, a, and the common difference, d.

6. In an arithmetic sequence, the first term, T_1, is 7 and the fifth term, T_5, is 19.

   (i) Find the common difference, d.

   (ii) Find, in terms of n, an expression for T_n, the nth term, and hence or otherwise, find T_{20}.

   (iii) Which term of the sequence is 100?

7. In an arithmetic sequence, the sum of the third term, T_3, and the seventh term, T_7, is 38 and the sixth term, T_6, is 23.

   (i) Find the first term, a, and the common difference, d.

   (ii) Find, in terms of n, an expression for T_n, the nth term.

   (iii) Show that $T_{19} = 5T_4$.

   (iv) For what value of n is $T_n = 99$?

8. The first four terms of an arithmetic sequence are 5, p, q, 11.

   (i) Find the value of p and the value of q.

   (ii) Find T_{10}, the tenth term.

9. The first five terms of an arithmetic sequence are p, q, 4, r, –2.

   (i) Find the value of p, the value of q and the value of r.

   (ii) Find T_{20}, the twentieth term.

Arithmetic sequence 3

To verify that a sequence is arithmetic, we must show the following:

$$T_n - T_{n-1} = \text{constant}$$

To show that a sequence is **not arithmetic**, it is only necessary to show that the difference between any two consecutive terms is not the same.

In practice, this usually involves showing that $T_3 - T_2 \neq T_2 - T_1$ or similar.

 EXAMPLE 1

T_n, the nth term, of a sequence is given by $T_n = 5n + 2$.
Verify that the sequence is arithmetic.

Solution:

$$T_n = 5n + 2$$
$$T_{n-1} = 5(n - 1) + 2 \qquad \text{(replace } n \text{ with } (n - 1))$$
$$= 5n - 5 + 2$$
$$\therefore T_{n-1} = 5n - 3$$
$$T_n - T_{n-1} = 5n + 2 - (5n - 3)$$
$$= 5n + 2 - 5n + 3$$
$$T_n - T_{n-1} = 5$$
$$\therefore T_n - T_{n-1} = \text{a constant}$$

Thus, the sequence is arithmetic.

EXAMPLE 2

T_n, the nth term, of a sequence is given by $T_n = n^2 + 3n$.
Verify that the sequence is not arithmetic.

Solution:

$T_n = n^2 + 3n$

$$T_1 = (1)^2 + 3(1) \qquad\qquad T_2 = (2)^2 + 3(2) \qquad\qquad T_3 = (3)^2 + 3(3)$$
$$= 1 + 3 \qquad\qquad\qquad = 4 + 6 \qquad\qquad\qquad = 9 + 9$$
$$T_1 = 4 \qquad\qquad\qquad\quad T_2 = 10 \qquad\qquad\qquad\quad T_3 = 18$$

$$T_3 - T_2 = 18 - 10 = 8 \qquad\qquad T_2 - T_1 = 10 - 4 = 6$$
$$T_3 - T_2 \neq T_2 - T_1$$

Thus, the sequence is not arithmetic.

Note: We could also have shown $T_n - T_{n-1} \neq$ a constant to show that the sequence is
not arithmetic.

Exercise 9.8

In questions 1–12, you are given the nth term, T_n, of a sequence. Show that the sequence is arithmetic.

1. $T_n = 2n + 3$
2. $T_n = 3n + 1$
3. $T_n = 4n + 5$
4. $T_n = 5n$
5. $T_n = 2n$
6. $T_n = 3n - 2$
7. $T_n = n - 4$
8. $T_n = 2n - 5$
9. $T_n = 7n + 1$
10. $T_n = 3 - n$
11. $T_n = 5 - 2n$
12. $T_n = 4 - 3n$

In questions 13–18, you are given the nth term, T_n, of a sequence. Show that the sequence is not arithmetic.

13. $T_n = n^2 + 2n$
14. $T_n = n^2 + 5n$
15. $T_n = n^2 - 3n$
16. $T_n = 2n^2 + n$
17. $T_n = 2n^2 - 1$
18. $T_n = n^2 - 4n + 3$

Series

When we add together the terms of a sequence, we get a series.

For example:

Sequence: 1, 4, 7, 10, . . .
Series: $1 + 4 + 7 + 10 + \cdots$

The commas are replaced by plus signs to form the series.
The sum of the series is the result of adding the terms.
The sum of the first n terms of a series is denoted by S_n.

$$\therefore S_n = T_1 + T_2 + T_3 + \cdots + T_n$$

Note: Even though each term is separated by a plus sign rather than a comma, we still write $T_1 = 1$, $T_2 = 4$, $T_3 = 7$, etc.

From this we have:

$$S_1 = T_1$$
$$S_2 = T_1 + T_2$$
$$S_3 = T_1 + T_2 + T_3, \text{ etc.}$$

Arithmetic series

An **arithmetic series** is the sum of the terms of an arithmetic sequence.

The sum of the first n terms of an arithmetic series is denoted by S_n.
The formula for S_n can be written in terms of n, a and d.

$$S_n = \frac{n}{2}[2a + (n - 1)d]$$

Note: Once we find a and d, we can answer any question about an arithmetic series.

EXAMPLE 1

The first three terms of an arithmetic series are $4 + 7 + 10 + \cdots$

(i) Find, in terms of n, an expression for S_n, the sum to n terms.

(ii) Find S_{20}, the sum of the first 20 terms.

Solution:

Note: Even though each term is separated by a plus sign rather than a comma, we still write $T_1 = 4$, $T_2 = 7$, $T_3 = 10$, etc.

(i) $4 + 7 + 10 + \cdots$

$$a = T_1 = 4 \qquad d = T_2 - T_1 = 7 - 4 = 3$$

$$S_n = \frac{n}{2}\left[2a + (n - 1)d\right]$$

$$= \frac{n}{2}\left[2(4) + (n - 1)(3)\right] \qquad \text{(put in } a = 4 \text{ and } d = 3)$$

$$= \frac{n}{2}\left[8 + 3n - 3\right]$$

$$S_n = \frac{n}{2}(3n + 5)$$

(ii) Find S_{20}.

Method 1:

$$S_n = \frac{n}{2}\left[2a + (n - 1)d\right]$$

$$S_{20} = \frac{20}{2}\left[2(4) + (20 - 1)(3)\right]$$

(put in $n = 20$, $a = 4$ and $d = 3$)

$$S_{20} = 10(65)$$

$$S_{20} = 650$$

Method 2:

$$S_n = \frac{n}{2}(3n + 5) \quad \text{(from part (i))}$$

$$S_{20} = \frac{20}{2}(3(20) + 5)$$

$$= 10(65)$$

$$S_{20} = 650$$

In some questions we are given values of S_n and T_n for two values of n. In this case, we use the method of simultaneous equations to find a and d.

EXAMPLE 2

In an arithmetic series, the fifth term, T_5, is 14 and the sum of the first six terms, S_6, is 57.

(i) Find the first term, a, and the common difference, d.

(ii) Show that: (a) $T_n = 3n - 1$ (b) $2S_n = 3n^2 + n$

Solution:

(i) We are given two equations in disguise and we use them to find a and d.

$$T_n = a + (n - 1)d$$

Given: $T_5 = 14$

$$\therefore a + (5 - 1)d = 14$$

$$a + 4d = 14 \qquad ①$$

$$S_n = \frac{n}{2}[2a + (n - 1)d]$$

Given: $S_6 = 57$

$$\therefore \frac{6}{2}[2a + (6 - 1)d] = 57 \quad (n = 6)$$

$$3(2a + 5d) = 57$$

$$2a + 5d = 19 \qquad ②$$

(divide both sides by 3)

Now solve the simultaneous equations ① and ② to find the value of a and the value of d.

$$2a + 8d = 28 \qquad ① \times 2$$

$$-2a - 5d = -19 \qquad ② \times -1$$

$$\overline{3d = 9}$$

$$d = 3$$

Knowing $d = 3$, the next step is to find a.

Put $d = 3$ into ① or ②.

$$a + 4d = 14 \qquad ①$$

$$a + 4(3) = 14$$

$$a + 12 = 14$$

$$a = 2$$

Thus, $a = 2$ and $d = 3$.

(ii) Show that $T_n = 3n - 1$ and $2S_n = 3n^2 + n$.

Replace a with 2 and d with 3 in the formulas for T_n and S_n.

(a)
$$T_n = a + (n - 1)d$$

$$= 2 + (n - 1)(3)$$

(put in $a = 2$ and $d = 3$)

$$T_n = 2 + 3n - 3$$

$$T_n = 3n - 1$$

(b)
$$S_n = \frac{n}{2}[2a + (n - 1)d]$$

$$= \frac{n}{2}[2(2) + (n - 1)(3)]$$

(put in $a = 2$ and $d = 3$)

$$S_n = \frac{n}{2}[4 + 3n - 3]$$

$$S_n = \frac{n}{2}(3n + 1)$$

$$2S_n = n(3n + 1)$$

(multiply both sides by 2)

$$2S_n = 3n^2 + n$$

In some questions we have to solve an equation in disguise to find the value of n.

EXAMPLE 3

Find the sum of the arithmetic series $7 + 9 + 11 + \cdots + 55$.

Solution:

The first step is to find the number of terms, n, that there are in the series.

$$a = T_1 = 7 \qquad\qquad\qquad d = T_2 - T_1 = 9 - 7 = 2$$

Equation given in disguise:

Given: $\qquad\qquad T_n = 55$

$\therefore\ a + (n - 1)d = 55$

$\qquad 7 + (n - 1)(2) = 55$

(put in $a = 7$ and $d = 2$)

$$7 + 2n - 2 = 55$$
$$2n + 5 = 55$$
$$2n = 50$$
$$n = 25$$

Thus, there are 25 terms.

$$S_n = \frac{n}{2}\left[2a + (n - 1)d\right]$$

$$S_{25} = \frac{25}{2}\left[2(7) + (25 - 1)(2)\right]$$

(put in $n = 25$, $a = 7$ and $d = 2$)

$$= \frac{25}{2}\left[14 + (24)(2)\right]$$

$$= \frac{25}{2}\left[14 + 48\right]$$

$$= \frac{25}{2}(62)$$

$$S_{25} = 775$$

Exercise 9.9

1. The first three terms of an arithmetic series are $3 + 5 + 7 + \cdots$.
    Find S_{10}, the sum of the first 10 terms.

2. The first three terms of an arithmetic series are $4 + 7 + 10 + \cdots$.
    Find S_{12}, the sum of the first 12 terms.

3. The first three terms of an arithmetic series are $1 + 5 + 9 + \cdots$.
    Find S_{18}, the sum of the first 18 terms.

4. The first three terms of an arithmetic series are $3 + 8 + 13 + \cdots$.

    (i) Find, in terms of n, an expression for S_n, the sum to n terms.

    (ii) Find S_{20}, the sum of the first 20 terms.

5. The first three terms of an arithmetic series are $10 + 13 + 16 + \cdots$.

    (i) Find, in terms of n, an expression for S_n, the sum to n terms.

    (ii) Find S_{30}, the sum of the first 30 terms.

6. The nth term of an arithmetic series is given by $2n + 3$.

    (i) Write down the first four terms.

    (ii) Write down the common difference.

    (iii) Find S_{16}, the sum of the first 16 terms.

7. In an arithmetic series, the fifth term, T_5, is 22 and the sum of the first four terms, S_4, is 38.

    (i) Find the first term, a, and the common difference, d.

    (ii) Show that: (a) $T_n = 5n - 3$ (b) $2S_n = 5n^2 - n$

8. In an arithmetic series, the eighth term, T_8, is 21 and the sum of the first six terms, S_6, is 18.

    (i) Find the first term, a, and the common difference, d.

    (ii) Show that: (a) $T_n = 4n - 11$ (b) $S_n = 2n^2 - 9n$

    (iii) Find: (a) T_{20} (b) S_{30}

9. In an arithmetic series, the seventh term, T_7, is 20 and the sum of the first five terms, S_5, is 40.

    (i) Find the first term, a, and the common difference, d.

    (ii) Show that: (a) $T_n = 3n - 1$ (b) $2S_n = 3n^2 + n$

    (iii) Find: (a) T_{30} (b) S_{30}

10. In an arithmetic series, the eighth term, T_8, is 27 and the sum of the first 10 terms, S_{10}, is 120.

    (i) Find the first term, a, and the common difference, d.

    (ii) Show that: (a) $T_n = 3(2n - 7)$ (b) $S_n = 3(n^2 - 6n)$

    (iii) Find: (a) T_{25} (b) S_6

11. In an arithmetic series, the sum of the first four terms, S_4, is 44 and the sum of the first six terms, S_6, is 102.

    (i) Find the first term, a, and the common difference, d.

    (ii) Find: (a) T_{20} (b) S_{20}

12. Find the sum of the arithmetic series $2 + 5 + 8 + \cdots + 59$.

13. Find the sum of the arithmetic series $1 + 5 + 9 + \cdots + 117$.

14. Find the sum of the arithmetic series $3 + 8 + 13 + \cdots + 248$.

15. The nth term of a series is given by $T_n = 3n + 2$.

    (i) Write down, in terms of n, an expression for T_{n-1}, the $(n - 1)$st term.

    (ii) Show that the series is arithmetic.

    (iii) Find S_{20}, the sum of the first 20 terms.

16. The first three terms of an arithmetic series are $10 + 20 + 30 + \cdots$.

    (i) Find, in terms of n, an expression for T_n, the nth term.

    (ii) Find, in terms of n, an expression for S_n, the sum to n terms.

    (iii) Using your expression for S_n, find the sum of the natural numbers that are both multiples of 10 and smaller than 2,001.

17. The first three terms in an arithmetic series are $1 + 3 + 5 + \cdots$.

    (i) Show that: **(a)** $T_n = 2n - 1$ **(b)** $S_n = n^2$

    (ii) Hence or otherwise, evaluate: **(a)** T_{20} **(b)** S_{20}

    (iii) How many terms need to be added to give a sum of 225?

18. The first three terms of an arithmetic series are $3a + 4a + 5a + \cdots$ where a is a real number.

    (i) Find, in terms of a, an expression for T_{10}, the tenth term.

    (ii) Find, in terms of a, an expression for S_{10}, the sum of the first 10 terms.

    (iii) If $S_{10} - T_{10} = 126$, find the value of a.

    (iv) Write down the first four terms of the series.

    (v) Write down, in terms of n, expressions for: **(a)** T_n **(b)** S_n

    (vi) Hence or otherwise, evaluate: **(a)** T_{20} **(b)** S_{20}

19. The general term, T_n, of an arithmetic series is given by $T_n = 2n + 5$.

    (i) Find the first term, a, and the common difference, d.

    (ii) For what value of n is the sum of the first n terms, S_n, equal to 160?

20. A pupil saves money each week. The pupil saves 40c in the first week, 60c in the second week, 80c in the next week, continuing this pattern for 50 weeks.

    (i) How much will the pupil save in the 50th week?

    (ii) How much will the pupil have saved after 50 weeks?

21. A woman accepted a post with a starting salary of €30,000. In each following year she received an increase in salary of €2,000. What were her total earnings in the first 12 years?

22. In a potato race, 10 potatoes are placed 8 m apart in a straight line. The object of the race is to pick up the first potato and place it in a basket 20 m in front of the first potato, then run to the second potato, pick it up and place it in the basket and so on.

The race begins at the basket. Find the total distance covered by a contestant who finishes the race.

23. A display in a grocery store will consist of cans stacked as shown.

    The first row is to have 18 cans and each row after the first is to have two cans fewer than the preceding row. How many cans will be needed in the display?

24. A man is given an interest-free loan. He repays the loan in monthly instalments. He repays €40 at the end of the first month, €44 at the end of the second month, €48 at the end of the third month, continuing the pattern of increasing the monthly repayments by €4 a month until the loan is repaid. The final monthly repayment is €228.

    (i) Show that it will take the man 48 months to repay the loan.

    (ii) Calculate the amount of the loan.

25. A ball rolls down a slope. The distances it travels in successive seconds are 2 cm, 6 cm, 10 cm, 14 cm and so on. How many seconds elapse before it has travelled a total of 18 m?

Given S_n of an arithmetic series in terms of n

In many problems we are given an expression for S_n in terms of n and we need to find a and d. In this type of problem, we use the fact that for all arithmetic series:

$$T_n = S_n - S_{n-1} \qquad \text{and} \qquad T_1 = S_1$$

Examples: $T_2 = S_2 - S_1$, $T_3 = S_3 - S_2$, $T_9 = S_9 - S_8$ and so on.

EXAMPLE 1

The sum of the first n terms, S_n, of an arithmetic series is given by $S_n = 2n^2 + n$. Find the first term, a, and the common difference, d.

Solution:

$$S_n = 2n^2 + n$$

$$S_1 = 2(1)^2 + (1) \qquad\qquad S_2 = 2(2)^2 + (2)$$
$$= 2(1) + 1 \qquad\qquad\qquad = 2(4) + 2$$
$$= 2 + 1 \qquad\qquad\qquad\qquad = 10$$
$$= 3 \qquad\qquad\qquad\qquad T_2 = S_2 - S_1$$
$$a = T_1 = S_1 = 3 \qquad\qquad\qquad = 10 - 3$$
$$\qquad\qquad\qquad\qquad\qquad = 7$$
$$\qquad\qquad\qquad\qquad d = T_2 - T_1 = 7 - 3 = 4$$

Thus, $a = 3$ and $d = 4$.

EXAMPLE 2

The general term, T_n, of an arithmetic sequence is given by $T_n = 2n + 5$. Find the first term, a, and the common difference, d. For what value of n is $S_n = 160$?

Solution:

$$T_n = 2n + 5 \qquad\qquad\qquad d = T_2 - T_1$$
$$T_1 = 2(1) + 5 = 2 + 5 = 7 = a \qquad = 9 - 7$$
$$T_2 = 2(2) + 5 = 4 + 5 = 9 \qquad\qquad d = 2$$

Thus, $a = 7$ and $d = 2$.
Equation given in disguise:

$$S_n = 160$$

$$\frac{n}{2}[2a + (n-1)d] = 160 \qquad \text{(we know } a \text{ and } d \text{, find } n\text{)}$$

$$\frac{n}{2}[2(7) + (n-1)(2)] = 160 \qquad \text{(put in } a = 7 \text{ and } d = 2\text{)}$$

$$\frac{n}{2}(14 + 2n - 2) = 160$$

$$\frac{n}{2}(2n + 12) = 160$$

$$n(2n + 12) = 320 \qquad \text{(multiply both sides by 2)}$$

$$2n^2 + 12n = 320$$

$$2n^2 + 12n - 320 = 0$$

$$n^2 + 6n - 160 = 0 \qquad \text{(divide both sides by 2)}$$

$$(n - 10)(n + 16) = 0$$
$$n - 10 = 0 \ \text{ or } \ n + 16 = 0$$
$$n = 10 \ \text{ or } \ n = -16 \qquad (\text{reject } n = -16)$$

Thus, $n = 10$.

Note: If n is a fraction or a negative number, reject it.

Exercise 9.10

1. The sum of the first n terms, S_n, of an arithmetic series is given by $S_n = n^2 + 2n$. Use S_1 and S_2 to find the first term, a, and the common difference, d.

2. The sum of the first n terms, S_n, of an arithmetic series is given by $S_n = n^2 + 3n$. Find the first term, a, and the common difference, d.

3. The sum of the first n terms, S_n, of an arithmetic series is given by $S_n = 3n^2 - 2n$. Find the first term, a, and the common difference, d.

4. The sum of the first n terms, S_n, of an arithmetic series is given by $S_n = 2n^2 - 3n$. Find the first term, a, and the common difference, d.

5. The sum of the first n terms, S_n, of an arithmetic series is given by $S_n = \dfrac{n(3n + 1)}{2}$.

    (i) Calculate the first term of the series.

    (ii) By calculating S_8 and S_7, find T_8, the eighth term of the series.

6. The sum of the first n terms, S_n, of an arithmetic series is given by $S_n = 2n^2 + n$.

    (i) Calculate the first term of the series and the common difference.

    (ii) Find, in terms of n, an expression for T_n, the nth term.

    (iii) Hence, calculate T_{10}.

    (iv) Show that $T_{10} = S_{10} - S_9$.

7. The sum of the first n terms, S_n, of an arithmetic series is given by $S_n = 2n^2 - 4n$.

    (i) Find the first term, a, and the common difference, d.

    (ii) Find, in terms of n, an expression for T_n, the nth term.

    (iii) Find T_{20} and verify that $T_{20} = S_{20} - S_{19}$.

    (iv) Starting with the first term, how many terms of the series must be added to give a sum of 160?

Differences 2

Earlier, we investigated differences between differences on some sequences. While these are not arithmetic sequences, it is still possible to find an expression for T_n, the nth term. When it takes *two* differences to see a constant, the formula for T_n will be of the form $T_n = an^2 + bn + c$.

Furthermore, it can be shown that when the second differences are 2, then $T_n = n^2 + bn + c$, and when the second differences are 4, then $T_n = 2n^2 + bn + c$.

Here is the sequence 3, 6, 11, 18, 27, . . .

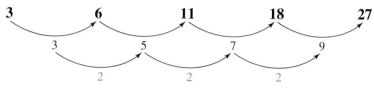

The general term of this sequence will be of the form $T_n = n^2 + bn + c$.

EXAMPLE

Find the general term, T_n, of the sequence 1, 5, 11, 19, 29, …

Solution:

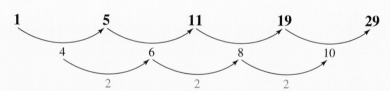

Because the second difference is 2, $T_n = n^2 + bn + c$. Now we need to find the value of b and the value of c.

We will use the first two terms to form two equations involving b and c and then use the method of simultaneous equations.

Given: $T_1 = 1$ and $T_2 = 5$

$T_n = n^2 + bn + c$

$T_1 = 1^2 + b(1) + c = 1$

$1 + b + c = 1$

$b + c = 0$ ①

$T_2 = 2^2 + b(2) + c = 5$

$4 + 2b + c = 5$

$2b + c = 1$ ②

$\begin{aligned} -b - c &= 0 & \text{① × } -1 \\ 2b + c &= 1 & \text{②} \\ \hline b &= 1 \end{aligned}$

$b + c = 0$

$1 + c = 0$

$c = -1$

Thus, $T_n = n^2 + 1n - 1 = n^2 + n - 1$.

Exercise 9.11

In questions 1–6, find an expression for T_n for the following sequences.

1. 3, 7, 13, 21, 31, . . .   2. 4, 9, 16, 25, 36, . . .

3. 2, 6, 12, 20, 30, . . .   4. 2, 5, 10, 17, 26, . . .

5. 0, 0, 2, 6, 12, . . .   6. 8, 15, 24, 35, 48, . . .

7. (i) Find T_n of the sequence 0, 4, 10, 18, 28, . . .

   (ii) Find T_{10}.

   (iii) Investigate whether T_{100} is less than or greater than 1,000.

8. A rocket is launched from ground level and its height is recorded each second after blast-off. The heights are 22 m, 36 m, 52 m, 70 m, . . .

   (i) Find T_n of the sequence.

   (ii) How high will the rocket be after 10 seconds?

   (iii) How high will the rocket be after 1 minute?

   (iv) Noting that the rocket does not rise uniformly, give a reason why a rocket would rise faster as time passes.

9. Mary is making rectangular patterns from counters. The length of each rectangle is one more than the width. The first three patterns are shown.

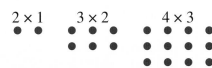

   (i) Each time, to get the next pattern, she increases the width by one more counter. Write an expression for the number of counters in the nth pattern.

   (ii) Mary notices that there is also a pattern in how many extra counters she needs each time to make the next pattern. How many extra counters does she need to make the $(n + 1)$th pattern from the nth pattern? Write your answer in the form $a(n + b)$.

ANSWERS

Exercise 1.1

1. 23   2. 4   3. −3   4. −6   5. −2   6. −10   7. −12   8. 8   9. 18

10. 16   11. 20   12. −100   13. −4   14. −2   15. 6   16. −1   17. 15

18. 0   19. 0   20. 2   21. 3   22. 9   23. 6   24. 12   25. 0   26. 39

27. −39   28. 9   29. 2   30. 2   31. 4   32. 8   33. $10\frac{1}{2}$ or 10·5

34. $\frac{1}{2}$ or 0·5   35. $\frac{1}{5}$ or 0·2   36. 30   37. 72   41. (i) 17   (ii) 27

42. $x, x+1, x+2$; $3x+3 = 3(x+1)$, which is divisible by 3

Exercise 1.2

1. $7x$ 2. $2x$ 3. $-3x$ 4. $-6x$ 5. $4x$ 6. $-7a$ 7. $-14y$ 8. $3b$ 9. $9x^2$

10. $2a^2$ 11. $3x^2$ 12. $6x^2$ 13. $-10x^2$ 14. $-12x^3$ 15. $10x^3$ 16. x^2 17. $12a^2$

18. $-15y^3$ 19. $8p^3$ 20. $x^2 + 5x + 6$ 21. $2x^2 - 3x - 20$ 22. $6x^2 - 19x + 10$ 23. a^2

24. $2x$ 25. a 26. $2ab$ 27. $2(a+4) + 8a = 10a + 8$ 28. 7   29. 3   30. 0   31. 0

32. (i) $4a$ (ii) $14x$ (iii) $4b$ 33. (i) $10x^2$ (ii) $6a^2$ (iii) $20x + 15$ or $5(4x+3)$ 34. $96y^2$

Exercise 1.3

1. 5   2. −4   3. 2   4. −3   5. 4   6. 3   7. −5   8. −3   9. 4   10. −6

11. 1   12. 2   13. 5   14. 6   15. 1   16. 5   17. 1   18. 3   19. 7   20. 4

21. 1   22. −2   23. 17   24. (i) 7   (ii) 6   (iii) 5   25. (i) $13x - 1 = 64$

(ii) 5   (iii) 24 cm   26. (i) $2x + 18$; $2x + 6$ (ii) $2x + 18 = 4x + 12$ (iii) 3

27. (i) $5n + 4$ (ii) 45   28. (i) $3x + 3 = 33$ (ii) 10   (iii) 10, 11, 12   29. (i) $\frac{x}{2} + \frac{x}{5} = 70$

(ii) 100   (iii) €20   30. 4   31. (ii) yes

Exercise 1.4

1. $x = 2, y = 1$ 2. $x = 4, y = 2$ 3. $x = 5, y = 3$ 4. $x = 5, y = 2$

5. $x = -2, y = -3$ 6. $x = 2, y = 3$ 7. $x = 7, y = 3$ 8. $x = 3, y = -1$

9. $x = 3, y = 2$ 10. $x = -1, y = 1$ 11. $x = 1, y = -4$ 12. $x = -1, y = -1$

13. $x = -2, y = -1$ 14. $x = 3, y = 4$ 15. $x = -1, y = 1$ 16. $x = 2, y = 3$

17. $x = 2, y = -3$ 18. $x = 3, y = 3$ 19. $x = 5, y = -1$ 20. $x = 2, y = -2$

21. $x = -1, y = -3$ 22. $x = 1, y = \frac{1}{3}$ 23. $x = \frac{3}{2}, y = \frac{5}{2}$ 24. $x = \frac{5}{2}, y = \frac{4}{3}$

25. $x = \frac{3}{5}, y = \frac{4}{5}$ **26.** $x = \frac{5}{2}, y = 1$ **27.** $x = \frac{3}{2}, y = \frac{1}{2}$ **28. (i) (a)** $7x + 3y = 82$

(b) $2x + y = 24$ **(ii)** $x = 10, y = 4$ **(iii) (a)** €10   **(b)** €4   **(iv)** €124

29. A $(3, -2)$, B $(-1, 23)$, C $(5, 2)$, D $(1, 4)$ **30. (i)** $x = 6, y = 2$ **(ii)** $x = 2, y = 1$

(iii) $x = 5, y = 3$ **31. (i)** $x = 50, y = 30$ **(ii)** $x = 40, y = 30$

32. $5x + 3y = 49$; $3x + 2y = 31$; $x = 5, y = 8$

33. $8x + 4y = 144$; $3x + 2y = 62$; $x =$ €0·10, $y =$ €0·16

34. (i) $P = 5, Q = 3, R = 4, S = 6$ **(ii)** $B = 8, C = 7, D = 2, E = 5$

35. apple = 10, lemon = 6, pear = 24, grapefruit = 16, grapes = 14 and banana = 8

Exercise 1.5

1. $(x + 1)(x + 3)$ **2.** $(x - 1)(x - 5)$ **3.** $(x - 2)(x + 4)$ **4.** $(x + 2)(x - 5)$

5. $(x - 1)(x - 4)$ **6.** $(x + 4)(x + 5)$ **7.** $(x - 3)(x + 4)$ **8.** $(x + 3)(x - 5)$

9. $(x + 3)(x + 10)$ **10.** $(x + 4)(x - 7)$ **11.** $(2x + 3)(x + 1)$ **12.** $(2x - 3)(x - 2)$

13. $(2x - 1)(x + 5)$ **14.** $(2x + 3)(x - 2)$ **15.** $(3x + 1)(x + 5)$ **16.** $(3x - 1)(x - 7)$

17. $(3x - 2)(x + 4)$ **18.** $(3x + 2)(x - 1)$ **19.** $(5x + 3)(x + 1)$ **20.** $(5x - 2)(x - 3)$

21. $(5x - 1)(x + 2)$ **22.** $(5x + 1)(x - 4)$ **23.** $(7x - 1)(x - 5)$ **24.** $(11x - 2)(x + 3)$

25. $x(x + 2)$ **26.** $x(x - 3)$ **27.** $x(x + 4)$ **28.** $x(x - 5)$ **29.** $x(x + 6)$ **30.** $x(x - 1)$

31. $x(x + 1)$ **32.** $x(2x + 3)$ **33.** $x(2x - 5)$ **34.** $(x - 2)(x + 2)$ **35.** $(x - 4)(x + 4)$

36. $(x - 5)(x + 5)$ **37.** $(x - 8)(x + 8)$ **38.** $(x - 10)(x + 10)$ **39.** $(x - 7)(x + 7)$

40. (i) $x^2 + 6x + 8$; $(x + 2)(x + 4)$ **(ii)** $x^2 + 5x$; $x(x + 5)$ **(iii)** $x^2 - 9$; $(x - 3)(x + 3)$

41. (i) $x + 4$ **(ii)** $2x + 1$ **(iii)** $x + 5$

Exercise 1.6

1. $(2x + 3)(2x + 1)$ **2.** $(4x - 1)(x - 5)$ **3.** $(3x + 1)(2x + 3)$ **4.** $(6x - 1)(x - 2)$

5. $(3x - 2)(2x + 1)$ **6.** $(8x - 1)(x - 3)$ **7.** $(4x + 5)(2x - 1)$ **8.** $(3x - 1)(3x - 5)$

9. $(5x - 3)(2x + 1)$

Exercise 1.7

1. $2, 3$ **2.** $-5, 4$ **3.** $3, -7$ **4.** $0, -3$ **5.** $0, 5$ **6.** $0, 8$ **7.** ± 6 **8.** ± 4

9. ± 10 **10.** $3, 4$ **11.** $-2, -4$ **12.** $-3, 5$ **13.** $1, 5$ **14.** $2, -5$ **15.** $4, -5$

16. $-1, 7$ **17.** $2, 7$ **18.** $-3, 8$ **19.** $0, 4$ **20.** $0, -6$ **21.** $0, 2$ **22.** ± 3

23. ± 5 **24.** ± 1 **25.** $-\frac{3}{2}, -1$ **26.** $\frac{3}{2}, 2$ **27.** $\frac{1}{2}, -4$ **28.** $\frac{2}{3}, -4$ **29.** $-\frac{5}{3}, 1$

30. $\frac{1}{3}, 2$ **31.** $\frac{1}{5}, -2$ **32.** $\frac{2}{7}, -1$ **33.** $\frac{3}{2}, -5$ **34.** $-3, 6$ **35.** $-2, 4$ **36.** $3, -5$

37. $0, -2$ **38.** $0, 4$ **39.** ± 6 **40.** $2x^2 - x - 15$; $-\frac{5}{2}, 3$ **41.** $-\frac{3}{2}, -2$ **42.** $-3, -4$

43. $-1, 3$ **44. (i)** $x(x + 8) = 64$ **(ii)** $x^2 + 8x - 64 = 0$ **(iii)** $-14, 6$ **45.** 2

46. (i) 5 (ii) 60   **47.** 3   **48.** 6 cm by 6 cm by 2 cm   **49.** $2x^2 + 8x = 90$; 5

50. (i) 90°; tangent and a radius are perpendicular to each other at the point of contact, T   (ii) 6

Exercise 1.8

1. $2\sqrt{2}$ **2.** $2\sqrt{6}$ **3.** $3\sqrt{5}$ **4.** $4\sqrt{2}$ **5.** $3\sqrt{3}$ **6.** $4\sqrt{3}$ **7.** $3\sqrt{6}$ **8.** $5\sqrt{5}$

9. $3\sqrt{10}$ **10.** $5\sqrt{2}$ **11.** (i) $1 \pm \sqrt{5}$ (ii) $-1.24, 3.24$ **12.** (i) $-1 \pm \sqrt{3}$ (ii) $-2.73, 0.73$

13. (i) $2 \pm \sqrt{5}$ (ii) $-0.24, 4.24$ **14.** (i) $-3 \pm \sqrt{2}$ (ii) $-4.41, -1.59$ **15.** (i) $3 \pm \sqrt{5}$

(ii) $0.76, 5.24$ **16.** (i) $-4 \pm \sqrt{3}$ (ii) $-5.73, -2.27$ **17.** (i) $-5 \pm \sqrt{2}$

(ii) $-6.41, -3.59$ **18.** (i) $5 \pm \sqrt{7}$ (ii) $2.35, 7.65$ **19.** (i) $-6 \pm \sqrt{3}$ (ii) $-7.33, -4.27$

20. $\dfrac{1 \pm \sqrt{3}}{2}$ **21.** $\dfrac{-1 \pm \sqrt{5}}{4}$ **22.** $\dfrac{-1 \pm \sqrt{2}}{3}$ **23.** $-2.24, 6.24$ **24.** $-0.78, 1.28$

25. $-1.84, 0.44$ **26.** (i) 1.32 (ii) 0.0224 **27.** (i) $2 \pm \sqrt{7}$ (ii) 4.65 or -0.65

(iii) $0.0225 < 0.1$ **28.** (ii) 5.2 (iii) 0.16

Exercise 1.9

1. 1, 2   **2.** 3, 4   **3.** −5, 3   **4.** −1, 2   **5.** $-\dfrac{1}{2}, 3$ **6.** $-3, \dfrac{1}{3}$ **7.** ±2   **8.** ±5

9. ±1   **10.** −3, 1   **11.** −6, 3   **12.** −2, 4   **13.** $\dfrac{1}{2}, 1$ **14.** −5, 4   **15.** $\dfrac{2}{3}, 1$

16. −2, 3   **17.** 1, 3   **18.** −4, 2   **19.** −4, 1   **20.** −3, 4   **21.** $-\dfrac{2}{5}, 4$ **22.** 0.4, 2.6

23. −0.8, 0.6   **24.** −1.6, −0.4   **25.** $1 \pm \sqrt{2}$ **26.** $2 \pm \sqrt{3}$ **27.** $1 \pm \sqrt{7}$

28. (i) $\dfrac{3x - 1}{(x + 1)(x - 3)}$ (ii) $-0.4, 5.4$ **29.** (i) $\dfrac{2x}{(x + 1)(x - 1)}$ (ii) $2 \pm \sqrt{5}$

Exercise 1.10

1. $x^2 - 5x + 6 = 0$ **2.** $x^2 - x - 2 = 0$ **3.** $x^2 - 3x - 10 = 0$ **4.** $x^2 - 3x - 4 = 0$

5. $x^2 + 5x + 6 = 0$ **6.** $x^2 - 9x + 20 = 0$ **7.** $x^2 - x - 12 = 0$ **8.** $x^2 + 5x - 24 = 0$

9. $x^2 - 9 = 0$ **10.** $x^2 - 4 = 0$ **11.** $x^2 + 2x = 0$ **12.** $x^2 - 5x = 0$ **13.** $x^2 - 1 = 0$

14. $2x^2 - 7x + 3 = 0$ **15.** $3x^2 - 5x - 2 = 0$ **16.** $2x^2 + 5x - 3 = 0$ **17.** $2x^2 - 3x - 5 = 0$

18. $6x^2 - 5x + 1 = 0$ **19.** $9x^2 + 3x - 2 = 0$ **20.** $8x^2 - 10x + 3 = 0$ **21.** $x^2 - 2x - 15 = 0$

22. $10x^2 + x - 2 = 0$

Exercise 1.11

1. (i) $x = 2$ and $y = -3$ or $x = 4$ and $y = -1$ (ii) $x = -1$ and $y = -1$ or $x = 3$ and $y = 11$

2. (i) (−2, 1) and (5, 8) (ii) (−4, −11) and (3, 3)

3. (3, 5), one point of intersection, therefore line is a tangent

4. $x = 3$ and $y = 2$ or $x = 2$ and $y = 3$ 5. $x = 2$ and $y = 1$ or $x = -1$ and $y = -2$

6. $x = 1$ and $y = 4$ or $x = 2$ and $y = 2$ 7. $x^2 + 6x + 9$ 8. $x^2 - 4x + 4$ 9. $y^2 - 2y + 1$

10. $y^2 + 6y + 9$ 11. $4 + 4x + x^2$ 12. $1 - 4x + 4x^2$ 13. $9 - 12x + 4x^2$

14. $9 - 30y + 25y^2$ 15. $x = -1$ and $y = 4$ or $x = 4$ and $y = -1$

16. $x = -3$ and $y = -4$ or $x = 4$ and $y = 3$ 17. $x = -1$ and $y = 0$ or $x = 0$ and $y = 1$

18. $x = 4$ and $y = 2$ or $x = -4$ and $y = -2$ 19. $x = -3$ and $y = -4$ or $x = 5$ and $y = 0$

20. $x = 2$ and $y = 3$ or $x = 3$ and $y = 2$ 21. $x = 5$ and $y = 1$ or $x = 0$ and $y = -4$

22. $x = 1$ and $y = 2$ 23. $x = -1$ and $y = 3$ or $x = 2$ and $y = -3$

24. (i) $x = 5$ and $y = 0$ or $x = 3$ and $y = 4$ (ii) $125, 91$ 25. (ii) 4 cm by 3 cm

26. (ii) $x = 3$ and $y = 9$; the lengths of the three sides are 6 cm, 8 cm and 10 cm

27. (i) $A(1, 2)$ and $B(8, 9)$ (ii) $\sqrt{98}$ or $7\sqrt{2}$ 28. $P(-6, 1)$ and $Q(2, 3)$

29. (i) $(-2, 10)$ and $(2, 10)$ (ii) $(-5, 16)$ and $(5, 16)$

Exercise 1.12

1. $x \geq 3$ 2. $x \leq 4$ 3. $x > 2$ 4. $x < 2$ 5. $x \leq 3$ 6. $x \geq -5$ 7. $x < -2$

8. $x \leq 1$ 9. $x \geq 1$ 10. $x \leq 3$ 11. $x \leq 2$ 12. $x \leq 4$ 13. $x > 5$

14. $x < 2$ 15. $2 \leq x \leq 5$ 16. $-1 \leq x < 4$ 17. $-2 \leq x < 3$ 18. $-3 < x \leq 7$

19. (i) (a) $x \geq 3$ (b) $x \leq 5$ (ii) $3 \leq x \leq 5$ 20. (i) (a) $x \leq 4$ (b) $x \geq -2$ (ii) $-2 \leq x \leq 4$

21. (i) $x \leq 6$ (ii) $x \geq -4$ (iii) $-4 \leq x \leq 6$ 22. (i) $x \geq -3$ (ii) $x \leq 1$ (iii) $-6 \leq x \leq 1$

23. (i) $x \leq 2$ (ii) $x > -3$ (iii) $-2, -1, 0, 1, 2$ 24. (i) $x \leq 1$ (ii) $x \leq 3$ (iii) $2, 3$

25. 3   26. $x \geq 5, x \leq 4$; nothing in common, no intersection   27. (i) $2, 4$ (ii) 1

(iii) $1, 4, 9, 16$ (iv) $2, 3, 5, 7$ 28. $3, 4, 5$ 29. $x > 1$ 30. (i) D (ii) A (iii) B

(iv) C (v) A (vi) C (vii) C (viii) A   31. (ii) $2 < x < 6$ 32. (i) $4, 5, 6, 7$ or 8

(ii) yes, Bernadette and Catherine, both aged 14, or Bernadette and Dermot, both aged 22   33. $(10, 7)$

Exercise 1.13

1. $\dfrac{b + c}{2}$ 2. $\dfrac{r - q}{3}$ 3. $\dfrac{c + d}{b}$ 4. $\dfrac{v - u}{a}$ 5. $\dfrac{5c - 3a}{2}$ 6. $\dfrac{4p + 2r}{3}$ 7. $\dfrac{2b + c}{2}$

8. $\dfrac{ac + d}{a}$ 9. $\dfrac{w - xz}{x}$ 10. $2b$ 11. $2a - 2c$ 12. $3r - 3s$ 13. $\dfrac{6c - 2b}{3}$ 14. $2r - p$

15. $3r + q$ 16. $\dfrac{b - 3a}{2}$ 17. $zy - xy$ 18. $\dfrac{sr - 2pr}{3}$ 19. $5q + 3r$ 20. $\dfrac{p + r}{s}$

21. $\dfrac{2a - 3c}{d}$ 22. $\dfrac{2c - 3b}{9}$ 23. $\dfrac{v^2 - u^2}{2s}$ 24. $\dfrac{b - 4a}{8}$ 25. $\dfrac{2s}{t^2}$ 26. $\dfrac{3v}{\pi r^2}$

27. $\dfrac{2s - 2ut}{t^2}$ 28. $\dfrac{1}{r - t}$ 29. $\dfrac{t}{r - p}$ 30. $\dfrac{y}{x - w}$ 31. (i) $\dfrac{v - u}{a}$ (ii) 40   32. (i) $\dfrac{2A}{a + b}$ (ii) 12

33. (i) $P = 2l + 2w$ (ii) $w = \dfrac{P - 2l}{2}$ (iii) $A = lw$ (iv) $w = \dfrac{A}{l}$ (v) $A = \dfrac{Pl - 2l^2}{2}$

34. (i) $2x + y = 18$ (ii) $y = 18 - 2x$ (iv) $x = 4$ and $y = 10$ or $x = 5$ and $y = 8$

35. (i) (a) $\dfrac{9c + 160}{5}$ (b) $\dfrac{9k - 2{,}297}{5}$ (ii) (a) 50   (b) −238

Exercise 1.14

1. 2^7 2. 5^9 3. 7^4 4. 3^7 5. 3^2 6. 2^3 7. 3^{-2} 8. 5^{-3} 9. 3^8 10. 5^6

11. 5^2 12. $3^{\frac{3}{2}}$ 13. $2^{\frac{3}{2}}$ 14. $3^{\frac{7}{2}}$ 15. $2^{-\frac{5}{2}}$ 16. $5^{-\frac{3}{2}}$ 17. a^2 18. a^3

19. a^2 20. a^4 21. 2^2 22. 5^2 23. 6^2 24. 3^3 25. 2^4 or 4^2 26. 7^2

27. 2^5 28. 3^4 or 9^2 29. 5^3 30. 2^7 31. 3^5 32. 6^3 33. 8   34. 9

35. 64   36. 25   37. 36   38. 125   39. 81   40. 125   41. 49   42. 16   43. 216

44. 1   45. $\frac{1}{3}$ 46. $\frac{1}{16}$ 47. $\frac{1}{125}$ 48. $\frac{1}{32}$ 49. $\frac{1}{9}$ 50. $\frac{1}{1{,}000}$ 51. 3   52. 5

53. 2   54. 4   55. 2   56. 6   57. 8   58. $\frac{1}{8}$ 59. 16   60. $\frac{1}{16}$ 61. 9   62. $\frac{1}{9}$

63. 2^6 or 4^3 or 8^2 64. 3^4 or 9^2 65. 2^3 66. 3^2 67. 5^2 68. 7^2 69. 2^4 70. 5^3

71. $2^{\frac{1}{2}}$ 72. $3^{\frac{1}{2}}$ 73. $5^{\frac{1}{2}}$ 74. $7^{\frac{1}{2}}$ 75. $2^{\frac{3}{2}}$ 76. 2^3 77. $2^{\frac{3}{2}}$ 78. $3^{\frac{3}{2}}$ 79. $5^{\frac{3}{2}}$

80. $5^{\frac{3}{2}}$ 81. $7^{-\frac{1}{2}}$ 82. $5^{\frac{5}{2}}$ 83. 2^3 84. 3^{-1} 85. 5^{-3} 86. 2^1 or 2   87. 5^3

88. 3^{-3} 90. 9^{-1} and 3^{-2}, both are equal to $\frac{1}{9}$ 91. (i) $(x^2 + x)$ m^2 (ii) $x^2 + x = 42; 6$

92. (i) $x^2 - x$ (ii) 3   93. (i) (a) a (b) b (c) x (d) $x + 3$ (ii) (a) $(x + 1)^2$ (b) $(x + 2)^2$

(iii) $2x + 3$ (iv) 3   94. (i) $x^{\frac{1}{2}}$ (ii) $x^{\frac{1}{3}}$ (iii) $x^{\frac{2}{3}}$ (iv) $x^{\frac{3}{4}}$

Exercise 1.15

1. 4   2. 3   3. 2   4. 1   5. 2   6. 1   7. 6   8. 2   9. 1   10. 4   11. 2

12. 1   13. $\frac{3}{2}$ 14. $\frac{3}{4}$ 15. $\frac{1}{4}$ 16. 2   17. −2   18. −3   19. −2   20. −1

21. $-\frac{5}{2}$ 22. $\frac{1}{2}$ 23. $\frac{1}{2}$ 24. −10   25. $4^2; \frac{3}{2}$ 26. $2^4; 3$ 27. −1, 2   28. $2^{\frac{3}{2}}; \frac{1}{4}$

29. (i) (a) $2^{\frac{1}{2}}$ (b) 2^3 (c) 2^4 (d) $2^{\frac{7}{2}}$ (ii) (a) 1 (b) $\frac{3}{2}$ (c) 2   30. (i) (a) $3^{\frac{1}{2}}$ (b) $3^{-\frac{1}{2}}$

(c) 3^4 (d) $3^{\frac{7}{2}}$ (ii) (a) $\frac{1}{4}$ (b) $\frac{1}{4}$ (c) $\frac{11}{2}$ 31. (i) (a) 5^3 (b) $5^{\frac{1}{2}}$ (c) $5^{\frac{5}{2}}$ (d) 5^5

(ii) (a) $-\frac{1}{6}$ (b) $-\frac{1}{4}$ (c) 3   32. (i) $x + 1$ (ii) 4   33. (i) $\frac{1}{2}bh$ (ii) (a) x^2 (b) 9

34. (i) 2^{k+2} (ii) (a) 3 (b) $\frac{1}{2}$ 35. (i) $\dfrac{8a}{c + 5}$ (ii) $\sqrt{2}$ or $2^{\frac{1}{2}}$

Exercise 2.1

1. (4, 3)   2. (5, 3)   3. (9, −3)   4. (−6, 5)   5. (−8, −3)   6. (−2, 2)   7. (3, 3)

8. (1, −1)   9. $\left(\dfrac{7}{2}, -2\right)$ 10. (3, 1)   11. $\left(2, -\dfrac{1}{2}\right)$ 12. $\left(\dfrac{3}{2}, \dfrac{5}{2}\right)$

13. (5, 2)   14. (−5, −1)   15. $p = 10, q = -5$ 16. $a = -2, b = 5$

17. $p = 6, q = -3$ 18. (4, 6), (6, 9), (8, 12)

Exercise 2.2

1. 5   **2.** 10   **3.** $\sqrt{5}$ **4.** $\sqrt{65}$ **5.** 3   **6.** 6   **7.** $\sqrt{40}$ or $2\sqrt{10}$ **8.** $\sqrt{50}$ or $5\sqrt{2}$

9. $\sqrt{40}$ or $2\sqrt{10}$ **10.** $\sqrt{72}$ or $6\sqrt{2}$ **11.** $\sqrt{5}$ **12.** $\sqrt{10}$ **13.** $|AB| = |BC| = \sqrt{34}$

14. 5   **15. (i)** A **(ii)** B **17.** $M(3, 1)$ **18. (i)** $P(1, -1)$ **(ii)** $Q(5, -4)$

19. (ii) parallelogram **(iii)** $|AD| = \sqrt{18}$ or $3\sqrt{2}$; $|AB| = \sqrt{26}$; $|BC| = \sqrt{18}$ or $3\sqrt{2}$;

$|CD| = \sqrt{26}$; yes **(iv)** (5, 2)   **21. (ii)** A-F-G-B **(iii)** Yes. Move R one unit closer to Q.

22. (i) C1(4, 2), C2(4, 6), C3(1, 10), C4(1, 14), C5(6, 16), C6(5, 14), C7(5, 10), C8(8, 6), C9(8, 2)

(ii) $32 + 8\sqrt{2}$ or 43·3 units **(iii)** 34 units

Exercise 2.3

1. (i) $\dfrac{2}{5}$ **(ii)** $\dfrac{1}{6}$ **(iii)** $-\dfrac{2}{3}$ **2. (i)** e and f **(ii)** c and d **(iii)** a and b **3.** 1   **4.** $\dfrac{3}{2}$

5. 1   **6.** $\dfrac{5}{3}$ **7.** -1 **8.** $-\dfrac{8}{11}$ **9.** -1 **10.** 10   **11.** -1 **12.** -2 **18.** $\dfrac{4}{3}$

19. $-\dfrac{3}{5}$ **20.** $-\dfrac{1}{3}$ **21.** -4 **22.** $\dfrac{1}{3}$ **23. (i)** $\dfrac{1}{2}$ m per year **(ii)** 13 m

24. (ii) S1–S2: $\dfrac{1}{2}$, S2–S3: $\dfrac{1}{7}$, S3–S4: $\dfrac{1}{3}$, S4–S5: $\dfrac{3}{10}$, S5–S6: $-\dfrac{3}{10}$, S6–S7: $-\dfrac{2}{15}$,

S7–S8: $\dfrac{1}{4}$, S8–S9: $-\dfrac{4}{5}$ **(iii)** we measure slope from left to right **(iv)** Beginners: S2–S3, S4–S5,

S5–S6, S6–S7, S7–S8; Experienced: S1–S2, S3–S4; Expert: S8–S9

25. (ii) $\dfrac{5}{2}$, 1, $\dfrac{1}{2}$, $\dfrac{3}{4}$, $-\dfrac{4}{3}$, $-\dfrac{2}{3}$, $-\dfrac{1}{2}$, $-\dfrac{3}{5}$ **(iii)** the roads go down the hill **(iv)** sections 2–4 and 6–8

26. yes: London

Exercise 2.4

1. on   **2.** on   **3.** not on   **4.** on   **5.** not on   **6.** on   **7.** not on   **8.** not on

9. on   **10.** not on   **12.** 7   **13.** 2   **14.** 3   **15.** -5 **16.** 4

Exercise 2.5

1. $2x - y - 7 = 0$ **2.** $3x - y + 2 = 0$ **3.** $x + y + 2 = 0$ **4.** $5x + y - 22 = 0$

5. $4x - y = 0$ **6.** $3x - 5y - 47 = 0$ **7.** $4x + 3y + 15 = 0$ **8.** $5x - 4y - 30 = 0$

9. $x + 6y + 15 = 0$ **10.** $5x + 7y + 17 = 0$ **11.** $2x - 5y - 9 = 0$ **12.** $x + 2y + 1 = 0$

13. (i) 70 minutes **(ii)** 130 minutes **(iii)** $20x - y + 30 = 0$ **(v) (a)** 90 minutes

(b) 110 minutes **(c)** $4\dfrac{1}{2}$ kg

Exercise 2.6

1. $x - y + 3 = 0$ 2. $2x + y - 10 = 0$ 3. $3x - y - 18 = 0$ 4. $x - 2y + 1 = 0$

5. $5x + 7y - 19 = 0$ 6. $3x - 5y + 13 = 0$ 7. $x + 2y + 9 = 0$ 8. $5x - 2y - 14 = 0$

9. $4x + 2y + 3 = 0$ 10. (i) $4x - 3y - 18 = 0$ (ii) $3x + 4y - 1 = 0$

11. (i) $2x - y - 6 = 0$ (ii) $x + 2y + 2 = 0$ 12. $2x + 3y - 7 = 0$ 13. $3x - 2y + 14 = 0$

14. (ii) (a) 117·5 cm   (b) 200 cm or 2 m   (iii) $15x - 2y + 100 = 0$ 15. (i) (4, 8), (12, 12)

(ii) $x - 2y + 12 = 0$ (iv) fixed charge: €6; charge per km: €0·50

Exercise 2.7

1. $y = -\frac{2}{3}x + 3$ 2. $y = \frac{5}{2}x - 6$ 3. $y = \frac{3}{2}x - 4$ 4. $y = \frac{4}{3}x + 7$ 5. $y = 3x + 8$

6. $y = \frac{2}{3}x - 5$ 7. $y = -\frac{1}{2}x + 8$ 8. $y = -\frac{1}{2}x + 2$ 9. $y = -\frac{5}{2}x - 5$ 10. $3x - y + 7 = 0$

11. $2x + y - 11 = 0$ 12. $8x + y + 5 = 0$ 13. $2x - 3y + 3 = 0$ 14. $3x - 5y - 30 = 0$

15. $x - 3y + 9 = 0$ 16. $3x + 4y + 36 = 0$ 17. $2x + 3y + 6 = 0$ 18. $5x + 6y - 24 = 0$

Exercise 2.8

1. -2 2. 3   3. 2   4. -3 5. $-\frac{2}{3}$ 6. $\frac{4}{3}$ 7. $-\frac{1}{4}$ 8. $\frac{1}{3}$ 9. $\frac{4}{3}$

10. $\frac{5}{7}$ 11. $\frac{3}{2}$ 12. $\frac{7}{10}$ 16. 6   17. 5

Exercise 2.9

1. $2x - y - 3 = 0$ 2. $2x + 3y = 0$ 3. $5x + 4y + 21 = 0$ 4. $3x + 4y - 14 = 0$

5. $5x - 3y + 10 = 0$ 6. $x + 2y + 5 = 0$ 7. $5x - 2y - 13 = 0$

Exercise 2.10

1. (2, 1)   2. (3, 2)   3. (1, 0)   4. (−4, 3)   5. (−3, −1)   6. (0, −5)   7. (1, 2)

8. (6, −1)   9. (−3, 7)   10. $\left(\frac{3}{5}, \frac{4}{5}\right)$ 11. $\left(\frac{3}{2}, -\frac{3}{2}\right)$ 12. $\left(\frac{6}{5}, \frac{2}{5}\right)$ 13. $\left(\frac{4}{5}, \frac{6}{5}\right)$

14. $\left(\frac{5}{2}, \frac{1}{2}\right)$ 15. $\left(\frac{10}{3}, \frac{10}{3}\right)$ 16. (−3, −3)   17. (−2, −4)

18. $A(2, 1)$; $B(1, -3)$; $4x - y - 7 = 0$

Exercise 2.11

26. (0, −7)   27. 3   28. $y = 3x + 2$ 29. $y = -\frac{2}{3}x - 3$

Exercise 2.14

1. 7   2. 13   3. 19   4. 9   5. $5\frac{1}{2}$ 6. 0   7. 20   8. 19   9. $13\frac{1}{2}$

10. 12   11. 10   12. 6   13. 12   14. 7   15. 9   16. 34   17. 37   18. 72

Exercise 2.15

1. (i) $\sqrt{20}$ or $2\sqrt{5}$ (ii) $M(0, 3)$ (iii) 5   (iv) $-\dfrac{1}{2}$ (v) $x + 2y - 6 = 0$ (vi) $2x - y - 7 = 0$

(vii) $P(4, 1)$ 2. (ii) 3   4. $B(3, -11)$ 5. (i) $(4, 0), (0, -6)$ (iii) 12

6. (i) $A(1, 3)$ (ii) $B(-5, 0), C(2, 0)$ (iii) $\dfrac{21}{2}$ 7. (ii) (a) $4x - 3y + 23 = 0$ (b) $D(-2, 5)$

(c) $M(5, 3)$ (d) 34   (e) $k = 13$ 8. (iii) $Q(-4, 1)$ (iv) $R(0, 9)$ (vi) 40

9. (i) $R\left(0, \dfrac{5}{2}\right)$ (ii) $2x + y - 5 = 0$ (iii) $Q(1, 3)$ (iv) 5   10. (ii) $B(5, 3)$

(iii) No. $m_l \times m_k \neq -1$ (iv) $2x - y - 10 = 0$ (v) $D(5, 0)$ (vi) $\dfrac{15}{2}$

11. (ii) $(0, -8)$ (iii) $x + 3y - 6 = 0$ (iv) $(0, 2)$ (v) $(3, 1)$ (vi) 15   12. 5 or 11

Exercise 2.16

1. $(5, 6)$ 2. (i) $(4, 5)$ (ii) $(1, 2)$ (iii) $(-6, 0)$ (iv) $(-8, 3)$ 3. (i) (a) $(7, -3)$ (b) $(1, 4)$
(c) $(-2, -4)$ (d) $(12, 3)$ (ii) $(-2, 3)$ 4. (i) $S(1, 6)$ (ii) $R(6, 2)$ (iii) $Q(0, 1)$
(iv) $P(-1, -1)$ 5. $h = 1, k = -1$ 6. $(5, -8)$ 7. $(-8, 7)$ 8. $(10, -2)$
9. (i) $(6, -9)$ (ii) $(0, 3)$ 10. $C(11, 5), D(3, 4)$ 11. (i) $B(5, -1)$ (ii) $(5, 0)$

Exercise 3.1

1. $x^2 + y^2 = 4$ 2. $x^2 + y^2 = 9$ 3. $x^2 + y^2 = 1$ 4. $x^2 + y^2 = 100$ 5. $x^2 + y^2 = 5$
6. $x^2 + y^2 = 13$ 7. $x^2 + y^2 = 17$ 8. $x^2 + y^2 = 23$ 9. $x^2 + y^2 = 25$ 10. $x^2 + y^2 = 13$
11. $x^2 + y^2 = 26$ 12. $x^2 + y^2 = 16$ 13. $x^2 + y^2 = 2$ 14. $x^2 + y^2 = 29$ 15. 4   16. 3
17. 1   18. $\sqrt{13}$ 19. $\sqrt{5}$ 20. $\sqrt{29}$ 21. $(-3, 0), (3, 0), (0, -3), (0, 3)$
22. $(-4, 0), (4, 0), (0, -4), (0, 4)$ 23. $(-7, 0), (7, 0), (0, -7), (0, 7)$
24. $(-8, 0), (8, 0), (0, -8), (0, 8)$ 25. $(-5, 0), (5, 0), (0, -5), (0, 5)$
26. $(-10, 0), (10, 0), (0, -10), (0, 10)$ 27. $x^2 + y^2 = 25$ 28. $x^2 + y^2 = 37$
29. $(-6, 3)$ 30. 40π 31. A–2, B–1, C–3

Exercise 3.2

1. on   2. outside   3. on   4. inside   5. on   6. on   7. inside
8. on   9. inside   10. outside   11. on   12. on   14. (ii) $(-5, -5), (-5, 5)$
15. $p = -2$ or 2   16. geraniums

Exercise 3.3

1. $(1, -2), (2, -1)$ 2. $(1, -4), (4, -1)$ 3. $(-4, 3), (-3, 4)$ 4. $(-3, -1), (3, 1)$
5. $(-1, 3), (3, 1)$ 6. $(-3, -2), (2, -3)$ 7. $(-3, 2), (2, -3)$ 8. $(3, 4), (5, 0)$

9. $(-1, 2), (2, 1)$ **10.** $(-6, 2), (-2, -6)$ **11.** $\sqrt{80}$ or $4\sqrt{5}$ **12.** $\sqrt{10}$

13. (i) $l : x - 2y - 5 = 0$ (ii) $(-3, -4), (5, 0)$ **14.** (i) $(0, 0)$, $\sqrt{52}$ km   (ii) $(-6, 4), (-4, 6)$

(iii) no: $\sqrt{8} < 10$ (iv) $C(-5, 5)$ (v) no: $\sqrt{52} - \sqrt{50} < 1$

Exercise 3.4

1. $(1, -1)$ **2.** $(2, -2)$ **3.** $(2, -1)$ **4.** $(1, -3)$ **5.** $(3, 1)$ **6.** $(1, -4)$

7. $(5, -1)$ **8.** $(1, 7)$ **9.** (i) $k : x^2 + y^2 = 5$ (ii) $(-2, 1)$

10. (ii) yes, it will pass through $(-3, 1)$ and $(-1, 3)$

Exercise 3.5

1. $(x - 2)^2 + (y - 3)^2 = 16$ **2.** $(x - 1)^2 + (y - 4)^2 = 25$ **3.** $(x - 2)^2 + (y + 1)^2 = 4$

4. $(x + 5)^2 + (y - 2)^2 = 1$ **5.** $(x + 4)^2 + (y + 3)^2 = 17$ **6.** $(x + 3)^2 + y^2 = 13$

7. $x^2 + (y - 2)^2 = 5$ **8.** $(x + 2)^2 + (y + 6)^2 = 29$ **9.** $(x + 1)^2 + (y + 1)^2 = 10$

10. $(x + 4)^2 + (y - 2)^2 = 12$ **11.** $(x - 1)^2 + (y - 2)^2 = 10$ **12.** $(x - 2)^2 + (y + 1)^2 = 41$

13. $(x - 4)^2 + (y + 3)^2 = 80$ **14.** $(x + 2)^2 + (y + 5)^2 = 50$ **15.** $(x - 1)^2 + (y + 1)^2 = 26$

16. $(x + 4)^2 + (y + 2)^2 = 20$ **17.** $(3, 2); 4$ **18.** $(-4, -5); 3$ **19.** $(1, -3); 5$

20. $(3, 5); 2$ **21.** $(2, 2); 7$ **22.** $(8, 7); 1$ **23.** $(5, -2); 5$ **24.** $(1, -5); 6$

25. $(0, 2); 8$ **26.** $(3, 0); 2$ **27.** $(x - 3)^2 + (y - 3)^2 = 5$ **28.** $(x + 1)^2 + (y - 2)^2 = 13$

29. (ii) $(x - 2)^2 + (y - 9)^2 = 25$ **30.** $(-5, 0), (1, 0), (0, -1), (0, 5)$ **31.** $P(2, 0), Q(8, 0)$

32. (i) $(x + 2)^2 + (y - 1)^2 = 20$ (ii) 8 **33.** (i) $(1, 2); \sqrt{13}$ (ii) $(x - 1)^2 + (y - 2)^2 = 13$

(iii) $(-2, 0), (4, 0)$ **34.** $s_2 : (x - 6)^2 + y^2 = 16; s_4 : (x - 18)^2 + y^2 = 16; s_5 : (x - 24)^2 + y^2 = 16$

35. (i) $(0, 0)$ (ii) $(3, 3)$ (iii) $x - y = 0$ **36.** (i) $(0, 0); 5$ (ii) $(5, 0)$ (iii) $(5, 5)$

(iv) $(x - 5)^2 + (y - 5)^2 = 25, (x + 5)^2 + (y - 5)^2 = 25, (x + 5)^2 + (y + 5)^2 = 25, (x - 5)^2 + (y + 5)^2 = 25$

37. (i) $(x - 4)^2 + y^2 = 16$ (ii) $B(8, 0)$ (iii) $C(12, 0)$ (iv) 12 (v) $(6, 0)$ (vi) $(x - 6)^2 + y^2 = 36$

(viii) $(x - 10)^2 + y^2 = 100$

Exercise 3.6

1. outside   **2.** outside   **3.** inside   **4.** inside   **5.** outside   **6.** outside

7. on   **8.** inside   **9.** inside   **10.** inside   **11.** outside   **12.** on   **13.** on

14. inside   **15.** $k = -6$ or 4 **16.** $p = 1$ or 7

Exercise 3.7

1. $3x + y - 10 = 0$ **2.** $2x - y - 5 = 0$ **3.** $5x + y + 26 = 0$ **4.** $3x - 2y + 13 = 0$

5. $x - 7y + 50 = 0$ **6.** $x - 4y + 17 = 0$ **7.** $2x + y - 10 = 0$ **8.** $5x + 2y + 29 = 0$

9. $2x - 3y - 27 = 0$ **10.** $2x + y + 4 = 0$ **11.** $3x - y - 25 = 0$ **12.** $6x - 7y + 41 = 0$

13. $x + y = 0$ **14.** $3x + 4y - 16 = 0$ **15.** $5x - 2y - 19 = 0$ **16.** $x + 3y = 0$

17. $5x + 2y - 25 = 0$ **18.** $3x - 4y - 15 = 0$ **19.** $x - 2y - 23 = 0$

Exercise 3.8

1. $(x - 4)^2 + (y + 2)^2 = 20$ 2. $(x + 5)^2 + (y + 4)^2 = 25$ 3. $(x - 4)^2 + (y + 4)^2 = 9$
4. $(x + 1)^2 + (y - 2)^2 = 9$ 5. $(5, -6); 8; (x - 5)^2 + (y - 6)^2 = 64$
6. $c : (x + 5)^2 + (y + 2)^2 = 36$ 7. (i) $(10, 6); \sqrt{20}$ or $2\sqrt{5}$ (iii) $2x + y - 16 = 0$
(iv) $R(8, 0)$ (v) $k : (x - 2)^2 + (y - 2)^2 = 20$ (vi) $P(-2, 0), Q(6, 0)$

Exercise 4.1

2. (i) 25   (ii) 169   (iii) 100   (iv) 841   (v) 10   (vi) 4   (vii) 16   (viii) 25   (ix) 7
(x) 1   (xi) 9   (xii) 4   3. (i) 25, 24, 7 and 12, 16, 20

(ii) 3, 7, $\sqrt{58}$ and 3, $\sqrt{7}$, 4   4. (i) $5, \dfrac{12}{13}, \dfrac{5}{13}, \dfrac{12}{5}$ (ii) $21, \dfrac{20}{29}, \dfrac{21}{29}, \dfrac{20}{21}$ (iii) $9, \dfrac{40}{41}, \dfrac{9}{41}, \dfrac{9}{40}$

(iv) $\sqrt{12}, \dfrac{1}{\sqrt{13}}, \dfrac{\sqrt{12}}{\sqrt{13}}, \dfrac{1}{\sqrt{12}}$ (v) $\sqrt{7}, \dfrac{\sqrt{7}}{4}, \dfrac{3}{4}, \dfrac{\sqrt{7}}{3}$ (vi) $\sqrt{13}, \dfrac{3}{\sqrt{13}}, \dfrac{2}{\sqrt{13}}, \dfrac{3}{2}$ 5. (ii) 4

6. (ii) $\cos Q = \dfrac{d}{x}, \sin Q = \dfrac{c}{x}$ 7. $42°$ 8. $55°$ 9. $7°$ 10. $17°$ 11. $63°$
12. $53°$ 13. $44°$ 14. $18°$ 15. (i) $< 90°$ (ii) $90°$ (iii) $> 90°$ (iv) $> 90°$

17. (i) $\dfrac{3}{5}, \dfrac{3}{4}$ (ii) (a) $\dfrac{16}{25} + \dfrac{9}{25} = 1$ (b) $\dfrac{4}{5} + \dfrac{3}{5} = \dfrac{7}{5} > \dfrac{3}{4}$ (iii) $37°$ 18. (i) $\dfrac{8}{17}, \dfrac{15}{17}$

(ii) $\dfrac{15}{17} + \dfrac{8}{17} = \dfrac{23}{17} > \dfrac{8}{15}$ (iii) $28°$ 19. (i) $\dfrac{24}{25}, \dfrac{7}{24}$ (ii) $\dfrac{576}{625} + \dfrac{49}{625} = 1$ 20. 20

21. (ii) $\dfrac{3}{4}$ 22. (i) 13 m   (ii) 12 m   65 cm   (iii) $\sqrt{16 + 16} = \sqrt{32}$

Exercise 4.2

1. $56°$ 2. $59°$ 3. $35°$ 4. $45°$ 5. $52°$ 6. $34°$ 7. $9·39$ 8. $28·84$
9. $26·36$ 10. (i) $2·5$ (ii) $37°$ 11. (i) 5   (ii) $39°$ 12. (i) 34   (ii) 64   (iii) $14°$

Exercise 4.3

1. $4·85$ m   2. $4·8$ m   3. $11·64$ m   4. (i) $3·5$ m   (ii) $71°$ 5. (i) 47 m   6. 426 m
7. (i) 84 m   (ii) $19°$ 8. (i) 1 m 28 cm   10. 11 km   11. (i) 40 km   (ii) 35 km
12. (i) 30 km   (ii) 60 km

Exercise 4.4

1. $80·00$ cm^2 2. $18·13$ cm^2 3. $31·01$ cm^2 4. $16·67$ cm^2 5. $47·55$ cm^2
6. $21·46$ cm^2 7. $21·33$ cm^2 8. $10·83$ cm^2 9. $17·55$ cm^2 10. $22·65$ cm^2
11. $29·73$ cm^2 12. $49·48$ cm^2 13. $45·11$ m^2 14. $62·99$ cm^2
15. (i) 3 cm   (ii) $2·16$ cm^2 (iii) $4·98$ cm^2 16. (i) 13.4 m^2 (ii) $45·1$ m^2
17. (i) $31·4$ cm^2 (ii) (a) $29·4$ cm^2 (b) 2 cm^2 18. 24 cm   19. (i) $0·56$ (ii) 26 m
20. $40°$

Exercise 4.5

1. 13·47   2. 4·88   3. 38°   4. 54°   5. 8·88   6. 27°   7. (i) 14 cm
(ii) 13 cm   8. (i) 65° (ii) 13·3 cm   (iii) 12·8 cm   9. (i) 24° (ii) 9 cm
10. (i) 17 m (ii) 50° (iii) 111 m² (iv) 14·37 m   11. (i) 23° (ii) 103 m (iii) 93 m

Exercise 4.6

1. 9·17   2. 15·68   3. 10·24   4. 41°   5. 57°   6. 95°   7. 106·6°   8. 29°
9. (i) 7 cm   (ii) 61°

Exercise 4.7

1. 8·64 km   2. $\sin^{-1}(1\cdot6) \rightarrow$ math error on calculator $\therefore$ impossible triangle   3. 204 cm
4. (i) 25·5 m   (ii) 17 m   (iii) 288 m²   5. 13°   6. 219 m
7. (i) 9·5 cm   (ii) 54·5 cm²   8. (i) 1,701 cm   (ii) 1,668 cm
9. (i) $|DA| = 52$ m $|BD| = 66$ m   (ii) 58 seconds, 24 seconds
10. (i) 2,552 m² (ii) 52·6972 m (iii) 48·427 m   11. (i) 65·2 km (ii) 19 km/h
12. (i) 37·2° (ii) 23·72 km   13. (i) 46 m   14. (ii) (a) $\sqrt{40}$ (b) $\sqrt{50}$ (iii) 63°
15. (ii) $x = 1\cdot5$ 16. (i) 893 m (ii) 2,693 m

Exercise 4.8

1. (i)

A	30°	45°	60°
$\cos A$	$\dfrac{\sqrt{3}}{2}$	$\dfrac{1}{\sqrt{2}}$	$\dfrac{1}{2}$
$\sin A$	$\dfrac{1}{2}$	$\dfrac{1}{\sqrt{2}}$	$\dfrac{\sqrt{3}}{2}$
$\tan A$	$\dfrac{1}{\sqrt{3}}$	1	$\sqrt{3}$
$\cos^2 A$	$\dfrac{3}{4}$	$\dfrac{1}{2}$	$\dfrac{1}{4}$
$\sin^2 A$	$\dfrac{1}{4}$	$\dfrac{1}{2}$	$\dfrac{3}{4}$
$\tan^2 A$	$\dfrac{1}{3}$	1	3

(ii)

B	0	$\dfrac{\pi}{2}$	$\dfrac{\pi}{3}$	π	$\dfrac{3}{2}\pi$	2π
$\cos B$	1	0	$\dfrac{1}{2}$	−1	0	1
$\sin B$	0	1	$\dfrac{\sqrt{3}}{2}$	0	−1	0
$\cos^2 B$	1	0	$\dfrac{1}{4}$	1	0	1
$\sin^2 B$	0	1	$\dfrac{3}{4}$	0	1	0

2. 1 **3.** 1 **4.** 4 **5.** $\frac{3}{2}$ or $1\frac{1}{2}$ **6.** $\frac{2}{3}$ **7.** $\frac{3}{2}$ or $1\frac{1}{2}$ **8.** $\frac{1}{4}$ **9.** $\frac{5}{8}$ **10.** 0

11. $-\frac{1}{2}$ **12.** $-\frac{1}{2}$ **13.** 1.732 **14.** undefined

Exercise 4.9

1. 0 **2.** 0 **3.** 1 **4.** 1 **5.** −1 **6.** −1 **7.** 0 **8.** 0 **9.** 0 **10.** −2
11. −3 **12.** 1 **13.** −1 **14.** 4 **15.** 0° or 360° **16.** 90° **17.** 270° **18.** 180°
19. 90° or 270° **20.** 0°, 180°, 360° **21.** 0°, 180°, 360° **22.** 1, −1

Exercise 4.10

1. $-\frac{1}{2}$ **2.** $\frac{1}{2}$ **3.** $\sqrt{3}$ **4.** $-\frac{1}{2}$ **5.** −1 **6.** $-\frac{1}{\sqrt{2}}$ **7.** $-\frac{\sqrt{3}}{2}$ **8.** $\frac{1}{\sqrt{3}}$

9. $-\frac{1}{\sqrt{2}}$ **10.** $-\frac{1}{\sqrt{3}}$ **11.** $-\frac{\sqrt{3}}{2}$ **12.** $-\frac{1}{\sqrt{2}}$

Exercise 4.11

1. 30°, 150° **2.** 60°, 120° **3.** 30°, 210° **4.** 60°, 300° **5.** 45°, 135° **6.** 60°, 240°
7. 45°, 225° **8.** 30°, 330° **9.** 240°, 300° **10.** 150°, 210° **11.** 225°, 315°
12. 150°, 330° **13.** 210°, 330° **14.** 120°, 300° **15.** 45°, 315° **16.** 24°, 156°
17. 83°, 277° **18.** 58°, 238° **19.** 143°, 217° **20.** 152°, 332° **21.** 222°, 318°

Exercise 5.1

6. (i) 6 (ii) 6 (iii) 6 (iv) 6 (v) 24 **7.** (i) 6 (ii) 6 (iii) 12 **8.** (iii) 24 (iv) 12
9. (i) (a) 120 (b) 216 **10.** (i) 1,572,480 (ii) 327,600 **11.** (i) 0000 (ii) 9999 (iii) 10,000

Exercise 5.2

1. 120 **2.** 720 **3.** 40,320 **4.** 362,880 **5.** 479,001,600 **6.** 30 **7.** 336
8. 5,040 **9.** 28 **10.** 120 **11.** 576 **12.** 64 **13.** 12,996 **14.** 126 **15.** 4
16. 20 **17.** 116 **18.** 1,329 **19.** 42 **21.** (i) 24 (ii) 12 **22.** (i) 5,040 (ii) 720
23. (i) 40,320 (ii) 1,440 **24.** (i) 5! = 120 (ii) 3! = 6 (iii) 5! − 4! = 120 − 24 = 96
25. (i) 9! = 362,880 (ii) 8! + 8! = 80,640 **26.** (i) 5,040 **27.** (5 − 1)! = 24

Exercise 5.3

3. (i) T (ii) P (iii) S **6.** (i) C (ii) A (iii) E (iv) B (v) D

Exercise 5.4

1. (i) $\frac{1}{3}$ (ii) $\frac{5}{12}$ (iii) $\frac{1}{12}$ (iv) $\frac{1}{6}$ **2.** (i) (a) $\frac{1}{4}$ (b) $\frac{3}{4}$ (c) $\frac{1}{4}$ (ii) $\frac{3}{4}$ **3.** $\frac{3}{8}$ **4.** $\frac{1}{20}$

5. (i) $\frac{1}{2}$ (ii) $\frac{5}{12}$ (iii) $\frac{1}{12}$ 6. (i) (a) $\frac{16}{25}$ (b) $\frac{9}{25}$ (c) $\frac{1}{5}$ (d) $\frac{4}{25}$

7. (i) (a) $\frac{3}{5}$ (b) $\frac{1}{5}$ (c) $\frac{27}{40}$ (d) 0 8. (i) (a) $\frac{1}{8}$ (b) $\frac{1}{4}$ (c) $\frac{1}{2}$

9. (i) $\frac{1}{52}$ (ii) $\frac{1}{2}$ (iii) $\frac{1}{4}$ (iv) $\frac{1}{13}$ (v) $\frac{3}{13}$ (vi) $\frac{3}{26}$ (vii) $\frac{5}{13}$ (viii) $\frac{12}{13}$ (ix) 0

10. (i) $\frac{1}{39}$ (ii) $\frac{1}{3}$ (iii) $\frac{1}{3}$ (iv) $\frac{1}{13}$ (v) $\frac{3}{13}$ (vi) $\frac{2}{13}$ (vii) $\frac{4}{13}$ (viii) $\frac{12}{13}$ (ix) 0

11. 20 12. 200 13. (i) $\frac{2}{5}$ (ii) 4 red discs 14. (i) $\frac{1}{5}$ (ii) $\frac{2}{5}$

15. (i) (a) $\frac{4}{5}$ (b) $\frac{1}{5}$ (ii) 3 16. (i) €20 (iii) $\frac{1}{5}$ (iv) $\frac{3}{5}$

17. (i) $\frac{2}{5}$ (ii) $\frac{3}{5}$ (iii) $\frac{1}{5}$ (iv) $\frac{7}{10}$ 18. (i) 9 (ii) $\frac{5}{9}$

19. (i) (a) $\frac{7}{15}$ (b) $\frac{1}{6}$ 20. (i) 4 (ii) $\frac{1}{2}$ 21. (i) (a) $\frac{7}{15}$ (b) $\frac{7}{30}$ (c) $\frac{18}{25}$

(d) $\frac{4}{25}$ (e) $\frac{1}{5}$ (ii) $\frac{1}{3}$ (iii) (a) $\frac{1}{4}$ (b) $\frac{9}{10}$ (iv) (a) $\frac{7}{23}$ (b) $\frac{11}{46}$ (c) $\frac{88}{115}$

22. (ii) (a) $\frac{2}{5}$ (b) $\frac{3}{5}$ (c) $\frac{3}{10}$ (d) $\frac{2}{5}$ (iii) $\frac{2}{3}$ (iv) $\frac{1}{5}$ 23. (i) (a) $\frac{1}{20}$ (b) $\frac{3}{5}$ (c) $\frac{3}{20}$

(d) $\frac{1}{2}$ (e) $\frac{1}{20}$ (ii) $\frac{1}{8}$ (iii) (a) $\frac{2}{3}$ (b) $\frac{7}{17}$

Exercise 5.5

1. (i) $\frac{1}{6}$ (ii) $\frac{1}{9}$ (iii) $\frac{5}{6}$ (iv) $\frac{1}{3}$ (v) $\frac{2}{9}$ (vi) $\frac{1}{9}$ (vii) $\frac{1}{12}$ 2. (ii) (a) $\frac{1}{5}$ (b) 0 (c) $\frac{6}{25}$

(iii) (a) $\frac{1}{5}$ (b) 0 (c) $\frac{6}{25}$ 3. (ii) (a) $\frac{3}{25}$ (b) $\frac{4}{25}$ (c) $\frac{6}{25}$ (d) $\frac{2}{5}$ (iii) $\frac{110}{25}=4\cdot4$ 4. $\frac{1}{2}$

5. (i) A1 A2 A3 A4 A5 A6

B1 B2 B3 B4 B5 B6

C1 C2 C3 C4 C5 C6

D1 D2 D3 D4 D5 D6

E1 E2 E3 E4 E5 E6

(ii) (a) $\frac{1}{30}$ (b) $\frac{1}{10}$ (c) $\frac{1}{5}$ (d) $\frac{2}{15}$ (iii) (a) $\frac{1}{30}$ (b) $\frac{1}{6}$ (c) $\frac{1}{5}$ (d) $\frac{2}{3}$

6. (i) 20 (ii) (a) $\frac{1}{5}$ (b) $\frac{1}{5}$ (c) $\frac{3}{10}$ and 4 (iii) 6

Exercise 5.6

1. 125   2. (i) $\dfrac{63}{100}$ (ii) 50   3. (i) 210   (ii) 90   4. (i) 45   (ii) 90

5. (i) $\dfrac{13}{60} = 0{\cdot}2166$ (ii) $\dfrac{1}{6} = 0{\cdot}1666$ 6. (i) $\dfrac{4}{7}$ (ii) 8

7. (i) $0{\cdot}3$ (ii) $0{\cdot}5$ (iii) (a) 160   (b) 400   9. green   11. (ii) (a) $\dfrac{13}{25}$

12. (i) $0{\cdot}1$ (ii) (a) 42   (b) 12   13. (i) 20   (ii) (a) $\dfrac{1}{20}$ (b) $\dfrac{3}{10}$

Exercise 5.7

1. (i) $\dfrac{1}{2}$ (ii) $\dfrac{1}{2}$ (iii) $\dfrac{2}{3}$ 2. $\dfrac{2}{5}$ 3. (i) $\dfrac{1}{3}$ (ii) $\dfrac{2}{3}$ (iii) $\dfrac{3}{4}$ (iv) $\dfrac{1}{4}$

4. (i) $\dfrac{1}{2}$ (ii) $\dfrac{1}{4}$ (iii) $\dfrac{2}{3}$ (iv) $\dfrac{1}{3}$ 5. (i) $\dfrac{1}{3}$ (ii) $\dfrac{1}{5}$ (iii) $\dfrac{7}{15}$ (iv) $\dfrac{8}{15}$

6. (i) $\dfrac{1}{9}$ (ii) $\dfrac{2}{9}$ (iii) $\dfrac{4}{9}$ (iv) $\dfrac{2}{3}$ (v) $\dfrac{1}{3}$ 7. (i) $\dfrac{7}{20}$ (ii) $\dfrac{11}{20}$ (iii) $\dfrac{3}{4}$ (iv) $\dfrac{17}{20}$

8. (i) $\dfrac{22}{45}$ (ii) $\dfrac{7}{15}$ (iii) $\dfrac{11}{15}$ (iv) $\dfrac{7}{45}$ (v) $\dfrac{11}{45}$ (vi) $\dfrac{1}{3}$ (vii) $\dfrac{2}{3}$ 9. (i) $\dfrac{1}{2}$ (ii) $\dfrac{7}{13}$ (iii) $\dfrac{7}{26}$

(iv) $\dfrac{19}{26}$ 10. (i) $\dfrac{2}{9}$ (ii) $\dfrac{11}{36}$

Exercise 5.8

1. (i) $\dfrac{2}{5}$ (ii) $\dfrac{3}{40}$ (iii) $\dfrac{23}{40}$ (iv) $\dfrac{7}{20}$ (v) $\dfrac{1}{20}$ (vi) 360,000   2. (i) 70   (ii) $\dfrac{29}{35}$ (iii) $\dfrac{1}{14}$

(iv) $\dfrac{1}{10}$ (v) $\dfrac{4}{7}$ 3. (i) $\dfrac{11}{20}$ (ii) $\dfrac{13}{40}$ (iii) $\dfrac{1}{100}$ (iv) $\dfrac{1}{50}$ (v) $\dfrac{193}{200}$ (vi) $\dfrac{129}{200}$ 5. (i) 27

(ii) they liked both wine and beer   (iii) $\dfrac{1}{9}$ (iv) $\dfrac{9}{34}$ (v) 190   (vi) 316 or 317   6. (i) $\dfrac{9}{10}$

Exercise 5.9

1. (i) $\dfrac{1}{12}$ (ii) $\dfrac{1}{4}$ (iii) $\dfrac{1}{3}$ (iv) $\dfrac{1}{6}$ 2. (i) $\dfrac{1}{5}$ (ii) $\dfrac{3}{10}$ (iii) $\dfrac{1}{2}$ (iv) $\dfrac{2}{5}$ 3. (i) $\dfrac{1}{7}$

(ii) $\dfrac{1}{7}$ (iii) $\dfrac{1}{49}$ (iv) $\dfrac{2}{49}$ (v) $\dfrac{1}{7}$ (vi) $\dfrac{6}{7}$ 4. (i) 4   (ii) $\dfrac{1}{4}$ 5. (i) $\dfrac{1}{5}$ (ii) $\dfrac{3}{20}$ (iii) $\dfrac{3}{5}$

(iv) $\dfrac{1}{20}$ (v) $\dfrac{13}{20}$ 6. (ii) $\dfrac{5}{9}$ (iii) $\dfrac{4}{9}$ 7. (i) $\dfrac{1}{9}$ (ii) $\dfrac{8}{9}$ (iii) $\dfrac{2}{9}$ 8. (ii) (a) $\dfrac{16}{33}$

(b) $\dfrac{14}{33}$ (c) $\dfrac{3}{33}$ 9. (i) (a) $\dfrac{1}{4}$ (b) $\dfrac{1}{16}$ (c) $\dfrac{3}{16}$ (d) $\dfrac{3}{8}$ (ii) (a) $\dfrac{1}{18}$ (b) $\dfrac{7}{18}$

10. (i) 0·6; 0·7; 0·2 (ii) (a) 0·12 (b) 0·48 (c) 0·4   **11.** (i) 8 (ii) $\dfrac{1}{8}$ (iii) $\dfrac{7}{8}$

(iv) $\dfrac{3}{8}$ (v) $\dfrac{1}{8}$

Exercise 5.10

1. (i) $-\dfrac{1}{2}$ (ii) not fair $\left(-\dfrac{1}{2}\text{ euro every game}\right)$ **2.** 5·5   **3.** (i) €3·5 (ii) lose, €12·50

(iii) €3·50   **5.** (i) (a) $\dfrac{1}{10,000}$ (b) $\dfrac{1}{500}$ (c) $\dfrac{9,979}{10,000}$ (iii) 3   **6.** (ii) $\dfrac{1}{12}$ (iii) $\dfrac{1}{4}$ (v) 8·5

7. €1·31, good value   **8.** (i) yes, $E(x) = 5$ (ii) change €10 to €40 is one possibility

9. (i) 0·101 (ii) 0·086 (iii) €616·91 (iv) €520·39

10. (ii) $E(x) = $ €3·75, charge €3·75 to play (iii) $E(x) = $ €4·375, not fair

Exercise 6.1

1. (i) 10 (ii) 19 (iii) 1 (iv) 4 (v) 6   **2.** (i) 13 (ii) −12 (iii) −2

(iv) −7 (v) 0 (vi) 4   **3.** (i) 18 (ii) 4 (iii) 0 (iv) −2 (v) 12

(vi) −5, 2   **4.** (i) (a) 10 (b) 4 (ii) 2   **5.** 3   **6.** (i) 3 (ii) −1

(iii) 8 (iv) −6 (v) −5, 3   **7.** (i) −1 (ii) −2 (iii) $\dfrac{1}{4}$ (iv) $\dfrac{14}{25}$

(v) 0, −2   **8.** (i) 15 (ii) 15 (iii) 27 (iv) $k = -5$ **9.** (i) −8 (ii) 100

(iii) 10 (iv) $k = 3$ **10.** (i) (a) 15 (b) 8 (c) 3 (ii) $k = -4$ (iii) −2, 2

11. (i) 4; 2 (ii) $k = 2$ (iii) 1   **12.** (i) (a) 6 (b) 54 (c) 2 (ii) 2

13. (i) (a) 20 (b) 1,280 (c) 5 (d) 10 (ii) 3   **14.** (i) 168 m (ii) 6 sec

15. (i) 300 m (ii) 48 m (iii) 2·5 sec, 10 sec   **16.** (i) 24 m/s (ii) 45 m

(iii) 2 sec, 8 sec   **17.** (i) 625 (ii) 24,414   **18.** (i) €11,776 (ii) €3,859

Exercise 6.2

1. 2   **2.** 4   **3.** 3   **4.** −10   **5.** 2   **6.** −4   **7.** $\dfrac{3}{2}$, 2   **8.** (i) 2 (ii) −3

9. −12   **10.** (i) 7 (ii) −3   **11.** $a = 3, b = -4$ **12.** $a = -7, b = -1$

13. (i) $a = 2, b = -3$ (ii) −1; 5 (iii) $-\dfrac{3}{2}, 4$ **14.** (i) $a = 5, b = -17$ (ii) $x \le 4$

15. (i) $a + b = 1; a - b = 5$ (ii) $a = 3, b = -2$ **16.** (i) $p + q = 7; p - q = -3$ (ii) $p = 2, q = 5$

(iii) $-3, \dfrac{1}{2}$ **17.** (i) $a + b = -1, 4a + 2b = 2$ (ii) $a = 2, b = -3$ (iii) 0, 1   **18.** (i) $c = -3$

(ii) $a = 4, b = -5$ **19.** (i) −6 (ii) −8, −3   **20.** (i) $-a + b = 0, -9a + b = -24$ (ii) $a = 3, b = 3$

21. (i) $ab^0 = 8, ab^1 = 32$ (ii) $a = 8, b = 4$ **22.** (i) $ab^1 = 4, ab^2 = 12$

(ii) $a = \dfrac{4}{3}, b = 3$ **23.** $a = 2, b = -3$ **24.** (i) $b = 1, c = -2$ (ii) $k = -2$

25. (i) $p = -3, q = -4$ (ii) $a = -1, b = 4, c = 6; \dfrac{3}{5}$ (iii) 4   **26.** (i) $a = 2, b = -5$ (ii) $h = -\dfrac{1}{2}, k = 3$

(iii) $-2, 3$ **27.** (i) $b = -2, c = 4$ (ii) $p = 2, q = -1$ (iii) $-5, 1$ **28.** $a = 2, b = -4$

29. (i) $a = -5, b = 2$ (ii) $k = 2$ **30.** $a = 6, b = 3$ **31.** (i) $a = 2, b = \dfrac{1}{2}$ (ii) $k = 8$

32. (i) $b = 3, c = -10$ (ii) $k = -10$ (iii) $0, -3$ **33.** (i) -3 (ii) $b = 2, c = -3$

Exercise 6.3

1. 5   **2.** 13   **3.** 11   **4.** 1   **5.** 34   **6.** 25   **7.** -16 **8.** -18 **9.** -9
10. 213   **11.** 210   **12.** 378   **13.** 192   **14.** 50   **15.** $\dfrac{1}{9}$

Exercise 6.4

1. (i) 7 (ii) -1 (iii) 4 (iv) 11 (v) -17 (vi) 19 (vii) -2 (viii) 5 (ix) -1
2. (i) $23 - 6x$ (ii) $3x - 3$ (iii) $17 - 2x$ (iv) $x - 10$ (v) $3x - 13$ (vi) $9x + 8$
3. (i) 66 (ii) 13 (iii) 18 (iv) 18 (v) 27 (vi) 11 (vii) $x^2 + 14x + 51$
4. (ii) (a) 2^{x+1} (b) $2^x + 1$ **5.** (i) 4 (ii) $-3, 3$ (iii) $0, 5$ **6.** $a = 15$ **7.** (i) 0 (ii) 4
8. (i) 4,320 (ii) €169·04 (iii) (a) €128 (b) €182 (c) €495·20 (iv) $20 + 1·08x$ (v) €614

Exercise 7.1

16. (i) $(2, -4)$ **17.** (i) $(1, 1)$

Exercise 7.2

9. (i) $(-1, -1)$ **10.** (i) $(-1, 4), (2, -5)$

Exercise 7.3

12. (ii) $(-3, 0), (-2, 3), (1, 0)$ **13.** (ii) $(-1, 5), (2, -10), (3, -7)$

Exercise 7.4

7. (ii) $(0, 1)$ **8.** (ii) $(-1, 6), (1·45, 1·1)$ **9.** (ii) $(-0·9, 0·25), (0·48, 2·25)$

Exercise 7.5

1. (i) $-1, 2$ (ii) $(0, 4), (2, 0)$ (iii) $4, 0$ (iv) 10 (v) $0 < x < 2$ (vi) $-0·7, 1, 2·7$
2. (i) $2·3$ (ii) $-2·4$ (iii) $4·75$ (iv) $1·1$
3. (i) $-3, -2, 1$ (ii) 6 (iii) $0·9, -6·1$ (iv) $-3·3, -1·5, 0·8$
4. (iii) $(-1, 11), (2, -16)$ (iv) $-1 < x < 2$ (v) $-2, 0·3, 3·2$

5. (i) (0, 5) (ii) −1, 1·4, 3·6 (iii) −0·7, 0·8, 3·9

6. (i) −2, 2, 3 (ii) −1, 0, 4 (iii) (−1, 12), (1, 6), (3, 0) (iv) $-1 < x < 1, 3 < x < 4$ (v) $1 < x < 3$

7. (i) 4, 0 (ii) (−1, 4), (1, 0) (iii) $-1 < x < 1$

8. (iii) −3·7, −0·25, 2 (iv) −6

9. (i) 1, 3·5 (ii) $1 < x < 3·5$ (iii) $-2 < x < 1, 3·5 < x < 4$

10. (iv) (−1·6, −5)   11. (iii) 31·25 bacteria (iv) 6 hours   12. (ii) 4 (iii) 7 rounds

13. (i) 16,777,216 bacteria   14. (i) 25% (iii) 26 days

Exercise 7.6

1. (ii) 34   2. 77   3. 32·5   4. 32   5. 67·5   6. 55

Exercise 8.1

1. $3x^2$ 2. $2x$ 3. 8   4. $\dfrac{1}{2}x$ 5. 0   6. x^2 7. −5   8. $\dfrac{5}{2}$ 9. 0   10. $2x - 3$

11. $3x^2$ 12. $\dfrac{x}{5} + 3$ 13. $2x - \dfrac{9}{2}x^2$ 14. $3x^2 + 8x + 1$ 15. −3   16. $\dfrac{3}{2}$ 17. $2x$

18. $1 - 3x^2$ 19. 3   20. $\dfrac{1}{10}x - 1$ 21. $\dfrac{3}{2} - \dfrac{3}{8}x^2$ 22. $2x - 1$ 23. $6x^2 - 4x + 4$

24. $-2 - 15x^2$ 25. $\dfrac{2}{3}x - \dfrac{3}{2}x^2$

Exercise 8.2

1. 10   2. 43   3. 23   4. −5   5. 6   6. 13   7. −37   8. −20   9. 10π

10. 36π 11. (i) 2 (ii) −3 (iii) −1 (iv) 3 (v) −3

Exercise 8.3

1. $24x + 12$ 2. $2 - 6x$ 3. 4   4. 0   5. $-12x$ 6. −2   7. $2a$ 8. $6px + 2q$

9. (i) −10 (ii) 6   10. (i) 73 (ii) −30   11. (i) −5 (ii) −4   12. −20   15. 3

Exercise 8.4

1. −1   2. − 7   3. 0   4. $3x - y - 6 = 0$ 5. $3x - y + 5 = 0$ 6. $x + y - 2 = 0$ and $x - y - 3 = 0$; yes

Exercise 8.5

1. (1, 1)   2. (−2, 13)   3. (3, 0); (−1, −4)   4. (2, −20); (−1, 10)   5. (1, 5)

6. (3, −9); (−2, −4)   7. (i) $p = -4, q = 2$ (ii) $\dfrac{1}{2}$ (iii) $y = \dfrac{1}{2}x^2 - x - 4$ (iv) $x - 1$ (v) (8, 20)

8. (ii) (a) $x^2 - 2x - 8$ (b) 7 (iii) (a) 18 (b) $y - 7x - 39 = 0$ (iv) −4 and 6

9. (i) 0 (iii) 3   10. −4   11. (i) $-2 = 4a + 2b$ (ii) $2ax + b$; $4a + b = 3$

(iii) $b = -5; a = 2$ 12. $p = 3; q = 4$ 13. (i) $3x^2 + 2ax$ (ii) −3

Exercise 8.6

1. $(2, -1)$ 2. $(-3, -8)$ 3. $(2, -5)$ 4. $(-3, 16)$ 5. $(-2, 9)$ 6. $(-2, 13)$

7. $\max(-1, 9)$; $\min(3, -23)$ 8. $\max(1, 13)$; $\min(-3, -19)$ 9. $\max(1, 6)$; $\min(2, 5)$

10. $\max(3, 54)$; $\min(-3, -54)$ 11. $\max(0, 0)$; $\min(4, -32)$ 12. **(i)** $x = 3$ **(ii)** 9

13. $R = 1$ 14. $S = \dfrac{5}{2}$ 15. $P = -4$; $Q = -1$ 16. $H = -3$; $K = 2$

17. **(i) (a)** 6·2   **(b)** 6·1   **(c)** 6·04   **(ii)** 6   **(iii)** as the chord becomes a tangent, its slope $= \dfrac{dy}{dx}$

18. **(ii)** 8·01   **(iii)** 16·040025   **(iv)** 8·005   **(v)** 8   **(vi)** as the chord becomes a tangent, its slope $= \dfrac{dy}{dx}$

19. $b = 4$; $c = 4$ 20. **(i)** $a = -3$; $(2, -2)$ **(ii)** $(0, 2)$ **(iii)**

21. **(ii)** $a = (-1, 0)$; $b = (0, 25)$; $c = (1, 32)$; $d = (5, 0)$

22. **(i)** $(4, -25)$ **(ii)** $2x - 8$ **(iii)**

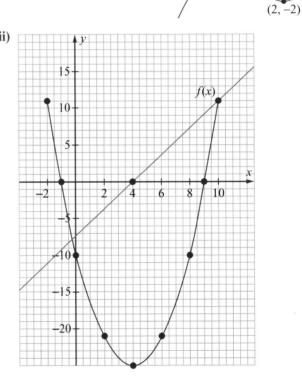

(iv) $f'(x)$ cuts the x-axis at $x = 4$, the x-coordinate of the minimum point.

23. (i) $(-1, 13)$; $(2, -14)$ (ii) $f'(x) = 6x^2 - 6x - 12$ (iii)

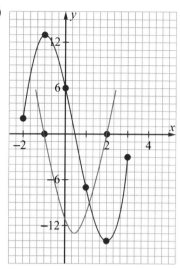

    (iv) $f'(x)$ cuts the x-axis at $x = -1$ and $x = 2$ the x-coordinate of the turning points

24. (i) $f(x) - b$ (ii) $f'(x) - c$ (iii) $f''(x) - a$

25. (i) $f(x) - b$ (ii) $f'(x) - a$ (iii) $f''(x) - c$

Exercise 8.7

1. (i) $x < 1$ (ii) $x > 1$ **2.** (i) $x < -3$ (ii) $x > -3$ **8.** (i) b, curve decreasing indicates negative slope   (ii) c (iii) a **9.** (i) D (ii) B (iii) 0 (iv) $\dfrac{dy}{dx} > 0$, curve increasing indicates positive slope

Exercise 8.8

1. (i) 4 km   (ii) $3t^2 - 6t + 3$ (iii) 12 km/h   (iv) 1 and 5 km   **2.** (i) $80 - 40t$ (ii) 2 hours (iii) 350 degrees   (iv) -120 degrees per hour   **3.** (i) 18,100   (ii) 1,185 people/year
4. (i) $2t - 6$ (ii) 900   (iii) 200 bears per year   **5.** (i) 1,600 hairs per year
(ii) 2,000 hairs per year   (iii) 40 years   **6.** (i) (a) 07:00   (b) 01:10
(c) between 08:00 and 09:00   (ii) (a) 80   (b) -21 cm per hour   **7.** (i) 3 m/sec   (ii) 20 secs
(iii) 860 m   (iv) 4 m/sec^2 **8.** (i) 405 m   (ii) 20 m/sec   (iii) 425 m   **9.** (i) 12 m/sec
(ii) 4 secs   (iii) 24 m   **10.** (i) $8 - 2t$ (ii) -4 cm^3/sec   (iii) 4 secs   (iv) (a) 6   (b) 3
11. (i) 300   (ii) -250 cm^3/sec   **12.** (i) $3t^2 - 12t + 9$; $6t - 12$ (ii) 9 m/sec   (iii) 6 m/sec^2
(iv) $t = 1$ or $t = 3$ (v) $t = 2$ (vi) $t = 3$ (vii) $t = 5$
13. (i)

t	0	1	2	3	4	5
h	8	25	32	29	16	-7

(ii) (a) $22 - 10t$ (b) solving $\dfrac{dh}{dt} = 0$ for maximum height gives $t = 2\cdot2$; maximum height $= 32\cdot2$ m

(iii) $4\cdot7$ secs   (iv) the height of the window above the ground $= 8$ m

14. (i)

t	0	2	4	6	8	t	8	10	12	14	16	18
$f(t)$	2,000	1,928	1,728	1,400	944	$g(t)$	944	800	624	416	176	−96

(ii)

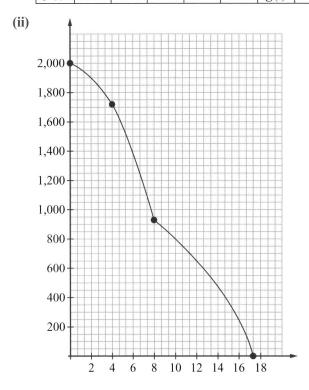

(iii) 17·3 secs **(iv)** −196 m/sec
(v) −88 m/sec **(vi)** yes, falling faster with no parachute

Exercise 9.1

1. 17, 21, 25, 29   2. 20, 15, 10, 5   3. −3, −1, 1, 3   4. 1, −2, −5, −8

5. 4·1, 4·5, 4·9, 5·3   6. 0·4, −0·2, −0·8, −1·4   7. 16, 32, 64, 128   8. 162, 486, 1,458, 4,374

9. 5, 7, 9, 11   10. 4, 7, 10, 13   11. 3, 7, 11, 15   12. 2, 7, 12, 17   13. −1, −3, −5, −7

14. −1, −5, −9, −13   15. 6, 9, 14, 21   16. 3, 8, 15, 24   17. $2, \frac{3}{2}, \frac{4}{3}, \frac{5}{4}$ 18. $1, \frac{4}{3}, \frac{3}{2}, \frac{8}{5}$

19. 2, 4, 8, 16   20. 3, 9, 27, 81   21. (i) 7, 12, 17   22. (i) 3, 6, 11   23. (i) $\frac{3}{2}, \frac{4}{3}, \frac{5}{4}$

Exercise 9.2

1. (ii) 1, 3, 5; yes: odd numbers   (iii) 2, 4, 6; yes: even numbers   (iv) yellow   (v) green
(vi) green   2. (i) 1, 4, 7   (ii) 2, 5, 8   (iii) 3, 6, 9   (iv) blue   (v) white   (vi) red

3. (i) 1, 4, 7, 10   (ii) 2, 5, 8, 11   (iii) 3, 6, 9, 12   (iv) yellow   (v) orange   (vi) 23   (vii) 28

4. (i) yellow: 1, 5, 9; purple: 2, 6, 10; green: 3, 7, 11; blue: 4, 8, 12   (ii) blue   (iii) purple
(iv) green   (v) 31   (vi) 41

Exercise 9.3

1. 3, 5, 7, 9; 2
2. 5, 8, 11, 14; 3
3. 1, 5, 9, 13; 4
4. 7, 12, 17, 22; 5
5. 1, −1, −3, −5; −2
6. 5, 2, −1, −4; −3
7. 2, 5, 10, 17; 2
8. −1, 2, 7, 14; 2
9. 2, 6, 12, 20; 2
10. 2, 4, 8, 16
11. 3, 9, 27, 81
12. 5, 7, 11, 19

Exercise 9.4

1. 2, 4, 6, 8, 10; linear
2. 2, 5, 8, 11, 14; linear
3. 5, 9, 13, 17, 21; linear
4. 1, 4, 9, 16, 25; not linear
5. 0, 2, 6, 12, 20; not linear
6. 3, 8, 15, 24, 35; not linear
7. 2, 4, 8, 16, 32; not linear
8. 0, 4, 18, 48, 100; not linear
9. (i) 5, 7, 9, 11
10. (i) 1, 4, 7, 10, 13 (iv) 3
11. (i) sequence B

12. (i)

Day	1	2	3	4	5
€	4	6	8	10	12

(ii) €22 (iii) €52 (v) €202 (vi) €18 (vii) 19 days

13. (i)

Day	1	2	3	. . .	10
€	1	4	7	. . .	28

(ii)

(iii) the values grow more quickly

14. (ii) Bill (iv) linear (v) day 18 (vi) no
15. (iii) yes; day 21 (iv) Jane
16. (ii) yellow flower (iii) yes

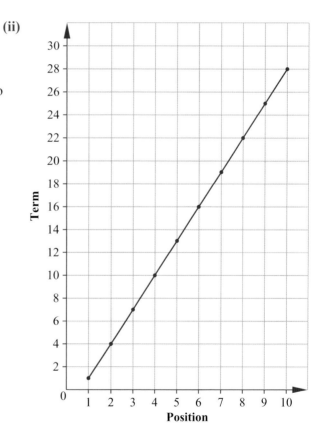

Exercise 9.5

1. $a = 1$; $d = 2$; $T_n = 2n - 1$ 2. $a = 2$; $d = 3$; $T_n = 3n - 1$ 3. $a = 3$; $d = 4$; $T_n = 4n - 1$

4. $a = 6$; $d = 5$; $T_n = 5n + 1$ 5. $a = 9$; $d = -2$; $T_n = 11 - 2n$ 6. $a = 4$; $d = -3$; $T_n = 7 - 3n$

7. $a = 8$; $d = -5$; $T_n = 13 - 5n$ 8. $a = 4$; $d = -6$; $T_n = 10 - 6n$ 9. $a = -5$; $d = 2$; $T_n = 2n - 7$

10. (i) $a = 1$, $d = 3$ (ii) $T_n = 3n - 2$; $T_{50} = 148$ (iii) T_{30} 11. (i) $a = 4$, $d = 5$

(ii) $T_n = 5n - 1$; $T_{45} = 224$ (iii) T_{50} 12. (i) $a = 40$, $d = -4$ (ii) $T_n = 44 - 4n$; $T_{15} = -16$

(iii) T_{11} 13. (i) $2n + 3$ (iii) $5n + 2$ (v) €55   14. (ii) $a = 5$, $d = 3$ (iii) (a) €2

(b) €3 (iv) $32\frac{2}{3}$ km   15. (i) 35 mins   (iii) $a = 35$, $d = 15$ (iv) $15n + 20$ (v) 155 mins (vi) $14\frac{2}{3}$ kg

16. T_{59} 17. T_{30} 18. (i) 28 months   (ii) $2n + 8$ (iii) $3n + 5$ (iv) 338 months

19. $k = 3$; 5, 7, 9   20. $k = 4$; 3, 7, 11   21. $k = 11$; 17, 23, 29, 35   22. (i) $k = 5$; 3, 11, 19, 27

(ii) $T_n = 8n - 5$; $T_{21} = 163$ (iii) T_{31}

Exercise 9.6

1. (i) 9, 11, 13   (ii) arithmetic   (iii) $2n + 1$ (iv) 101

2. (i)

Pattern	1	2	3	4	5
No. of tiles	7	13	19	25	31

(ii) $6n + 1$ (iii) pattern 42   3. (i) 17, 21   (ii) $4n + 1$ (iii) shape 12

4. (i) 40   (ii) 10

5. (i)

Rectangle	1	2	3	4	5	6
Number of white squares	5	6	7	8	9	10
Number of red squares	4	6	8	10	12	14
Total number of squares	9	12	15	18	21	24

(ii) 14   (iii) $n + 4$ (iv) $2n + 2$ (v) 22   (vi) 36   (vii) $3n + 6$

6. (i) 38   (ii) $7n + 3$ (iii) 143   (iv) $a = 4$, $b = 3$ (v) 9th diagram

7. (i) 4 cm   (ii) 18 cm^2 (iii) 22 cm^2 (iv) 42 cm^2 (v) $(4n + 2)$ cm^2

8. (ii)

Diagram	1	2	3	4	5
Number of dots	5	8	11	14	17

(iii) $3n + 2$ (v) odd   9. (i) 1, 3, 6, 10   (iii) 0, 1, 3, 6   10. (i) 14, 20, 26   (iii) $6n + 8$

(iv) pond 15   (v) 4, 5, 6   (vi) $n + 3$ (vii) 18 slabs × 33 slabs

Exercise 9.7

1. $a = 3, d = 2$ 2. $a = 1, d = 3$ 3. $a = 7, d = 4$ 4. $a = 3, d = 5$ 5. $a = 5, d = 6$

6. (i) $d = 3$ (ii) $3n + 4$; 64   (iii) T_{32} 7. (i) $a = 3, d = 4$ (ii) $4n - 1$ (iv) $n = 25$

8. (i) $p = 7, q = 9$ (ii) 23   9. (i) $p = 10, q = 7, r = 1$ (ii) -47

Exercise 9.9

1. 120   2. 246   3. 630   4. (i) $\frac{n}{2}(5n + 1)$ (ii) 1,010   5. (i) $\frac{n}{2}(3n + 17)$ (ii) 1,605

6. (i) 5, 7, 9, 11   (ii) 2   (iii) 320   7. (i) $a = 2, d = 5$ 8. (i) $a = -7, d = 4$ (iii) (a) 69

(b) 1,530   9. (i) $a = 2, d = 3$ (iii) (a) 89   (b) 1,365   10. (i) $a = -15, d = 6$

(iii) (a) 129   (b) 0   11. (i) $a = 2, d = 6$ (ii) (a) 116   (b) 1,180   12. 610

13. 1,770   14. 6,275   15. (i) $3n - 1$ (iii) 670   16. (i) $10n$ (ii) $5n(n + 1)$ (iii) 201,000

17. (ii) (a) 39   (b) 400   (iii) 15   18. (i) $12a$ (ii) $75a$ (iii) $a = 2$ (iv) 6, 8, 10, 12

(v) (a) $2n + 4$ (b) $n(n + 5)$ (vi) (a) 44   (b) 500   19. (i) $a = 7, d = 2$ (ii) 10

20. (i) €10·20   (ii) €265   21. €492,000   22. 1,120 m   23. 90   24. (ii) €6,432

25. 30 seconds

Exercise 9.10

1. $a = 3, d = 2$ 2. $a = 4, d = 2$ 3. $a = 1, d = 6$ 4. $a = -1, d = 4$ 5. (i) 2   (ii) 23

6. (i) 3; 4   (ii) $4n - 1$ (iii) 39   7. (i) $a = -2, d = 4$ (ii) $4n - 6$ (iii) 74   (iv) 10

Exercise 9.11

1. $n^2 + n + 1$ 2. $n^2 + 2n + 1$ 3. $n^2 + n$ 4. $n^2 + 1$ 5. $n^2 - 3n + 2$ 6. $n^2 + 4n + 3$

7. (i) $n^2 + n - 2$ (ii) 108   (iii) greater   8. (i) $n^2 + 11n + 10$ (ii) 220 m   (iii) 4,270 m

9. (i) $n(n + 1)$ or $n^2 + n$ (ii) $2(n + 1)$